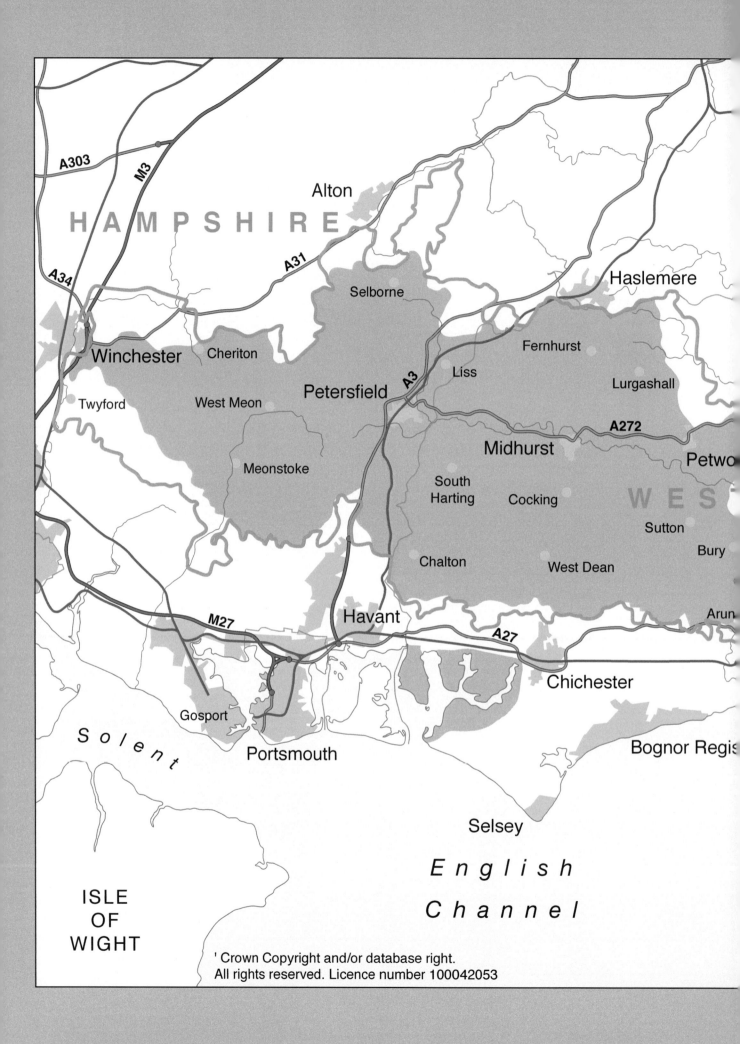

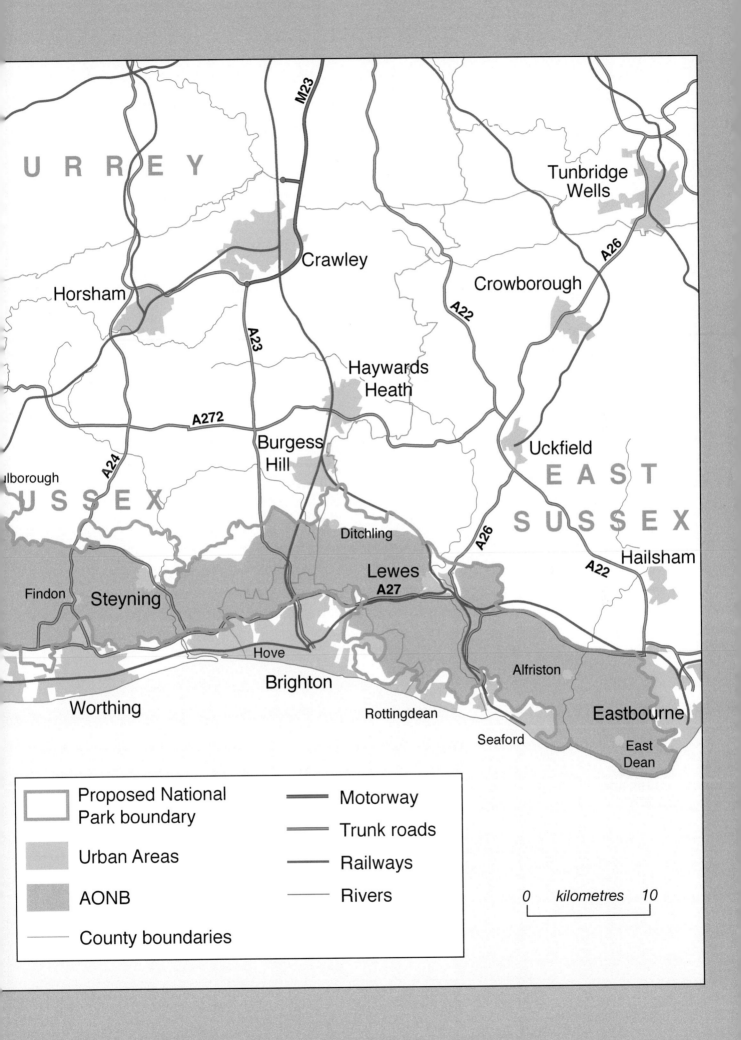

S U R R E Y

M23

Crawley

Horsham

A23

Tunbridge
Wells

Crowborough

A22

A26

Haywards
Heath

Burgess
Hill

A272

ilborough

A24

S U S S E X

Uckfield

E A S T

S U S S E X

Ditchling

A26

Hailsham

Findon

Steyning

Lewes

A27

Alfriston

Hove

Brighton

Eastbourne

Worthing

Rottingdean

Seaford

East
Dean

Proposed National Park boundary	Motorway
Urban Areas	Trunk roads
AONB	Railways
County boundaries	Rivers

0   kilometres   10

The Future of the
SOUTH DOWNS

Frontispiece
An aerial view of Alfriston, East Sussex, taken from the south-east with the escarpment of the South Downs in the background, dip-slope on the left and the steep, north-facing scarp-slope to the right. Photo: English Heritage.

Previous page
Butser Hill, Hampshire, in snow, looking north.
Photo: Garrick Palmer, courtesy of the South Downs Joint Committee (SDJC)

The Future of the
SOUTH DOWNS

Landscape, Ecology, Land Use and Conservation

Gerald Smart and Peter Brandon
Editors

PACKARD PUBLISHING LIMITED
CHICHESTER

'What Future for the South Downs?'
– the cover of a CPRE leaflet of the 1990s.
Courtesy of the Campaign to Protect Rural England/SDJC.

The Future of the SOUTH DOWNS

© The authors of the respective chapters 2007

First published in 2007 by **Packard Publishing Limited, Forum House, Stirling Road, Chichester, West Sussex, PO19 7DN, UK**.
Telephone & facsimile 01243 537977;
e-mail info@packardpublishing.co.uk;
website www.packardpublishing.com

ISBN – 10: 1 85341 137 X

ISBN – 13: 978 1 85341 137 3

A CIP record of this book may be obtained from the British Library.

Cover painting of Black Cap, Ditchling Beacon by Roy Adams, 1992.

Title-page photograph of the Cuckmere Valley at sunrise, courtesy of the South Downs Joint Committee (SDJC).

Vignettes and line drawings at the end of chapters are taken from the book of drawings by students of the City of Chichester School of Art, *West of the Arun*, 1932.

This book was commissioned, prepared for press and indexed by Michael Packard.

Layout of text by Russell Townsend; layout of cover, colour plates and reprographics by Hilite Design & Reprographics, Southampton, Hampshire.

Maps prepared by the University of Southampton Cartographic Unit and sponsored by Natural England.

Printed and bound in the United Kingdom.

Table of Contents

IMPORTANT NOTICE

Printing of the *Future of the South Downs* was virtually complete when the report of the Designation Order Public Inquiry Inspector was released in early July 2007. Consequently the proposed National Park boundary shown on the maps is based on the original Order rather than the reduced area and other changes recommended by the Inspector. Nevertheless, for comparison, the latter area can be seen in the endpapers at the back of the book.

    While welcoming the Inspector's support of National Park status in principle, the Editors consider that strong arguments can be advanced broadly in favour of the originally proposed wider boundary.

Foreword

Though I have now travelled the Sussex downs upwards of thirty years, yet I still investigate that chain of majestic mountains with fresh admiration year by year; and think I see new beauties every time I traverse it.

Gilbert White wrote those words to Daines Barrington on 9 December 1773. In the same letter, published in his book, *The Natural History of Selborne* of 1789, he makes observations on the breeds of sheep favoured by local shepherds, on the local gentry's taste for roast wheatears and on the magic of the Sussex chalk-hills themselves. Gilbert White recognized how the farming practices had helped to fashion this beautiful landscape and how the wildlife had influenced the local way of life. Over two hundred years later, we can share Gilbert White's exhilaration at the views afforded by the South Downs, both in Sussex and Hampshire, but these views are not the same. The wheatears are not so plentiful, though they are no longer consumed as a delicacy in Brighton. These 'majestic mountains' are now within one of Europe's more prosperous regions, with thousands either living or working in close proximity. The number of visitors each year must now be measured in millions.

The Secretary of State for the Environment, Food and Rural Affairs (DEFRA) is expected to determine soon whether there should be a National Park in the South Downs and, if so, what powers should be conferred on a National Park Authority. Views differ as to how the governance of the South Downs might best be organized for their most effective future conservation, but there is no disagreement on the national, indeed international, importance of this vulnerable tract of chalkland and its surroundings. This beautiful expanse of downland is greatly cherished by a wide range of people, all of whom have a legitimate interest in ensuring that their views are taken into account when critical decisions are finally made on the conservation and management of the South Downs, and including the Western Weald. These include residents, landowners, land managers, planners, environmental and landscape champions, historians, geographers and many others besides. Those who are ultimately charged with responsibility for putting in place management strategies for the South Downs will depend on a wide-ranging, inclusive dialogue in which all interests can participate so that appropriate policies which reconcile competing requirements can be formulated. This dialogue will be greatly assisted by the fourteen acknowledged experts who have each contributed to this timely book. The authors have between them an unrivalled knowledge of the cultural heritage of the South Downs, and bring together in one book a wealth of expertise to inform the consideration of their future management.

In my lifetime the Downs have been transformed by road improvements, urban development and changing agricultural practices, all of which have eroded the archaeological heritage, the wildlife and the landscape. The recent changes in the Common Agricultural Policy, however, have introduced new, more environmentally friendly policies for agricultural support. Once the present uncertainty on the future governance of the South Downs has been resolved, there is every reason to believe that we might then have an opportunity to put in place management strategies which could deliver lasting benefits for the conservation of what we most value, and which are compatible with the need to support the local rural economy. I believe that this book will be a valuable tool to ensure that we do not let this opportunity pass.

John Selborne

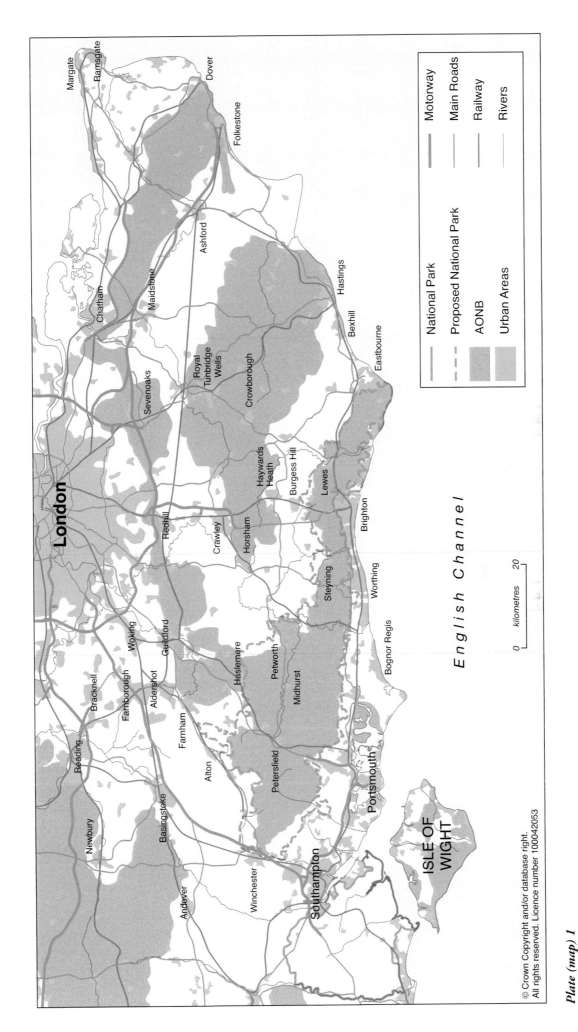

——	Motorway
——	Main Roads
——	Railway
——	Rivers

——	National Park
-- --	Proposed National Park
▨	AONB
▨	Urban Areas

English Channel

0   kilometres   20

ISLE OF WIGHT

© Crown Copyright and/or database right.
All rights reserved. Licence number 100042053

Plate (map) 1

The South Downs in their regional setting.
Map produced by the University of Southampton Cartographic Unit.

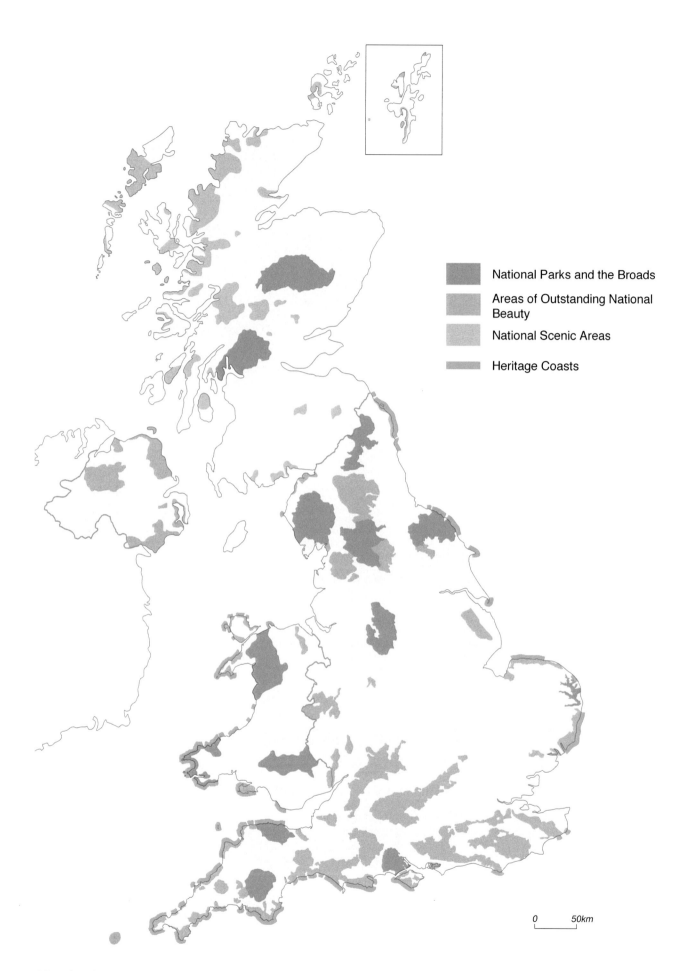

Legend:
- National Parks and the Broads
- Areas of Outstanding National Beauty
- National Scenic Areas
- Heritage Coasts

0   50km

Plate (map) 2
The extent of protected landscapes and heritage coasts in the United Kingdom.
Map by the University of Southampton Cartographic Unit.

Introduction

The South Downs, outlined in Plate (map) 1, are among the best loved landscapes in southern England. The beauty of their rolling chalk hills and steep escarpments, open river valleys, dramatic sea cliffs, sandy wealden ridges and woodlands, and colourful wildlife, has been an inspiration to writers and artists for centuries. This beauty is enjoyed daily by the 120,000 residents of local towns and villages, and the area attracts nearly 40 million visits a year, a total which is more than for any National Park. The Downs are, nevertheless, essentially working countryside, landscapes that have changed and are still changing in response to farming and forestry practice. *The Future of the South Downs* aims to describe in a readable way the local, national and indeed international value of the Downs, the problems arising from their multiple use, and the steps that have been, and can be, taken to conserve them.

The book is published at a critical time. The long-term 'health' of this whole area, a matter of concern for years among lovers of the countryside, is at last under formal scrutiny by central and local government and is openly debated, with the designation of a South Downs National Park in mind. Nearly 60 years have passed since British planning legislation first set out to designate areas of national landscape value and to promote their conservation. The family of protected landscapes now consists of 14 National Parks in England, Wales and Scotland, some 40 Areas of Outstanding Natural Beauty in England and Wales and nine in Northern Ireland, and some 36 National Scenic Areas in Scotland (Plate (map) 2). Although the Sussex Downs have often been seen as a potential National Park, and were officially proposed as such in 1947, this did not come about for a variety of reasons. Instead, in the 1960s the chalk and wealden landscapes in both Sussex and East Hampshire were designated as Areas of Outstanding Natural Beauty. AONBs, as such areas are usually known, are regarded as equivalent in landscape value to National Parks, but they do not get the same level of national funding and the leadership of a statutory Authority.

It took time for the County Councils of East and West Sussex and Hampshire to set up organizations to mastermind conservation in each AONB. Hampshire was the first, establishing a very active Joint Advisory Committee, and Sussex soon went markedly beyond this to create, with strong backing from the Countryside Commission and local people, the more highly-powered Sussex Downs Conservation Board, an experiment that was later to provide a basis for national legislation. These two have merged to form the South Downs Joint Committe. Meanwhile, visitor and other pressures in each AONB continue to increase, and, coming full circle, the Countryside Agency made a Designation Order in 2002 to establish a South Downs National Park for the whole area. It had recently done this for another unique southern England landscape, the New Forest, where the Order has now been confirmed. A National Park would have significantly more power and resources than a Conservation Board, and although the proposal was widely welcomed, especially by the strong South Downs Campaign, some local authorities voiced their opposition. If approved by the Government, it will signify a step-change in conservation and recreational provision in the area, coming at a time when other major countryside initiatives are in hand, including the reform of the EU Common Agricultural policy.

This brief history of administrative measures sets a necessary context for the timing and coverage of the book; it is of course spelled out more fully, amongst many other issues, in the text itself. *The Future of the South Downs* takes the form of related essays by fourteen authors, some written jointly. Acknowledged experts in the history, character and environmental assets of the Downs, they look in turn at the area's very special resources, the pressures that bear on them, and how adverse impacts might be mitigated. This leads to a concluding chapter, the theme of which is sustainable use and integrated measures to achieve it. Busy people as these authors are, mostly engaged in the day-to-day management of natural and community resources in Sussex and Hampshire, they have come together with a sense of mission. They believe that a book of this kind, running in parallel with official documents, will be of interest to all who care for the Downs, be they residents or visitors, landowners and managers, farmers, foresters, people in government and the professions, teachers and students. Above all, they hope that *The Future of the South Downs* will be a helpful, influential background for decision-makers preparing policies and action for a South Downs National Park Authority, or for any alternative joint organization that may come about.

Structurally, the book consists of three main parts, for each of which there is a contextual introduction and a concluding commentary that draws the threads together. Part One gives a set of historical, cultural and scientific perspectives of the Downs. Part Two goes on to examine the impacts on these of trends in the local economy and community structure, farming, forestry and water management, the pressures of countryside recreation and of changes in the town and village environment. In Part Three, the reader will find an explanation of the steps taken to conserve the area by the existing countryside-management organizations for the two AONBs. This is followed by an account of the Countryside Agency's proposals to establish a National Park Authority, and the local reaction to this. A final chapter, arising from the book as a whole, then depicts a sustainable vision for the Downs of the future, and discusses the implications of this for the task of management, preferably by a National Park Authority.

The message from *The Future of the South Downs* is that, whether or not the Downs become a National Park, there are many things that can be done to bring together finance, policies and action to maintain and enhance the qualities of this wonderful area for present and future generations. It is a challenge that must be taken up. Indeed, the authors have no doubt that the will is there to accept it, from the grass-roots of informed public opinion, leading, in due course, to the necessary political resolve.

Acknowledgements

The editors would like to record that the production of this book has only been made possible by the hard work and enthusiasm of the contributing authors, the support in spirit and in kind of the South Downs Conservation Board, the East Hampshire AONB Joint Advisory Committee (who now, in combination, form the South Downs Joint Committee) and the Countryside Agency (now forming part of Natural England). They also wish to express their sincere thanks to the publisher, Michael Packard, for his expertise, to Tim Aspden and Southampton University's Cartographic Unit for its skill in production of the necessary maps and to Russell Townsend for preparation of one of the figures in Chapter 2 and the layout of the book. To all, they owe an immense debt of gratitude.

Gerald Smart & Peter Brandon

A Note to the Reader

The Naming of Conservation and Other Countryside Organizations

The chapters in this book frequently refer to public institutions and non-governmental organizations concerned with nature and landscape conservation whose names differ from time to time and may cause confusion. For example, in October 2006 **Natural England** was formed from **English Nature** and parts of the **Countryside Agency** and the **Rural Development Service**.

Prior to that merger, **English Nature** (1991–2006) had been called the **Nature Conservancy Council** (1973–1991), and before then it was the **Nature Conservancy** (1949–1973). In turn the **Countryside Agency** (1999–2006) had incorporated the **Rural Development Commission** in 1999 when it became an 'agency'; previously it had been called the **Countryside Commission** (1968–1999), and before that the **National Parks Commission** (1949 –1968).

In 1996 the **Environment Agency** changed from being the **National Rivers Authority** – set up in 1989 as an amalgamation of ten regional water authorities.

Non-governmental organizations (NGOs) have from time to time altered their names as their focuses or remits have changed. The CPRE was founded in 1926 as the **Council for the Preservation of Rural England**. In 1969 it changed the word **Preservation** to **Protection** in its title. In 2003 the CPRE became the **Campaign to Protect Rural England**. The **Country Land & Business Association** (CLBA) changed its name in 2001 from the **Country Landowners Association** (CLA), founded in 1907. The **Open Spaces Society** was founded in 1865. After several changes in name, its current full title is the **Commons, Open Spaces and Footpaths Preservation Society**, but it is known by its abbreviated name of the **Open Spaces Society**. The **Society of Sussex Downsmen**, founded in 1923, became the **South Downs Society** in April 2005.

Other well-known organizations mentioned in the text, such as the **Forestry Commission**, the **National Trust**, the **Royal Society for the Protection of Birds** (RSPB) or the **Ramblers' Association**, have not changed their titles since they were founded.

The Authors use the name of an organization applying at the time of the actual matter being discussed. It was felt that too many uses of 'the former' or 'formerly known as' would impede the flow of the text. The index has separate page references to the different institutional names.

PART 1

The Historical, Cultural and Scientific Background

Introduction to Part 1

The purpose of dividing the book into three parts has been explained in the general introduction. Part 1, which now follows, offers a perspective of the character of the South Downs, setting the context for the book as a whole. Part 1 describes the landscape, especially as seen through the eyes of writers; its geological origins; its archaeological heritage; changes in its use; and the variety of its wildlife habitats.

Thus, in Chapter 1, Peter Brandon traces attitudes towards the landscape of the South Downs, from the days when writers regarded it as 'ugly' or 'dreary' by comparison with mountains and moorland, to the mid-nineteenth century when an almost idyllic view began to be expressed, the Downs being 'England', symbolized by sheep. Dr Brandon feels passionately about the beauty of the landscape, and he rues the destruction wrought on downland by government agricultural policies from 1939 until very recently. From his intimate knowledge of the whole area, he shows how the chalk landscape changes from east to west, and how, beyond the chalk, subtle differences are to be found in the often more enclosed countryside of the Western Weald.

Chapter 2, by Rendel Williams, gives a lucid and scientific account of the geological development of the landscape. He describes the million-year-old laying down of chalk, the structural basis of the escarpments, dip-slopes and valleys, and of the cliffs and shore platforms of the coastal strip. He then looks at the sands, sandstones and clays, predating the chalk, that create the closely varied landform of the wealden 'borderland'. Dr Williams points out that no other National Park has chalk within its boundary, and few parts of lowland Britain can offer such diversity of geology and scenery. The South Downs well deserve National Park status and the better understanding and enjoyment of its special features that go with this.

In Chapter 3, David McOmish and Peter Topping describe the very significant archaeological remains that exist in the South Downs and their immediate environs, among the richest cultural landscapes in England. Following a time-sequence from the palaeolithic through to the post-Roman period, they give a short, authoritative account of the evidence of settlement in each, including recent fieldwork. They comment on the disastrous impact of twentieth-century agriculture on archaeological sites, particularly fields and settlements, and, consequently, the important potential of discoveries yet to be made in woodland areas. They conclude with suggested aims for archaeological conservation and interpretation in the area.

Chapter 4, again by Peter Brandon, outlines the history of the South Downs landscape from before the Roman era up to recent times. Significant in this are changes in economic and social conditions: the development of farming, especially for sheep, the effects of the Black Death, of poverty, prosperity and of the pattern of land-ownership. He points out the aesthetic contribution of traditional buildings, barns, churches, mills and cottages, and of building materials, especially flint. He stresses the need to promote a better understanding of this history, and the conservation of the features that are such a vital part of it.

In Chapter 5, Tony Whitbread describes the semi-natural habitats of the South Downs: grassland, heath, scrub, hedgerows, woods, sandy ridges and clay vales, and their characteristic wildlife. He emphasizes the need to plan for a 'whole landscape' in which these habitats and their inter-connections can survive, a need towards which agricultural and land-management policies must contribute. Commenting on the importance in the area of land uses such as recreation, and of the effect of trends such as climate change, Dr Whitbread expresses an optimistic view of the future, with social, economic and environmental objectives combined to enable the Downs to be managed sustainably.

CHAPTER 1
The South Downs before and after 1939

PETER BRANDON

The South Downs (see Plate (map) 1) are among the noblest examples of countryside left in southern England, and there are few places where the beauty of the countryside is more lovely than in the view of the South Downs from the north which Alice Meynell (1899), who lived at Greatham near Pulborough, thought one of the finest in the world. H. G. Wells summed up their qualities by saying 'There is something in these downland views, which like seaviews, lifts a mind out to the skies' (Wells, 1915), and Virginia Woolf (1947), who absorbed the spirit of the Downs into her very being, acknowledged that 'It feeds me, rests me, satisfies me, as nothing else does'.

The South Downs are now at a critical moment in their development. They are a gift of history which is literally priceless, precious as well as vulnerable. It was an organic biodiverse before 1940 but modern farming practices have degraded much of the area's wildlife and landscape resources. Moreover, although nominally a well-protected stretch of land as an Area of Outstanding Beauty, the Downs have suffered from fifty years of insidious development, and pious plans made for their conservation have been often followed by actions which were the very opposite. Since the 1920s the South Downs have demonstrated that man's capacity to destroy their beauty is not matched by his ability to maintain or restore them. How to ruin downland was demonstrated at Twyford Down (see Chapter 11 and Plate 3), where the M3 motorway extension was cut through the Hampshire Downs at Winchester in 1992. The lesson from that experience is that no site in the South Downs, however well protected, can be deemed safe from the road engineer.

This chapter is concerned primarily with the past as well as the present, but solely from the standpoint that knowledge of it may inform and influence decisions on the management of the Downs in the future. It thus attempts in historical perspective to separate reality from myth, and identifies the memorable characteristics of the salient features of the Downs before 1939, which made the exhilarating loveableness of the South Downs the most familiar hills in England. It goes on to examine the present-day character of the proposed National Park for the South Downs, and makes some suggestions for new landscapes for which the consequences go wider than appears at first sight. Two implications stand out. The first is that different localities in the South Downs are bound to have different priorities by way of landscape changes. The second is that a knowledge of what people admired in the Downs before the Second World War, or at the present day, should be of use in planning the landscapes of the future. In the immediate post-war years it was held that the past should not be allowed to stand in the way of the future. Old habits, practices, old traditions, old ways of life were ruthlessly jettisoned in favour of 'modernization' and a restless search for profit. Public faith in this goal has now dribbled away. The history of the past half-century has one sure lesson. It is that policies imposed from the top without the backing of the public do not produce the desired

3

results. If change is to stick at this time of public disenchantment it must be based on a mutual understanding between landowners, farmers, consumers and environmentalists. This understanding can only be built on a wide-ranging, uninhibited discussion by the key participants shaping the policy process. It is this type of debate that this book hopes to generate. It implies that we are learners amongst other learners, and that each of us has valuable experience to communicate, including the un-monied voices who have hardly spoken yet.

THE 'OLD' DOWNS

The notion that the South Downs were immeasurably beautiful and a remarkable historic landscape of international importance was firmly established between 1900 and 1939. Rudyard Kipling, Hilaire Belloc and other writers crowded the stage to popularize them with ineffable gusto. Dazzled trippers devoured an avalanche of best-selling guidebooks, 'country' writing and verse. Handicraftsmen, artists and writers colonized downland villages. The Curwens (1929), father and son, explored the development of successive prehistoric cultures, contributing to knowledge of the early civilization of Britain with their famed team of archaeologists. Few lines of hills caught the public imagination as much as the steep northward-facing escarpment of the Downs (Plate 4), whether rising smooth-shaven from the flat Weald, 'so noble and so bare' in Belloc's phrase, or mantled with hanging woods. The Downs were sketched, painted, photographed, and otherwise advertised and mimicked, more than any other English landscape. Moreover, they became the object of a veritable popular cult which projected them as the halcyon image of a landscape embodying what was claimed to be the quintessence of English ideals. Thus to many the South Downs stood for England; others considered it the spoilt child of English landscape. Retired persons took the valuation of Kipling, Belloc and other writers, saying, in effect, 'If the Downs are such an ideal place, why not plan to end our lives there?', even to the point of weeping over the destruction of what they revered. In 1940 images of the Downs were used as recruiting posters. Frank Newbould depicted the fair on Alfriston Tye and another was of a shepherd striding out with his dog and flock from Birling Farm in the morning towards the sheep-nibbled grass backed by the Belle Tout lighthouse (Plate 5). They bore the legend: 'Britain; Fight for it now'. Ironically, much of the legendary beauty of the Downs was extinguished as finally and indiscriminately as were the lives of so many men and women who went to war to defend them (Brandon, 1998).

This public adulation of the Downs is, from an historian's point of view, a relatively recent phenomenon, and is a classic example of changing taste in landscape. As Jane Austen famously declares in *Sense and Sensibility* (1786), admiration of scenery had by then become a mere jargon. William Gilpin (1792), the originator of the Picturesque, held the general public in thrall for two generations, and what he professed to be beautiful was met with general approval. Gilpin's ideal scenery was rocky, abrupt and varied, with water features and many trees, preferably blasted and crooked. The smooth, rounded, forms of chalk scenery with their flowing curves were so abhorrent to him that he pronounced chalk scenery as 'ugly' and 'disgusting'. Consequently, the pioneer Regency visitors to Brighton, whilst admiring the resort, spoke slightingly of its downland setting as 'drear'. Dr Johnson thought that, although Brighton's setting was so dull, a man overcome by its dismalness would not be able to find a tree whereon to hang himself (Piozzi, 1984). The early Brighton doctors extolled the tonic qualities of the Brighton air but apologized for its bare and sterile-looking Downs. It is significant that Constable is silent on the scenic qualities of the Downs but goes into raptures at the sight of the patchwork of fields in the Weald below the Devil's Dyke (Leslie, 1931). Such deprecatory assessments of the Downs continued into the 1860s, when, for example, the botanist Mrs Merrifield (1864) noted the fascination of the downland flora but conceded that the Downs themselves were uninviting. When M.A. Lower (1854) wrote an essay about the Downs, he described them defensively as an 'amenity'. He felt obliged to 'sell' the Downs visually, knowing that he would have unappreciative readers still held in Gilpin's thrall. He was right, for deprecatory assessments of the Downs continued. As recently as the 1880s the famous preacher F.W. Robertson of Brighton was struggling to promote Brighton's Downs still thought ' prosaic' (Brooke, 1865), and even later August Hare (1894) must have put off thousands of potential visitors of the Downs by describing them as 'excessively dreary'. The poet, John Davidson (1898), although now regarded as one of the 'first of the moderns', found the nakedness of the Downs near Shoreham repelling, and compared their rolling bare slopes to the 'limbs and shoulders of plucked fowls'. He endured the ugliness as the 'prime cost of Southdown mutton' and yearned for them to be clothed in trees.

It is instructive to compare the denigration of the Downs during the course of most of the nineteenth century with the naturalist Gilbert White's admiration of them in his famous *Natural History of Selbourne* of 1798 (Plate 6). His love of the Downs is manifest in his description of them as 'delectable mountains', and his journeys to Ringmer through Lewes led him to describe the latter town as ringed in 'an amphitheatre of mountains'. In calling the Caburn and Firle Beacons 'mountains', White was following a tradition dating back to the seventeenth century and earlier before the current orthodoxy became

Plate 3

Environmental vandalism at its worst: the cutting through Twyford Down for the M3 Motorway, near Winchester, Hampshire.
Photo: Alison Tingley, courtesy of SDJC.

Plate 4

The Fulking escarpment, East Sussex, looking west from the Devil's Dyke area. The steep scarp-slope can be clearly seen.
Photo: John Tyler, courtesy of SDJC.

Plate 5

A poster painted by Frank Newbould as encouragement during the Second World War. The scene nowadays is well preserved by Eastbourne Borough Council. Courtesy of the Imperial War Museum, London.

established, that a mountain must be over 1000 feet high. Even in today's jargon it can be claimed that White knew what he was talking about. The Lewes hills rise so steeply and abruptly from the low-lying meadows in the Brooks that they are more impressive than many English hills and mountains which are higher. Moreover, as any traveller in early morning in spring and autumn will confirm, the steepest Downs are magnified by swirling mist – 'foxes' brewings' – and take on the stature and grandeur of mountains. The first to champion White on this matter was A. Hadrian Allcroft (1924). It is extraordinary that White's admiration for the Downs took so long to become established among the general public.

Yet the charge of insipidity planted by Gilpin and his followers was on the wane in late Victorian times and the South Downs came to take its place in the national psyche it holds today as an over-described, over-written, over-painted and, consequently, over-visited landscape. The story behind this extreme popularity in the modern era is one of the more fascinating in the history of the appreciation of national landscape. The new admiration of downland is doubtless in part to be connected with the frenetic rush of steam and urbanization which put a psychological strain on those living in London and larger towns. The growth of London, in particular, and its changes in lifestyle, had much to do with this growing fondness of the Downs. *Pace* eighteenth-century Dr Johnson, there was no longer in High Victorian London all that life would provide. Hanoverian London had previously been relatively compact and coherent, enveloped in its market gardens and fields which could be reached on foot. Mid-Victorian London, was by contrast a new city, which was more cut-about, more rebuilt and extended than at any time in its previous history. It is at this time that the Downs offered a complete and credible alternative world of comfort and relaxation. To people who had never longed so ardently or never so pined and wearied for the freedom of pure air and open country, the gently swelling curves so detested by Gilpin were now felt to be soothing and therapeutic. The ensuing wave of fashionable approval of open downland scenery is one of the swifter changes in the history of landscape taste. One of the first signs is the popularity of Copley Fielding's paintings of the eastern towns for the Victorian gentry.

Another partial explanation for the new admiration of the Downs lies in how their salient characteristics were treated in literature. People who fell deeply and desperately in love with the Downs invariably quoted Kipling and Belloc. In actuality these authors had shaped and directed the Downs as they intended them in their own minds. In a real sense they reinvented them as an idyllic version which was partly mythological. They celebrated neither the actual nor

the imaginary Downs, rather something in between; not the Downs as they were, but as they might have been dreamt of. So there is always something never altogether true, or entirely mistaken, in the poetic descriptions of the South Downs which praised them to the skies. In modern language there was an element of 'hype', as there was in Gilpin's landscape theories. People began to admire what they were taught to admire (Plate 7), and they could not believe that what had existed was no longer there. Even government reports were not exempt from this failing. Sir Arthur Hobhouse's description of the South Downs in his 1947 *Report of the National Parks Committee* reads like a kind of fairy-tale which was hopelessly out of touch with what was actually happening. He wrote that 'Here the town dweller can enjoy, often in surprising solitude, the sweeping views of the chalk uplands, the springy turf under his feet, lark song and the crooning of turtle doves and the scent of wild thyme and hawthorn'. As they read these lyrical words, local residents were witnessing with dismay the destruction of these very characteristics all around them by intensive agriculture. It is a vivid example of a generation which talked rather than acted.

It is said that there are landscapes, like some books and some people, of whom we form an indulgent opinion without finding it easy to justify our liking. The South Downs gives us an example. But what was the secret of their appeal? No single person can give a definitive answer to this matter. The essence of the Downs has always defied analysis (Plates 8 & 9). Their rural character before 1940, when they began to undergo irrevocable change, is particularly hard to define, so terribly difficult to convey, yet so unmistakeably there. Can it be recaptured and made comprehensible to us? We have to pick our way through the idyllic in the hope of finding the actual, but when we think we have found the latter, writers tell us that it is beyond their powers of description. Virginia Woolf (1947) came to realize this when returning to Rodmell on a summer's evening. Even with her exceptional powers of description, she could not catch and hold all the beauty 'more extravagantly greater than one could expect…I cannot hold this – I cannot express this – I am overcome by it – I am mastered'.

Furthermore, the Downs before 1939 were so different to those of today that Eric Gill warned that only persons who had shared the earlier experience of the Downs could convey them to persons who had not known them. 'If you had been a little child brought up in these hills, and in those days, you will understand their mortal loveliness. If, in your childhood, you have walked over them, and in them and under them …Then you will known what I am talking about, but not otherwise. No one who was not there as a child can know that heaven, no grown-up can capture it'. Gill was writing in 1940 of his experience in childhood and as a sculptor and letter-cutter at Ditchling between 1909 and 1924.

Certain elements of the Downs were singled out for especial praise. Notable amongst these was the north-facing escarpment, which was not seen as matched anywhere in the English chalkland for a wavy formidableness far superior, for example, to the Dorset or the North Downs. Then there was the openness of the Downs and their extensive spreads of unbroken and unfenced rolling country moulded in beautiful swelling curves which added a thrilling sense of ease and freedom, and of space as well as of height. The huge amounts of chalk which had been steadily sculpted to shape the muscular hills and hollow combes were also prized as reminiscent of broad, bare, rounded and smoothed sensuous outlines of the human figure.

The extensive spreads of old chalk grassland had been singled out as early as 1691 by the eminent botanist John Ray as one of the 'chief glories' of the Downs on account of its rich store of wild plants (Lankester, 1948). Increasingly, the springy turf with its wild aromatic herbs also became valued as a leisure-resource. Its soft velvety nature made sitting down seem like being on a comfortable cushion (provided one steered between the thistles!). Stepping on it was like being on a soft carpet and the springiness underfoot seemed like walking on India-rubber, the elastic spring carrying one forward at the rate of over four miles an hour without pain or rest. Unwearied by this motion everyone was fleeter of foot; sturdy ramblers donned 'seven-league' boots and strode, or leapt for joy; cyclists ground their pedals with the sensation of flying through the air. Horses became things of wings. Hounds, hare and foxes ran faster than anywhere else and the turf was superb for playing cricket. The old chalk grassland was even then among the rarest habitats in western Europe, and was regarded as peculiarly English by Lord Avebury in his *The Scenery of England* (1902)

The old chalk grassland owed itself to sheep grazing over millennia. Poets depicted the Downs as a sheepwalk in Arcadia. It was a modern version of the English pastoral that had never lost its savour and which began in the sixteenth century with Spenser's *Shepheards Calender*. Between 1900 and 1939 sheep became the symbol of Britain's best-loved landscape. The custodians of the Downs were then huge flocks of native-bred 'Southdowns' (Plate 10) and 'Hampshire Downs' (Plate 11) which grazed the open hills by day, so keeping them free of weeds and scrub, which would have overtaken them within weeks. These ancient breeds are recognizable in monastic records of the thirteenth century and were doubtless improved from prehistoric stocks. Traditionally, farmers fattened the Southdowns for mutton which had a distinctively thymey flavour derived from their herby pasture. They were half

the weight of present-day sheep, needing to be agile enough to return to the 'fold' at night, and put on the fat which has now fallen out of favour with consumers. The ewes, moreover, normally produce only a single lamb.

To many visitors the visitable antiquity of the Downs was a special allure. Spread far and wide on the turf was the outline of prehistoric tumuli, habitations, field-systems, enclosures and hill forts more extensive and unspoilt than anywhere in the British Isles. Moreover, farming practices and equipment seemed to have survived unchanged for more than a thousand years. There was still the sight of sturdy oxen dragging a heavy wooden plough along the slopes of the chalkland, and heavy horse-drawn wagons. Such scenes evoked a sense of 'Saxondom', as did the little squat downland churches nestling against some hillsides, and the homely working farms, little villages and hamlets. The novelists George Moore (1911), D. H. Lawrence (1912) and John Cowper Powys (1967), together with naturalists W. H. Hudson (1900) and Bob Copper (1971) of more recent times, with others, have remarked that the South Downs were the most 'Saxon' part of England. To Helen Thomas (1988), wife of the poet Edward Thomas, the age-old appearance of the higher Downs nourished her sense of continuity with oldest England, and gave her an almost religious sense of belonging to its soil.

Such single elements in the character of the 'old' Downs have been recalled by numerous observers, and the reminiscences of the actor Dirk Bogarde (1992) of Lullington and Lullington Heath, S. P. B. Mais's accounts of his mass walking parties and Bob Copper's recollection of Rottingdean at the beginning of the last century, come readily to mind. It is so much harder to find evidence which recaptures the character of the Downs before the last War as a whole. Anyone over the age of seventy years, when asked what is best remembered of the Downs of their childhood, invariably recalls wistfully a prospect paradisal in its emptiness, with bees buzzing round the wild flowers, myriads of butterflies and goldfinches singing on the tops of thistles. A more realistic description is that of the Worthing postman, J. H. Pull whose ecstasy at the then visible signs of the Black Patch flint mines on ' wild pasture lands on the vast turf-covered tracts on the upper slopes' dotted with juniper bushes, is one of the highlights of the archaeological literature of the Downs (Pull, 1932).

It is noticeable that few nostalgic visions of the 'old' Downs make reference to its arable land. It is almost as if observers were 'brainwashed' to keep silent about it. This is the note struck by the naturalist W. H. Hudson in his little masterpiece, *Nature in Downland* (1900). From his first chapter set in the sheep pastures on Kingston Hill, near Lewes, he avoids contact with human life as instinctively as the

Plate 6
The village of Selborne, Hampshire, where the naturalist Gilbert White lived, viewed from Selborne Hanger.
Photo: Mike Read.

Plate 7 *(centre left)*
Visitors to Beachy Head. A *Punch* cartoon of 1935.

Plate 8 *(centre right)*
The Woodingdean teashop in the 1930s, East Sussex, sited to cater to the increasing numbers of visitors to the area. From Mercer, P. & Holland, D. (1930) *The Huns Mere Pit: the Story of Woodingdean and Balsdean*, Lewes, courtesy of Peter Brandon.

Plate 9
Birling Gap, East Sussex, looking east, in 1931; increasing use of the motor car enabled such formerly remote sites to become popular. Severe cliff erosion has taken place since then: the cottage centre left has now fallen into the sea. Photo from an old postcard, photographer unknown, courtesy of Paul Millmore.

Plate 10
In the Eastern Downs near Lewes, flocks of Southdown sheep grazed the hills by day. Photo from an old postcard, photographer unknown, courtesy of Rendel Williams.

Plate 11
Hampshire Down sheep, specially bred for the conditions of the Western Downs.
Photo: Nick Heasman, courtesy of SDJC.

Plate 12
Getting ready to plough, Falmer, East Sussex, 1940.
Photo from a national newspaper in World War II, photographer unknown, courtesy of Peter Brandon.

Plate 13
Dust from ploughing, near Shoreham, West Sussex, September 1989; the fragile downland soil has been constantly reworked, and is now in danger of being severely eroded.
Photo: Phil Belden.

Plate 14
The Seven Sisters, Sussex Heritage Coast, viewed from Hope Gap, Seaford Head, East Sussex, August 1984.
Photo: Phil Belden.

wheatear and the stonechat. When he mentions corn it is with reference to the rabbit, not the ear or the sower or reaper. He also says almost nothing about the market towns, villages and human life in the Downs. He wrote: 'I seldom care to linger long in their cultivated parts. It seems better to get away, even from the sight of labouring men and oxen, and of golden corn and laughing birdweed, to walk on the turf.' Kipling, Belloc and almost all other writers had a similar aversion to ploughed land. Consequently, to this day, writers of the 'old' Downs have a one-sided view of 'pastoral' Downs. Nothing could be further from the truth. Sheep and corn traditionally existed in symbiosis. Without the dung of the sheepfold and the consolidation of the thin soils with the sheeps' hooves corn, the principal commodity on the Downs, could not have been grown (the sheep being principally in the nineteenth century kept for manuring the land).

For an antidote to the romantics' visions of the Downs we can turn to William Cobbett (Cole, 1930). As a keen horseman he made instinctively for the velvety turf, and the sight of several hundred sheep wending their way down to the fold moved him almost to tears with the recollection that as a boy he had worn a smock-frock and carried a wooden bottle for drink like any other shepherd's lad. But he was also impressed by the large-scale arable farming and its productiveness, and the large size of the fields. He recalled near Shoreham in 1832 the sight of four teams of oxen, six in a team, ploughing in preparation for wheat while several pairs of horses were harrowing and rolling in the same field. In fact, as he himself stated, each farm had its proportion of down, arable and meadow. The former lay almost entirely on the high ground along the present South Downs Way; the arable occupied the middle slopes of the farm and the floors of the combes, where also the farmhouse was sited; the meadow lay in the river valleys which furnished young grass in spring for lambs and pasture for cattle. The actual proportions varied according to time and environmental conditions. As we shall see, ploughing up of old chalk grassland occurred at times of high corn prices, as in wartime, but broadly speaking about one-third of a downland farm in 1900 was downland, over one-third arable and the rest meadow, parkland or woodland. John Godfrey's detailed examination of the land use on the Downs between the Arun and Adur valleys at dates from the 1840s to the onset of War in 1939 (Godfrey, 2002) is not at variance with this generalization. The extreme contraction of old chalk grassland at Applesham appears to have been exceptional (see Chapter 7).

The description by Pull in the 1920s of the downland sward as 'wild pastures' suggests rural dereliction. After the prosperous years of the mid-nineteenth century came a period of acute difficulty with falling prices for corn and wool, and lower rents which fell to ludicrous levels in the bottom of the depression in the 1930s. As early as 1867 poor land in the Western Downs was of little value agriculturally. Less than half of Up Waltham parish was then cultivated, and in Graffham parish only one-quarter. The greater part of the downland there was 'scarcely of value as sheepwalk'. Unsurprisingly labourers lacked work, were poor and badly housed; some were forced to emigrate to the Argentine and Patagonia. When Rider Haggard (1901) visited the Western Downs as part of his investigation into the state of English farming, he found the downland farms in such a sorry condition that they were capable of producing 'but little grass and less corn'. On the Eastern Downs the situation was little better. Farms were let rent-free and lacked tenants for two years or more at a time. The most successful farmers abandoned sheep-and-corn farming and went into dairying and beef production, as did the Brands of Glynde.

Much derelict land was improved during the First World War but, after the repeal of the Corn Production Act 1921, downland agriculture soon swung back into its old state of neglect. Thousands of acres were given over to ragwort, thorn bushes and rabbits. By 1939 dozens of farms, which had once employed many men, kept pedigree prize-winning flocks and produced bountifully wheat, barley and oats of the first quality, lay in desolation. George Mitchell of Pyecombe, the last of the Sussex crook-makers, was not making crooks for shepherds in 1939, but only for bishops. His smithy then looked out on sheepless downs where he remembered a thousand Southdowns grazing. He recalled that in the 'old days' the sward between Pyecombe and Lewes was like a 'billiard table', but then the grass was up to the knees. Despite this crisis, people thought the Downs were as resilient as diamonds and that the sheep would return in the same numbers as before when economic conditions improved. This was the view of Arthur Beckett, the valiant President of the Society of Sussex Downsmen in the 1930s, who held that Southdowns were the natural inhabitants of the Downs, and the Duke of Norfolk, in his review of Barclay Wills's book (1938) on the old shepherds, thought that memories of them would keep them green in people's minds 'against their return'. But the shepherds did not return, and it is surprising that so many persons thought they would. Somehow Sussex people assumed that, although the corrosion of English downland was inevitable, the South Downs would prove the one saving exception. Had sheep been profitable under the traditional system of management practised for centuries, little of the downland would have been touched by the plough. As we have noted, sheep grazing on unimproved pasture had been dying out from the 1870s, was greatly reduced in 1939, and ended completely with the aftermath of war.

From 1940 landscape-destroying intensive farming was promoted by successive governments to provide a greater sufficiency of home-produced food (Plate 12), especially cereals, and by means of subsidies and grants farmers were encouraged to plough up old grassland, scrub and similar unproductive land (Shoard, 1980). The introduction of artificial fertilizer made corn-growing independent of sheep dung, and with the coming of the tractor and bulldozer, and that of the combine harvester and other new equipment such as the deep subsoil disc harrow, the onerous task of dealing with the remaining turf and scrub was greatly eased (Plate 13). Another important change occurred in arable farming. The system of ley farming, which had supported mixed farming, died out in the face of subsidies for grain (see Chapter 7). The success of the ploughing-up policy was completed by crop-breeding which produced crops that resisted pests and yielded more. Everything environmentally that had been held traditionally was rated second best.

In a more favourable epoch a master-plan for the Downs might have provided for a more diversified farming economy consistent with the various soils and degree of slope. That cereal monoculture with agrochemicals, devised as being for the public good in the era of the ration book, should persist into the quite different world of the early twenty-first century, when public opinion has turned in favour of conservation, and consumer demands are different, is one of the anomalies of the present day which needs redress. The result was a disaster – environmentally, culturally, socially and morally – which has threatened the demolition of the Downs. One aspect which has long-term implications is Dr John Boardman's twenty-five year study by Oxford University's Environmental Change Institute (Boardman, 2003). He considers that soil conservation has been negligible, and that soil erosion is causing serious damage to the Downs. He questions the long-term viability of agriculture and argues that current farming systems are unsustainable.

With hindsight, the unmerciful harrying of the Downs was part of the 'commodification' of land which produced a number of disasters including inhuman tower blocks, urban motorways that tore the heart out of many city centres, polluted rivers, building on floodplains, and other instances of the erosion of public trust. There is now a dramatic change in public mood which means these practices are not inherently unchallengeable. Farmers were considered to be pursuing the public interest in the immediate post-war period, but this is no longer axiomatic. There is a new sense of the public interest and a willingness on the part of people to assert themselves in its cause. Whether we like it or not, this is a consumer age. People demand services that are tailored to their individual needs. They want choice and expect quality. They are also now much more conscious of environmental considerations. Clearly there is a need for these considerations to be resolved and for the enhancement of the environment of the Downs. These are challenges which cannot be ignored. They certainly challenge anyone concerned about the future of the South Downs, and the great question as to how to meet this challenge is the central theme of this book. Revolutions, we are told, usually blow themselves out sooner or later. 'The initial flush of exaltation pales: blissful dawn gives way to a banal afternoon.' It is the counter-movement we must now wrestle with, and countervailing, or at least mitigating, changes must be comprehensively applied. Nothing less will suffice to remedy the gross lack of foresight on the Downs. The watchwords of the new accountability would be locality, particularity, diversity, rehabilitation and difference. Such policies would go far to achieve the former Environment Minister Michael Meacher's aim announced in September 1999 to 'restore the area to its natural splendour and beauty'. It would also obviate the fear of the author H. E. Bates (1938), who remarked that we rightly regard as catastrophic the loss of such habitats as woodland, heathland or downland, but that an even greater catastrophe would the loss of the particular kind of beauty we take as naturally for granted as the air we breathe – our farmed landscape. No one who cares about farming wants to be reminded of that, for there is no other way to conserve the natural environment.

REGIONAL DIFFERENCES

Although the South Downs constitute a distinctive tract of chalkland which can be considered a self-contained entity in its own right, there are appreciable changes in character between east and west, and the river valleys which cut across them and the land immediately below the north-facing escarpment also create variations. In consequence the scenic and cultural heritage of the various parts of the Downs varies from one another in several respects. Thus the South Downs may be said to have three component parts, the Eastern Downs (with the sub-division of the downs forming the setting of the City of Brighton and Hove), the Western Downs of Sussex and the East Hampshire Downs, together with the river valleys and the scarp-foot along the north.

The Eastern Downs

It is the primordial shapes and ancient presences of the massive sweeps of bare rounded hills of the Eastern Downs that people regarded as archetypal downland and the epitome of the Downs scenery with which they fell so deeply and desperately in love before the last War. It is this section of the Downs that acquired world-wide fame with Kipling's verses that forms the 'blunt, bow-headed, whale-backed downs' in his own phrase. Here are the magnificent white towering cliffs and the sea, still breathtaking wonders. The Seven Sisters (Plate 14) and Beachy Head are more impressive than the White Cliffs of Dover and, largely thanks to the Society of Sussex Downsmen (now the South Downs Society), Eastbourne Council and East Sussex County Council, are much less spoilt. It is the sheer scale and dramatic profile of the Seven Sisters that wins peoples' hearts. Adrian Berg RA has recently been moved to capture the cliffs at varying hours and seasons, and the American artist Charles Wildbank, after travelling all over Britain, chose the image of the Seven Sisters for a giant mural of the cliffs on the new cruise-liner, the *Queen Mary 2*. The absence of trees or hedges bestows a striking individuality on the shape and form of the land because the chalk, whether grazed or cultivated, retains an impressive and monumental simplicity wherever its curving lines are not masked by woodland or engulfing scrub, which makes the forms of the hills barely discernible. Any form of development on these bare downs breaks the smooth outline and cannot be hidden from the public eye.

Traditionally these Eastern Downs were the principal sheep-rearing area of the South Downs and the most arable. Its glory was the sweet short turf and its most distinctive feature. This was very much the creation of sheep, it being a 'sheep-adapted' community of plants which were capable of sustaining their constant cropping. Consequently it is a type of vegetation that is entirely dependent on grazing by sheep both for its initiation and continued existence. Since the last war, almost all this habitat of old chalk grassland has been lost to ploughing, and although the billowing swells of the chalk are as distinctive under corn as under turf, much of the special charm of the Eastern Downs has been lost. It is now like an efficiently-run factory, where most of the wildlife in the regimented wheat has been killed off by pesticides and artificial fertilizers. The skies are emptier, too, and much of the archaeological heritage has been obliterated. As shown in Chapter 7 (and see Fig.7.4), a good deal of former arable land has been entered into the ESA scheme as pasture, and this greater variety of landscape is to be welcomed. The emptiness is eerie in the Devil's Rest Bottom, near Seaford, where ploughed-out lynchets can be made out, and which gives way to fragments of old chalk grassland overlooking Willingdon and Folkington. The heart of this country is Jevington, a beautiful flint village set in magnificent folds, with an ancient church and its Saxon antiquity. Appropriately, Bob Copper's career as a folk-singer was launched in 1950 with a radio broadcast from the Eight Bells inn (Copper, 1971). Nearby is the great profile of the escarpment stretching to Mount

Harry and Ditchling Beacon. This leads on to Wolstonbury and Newtimber Hills which afford finer views of the Western Downs beyond Chanctonbury Ring than from the Devil's Dyke.

Brighton's Downs are a disgrace. David Bangs has described Whitehawk Hill as a place that 'remains a wretched mess, neglected, unrecognised and scarcely funded' (Bangs, 2004) and much the same could be said of the rest of the environs of the resort. Scrub and bramble are slowly advancing; semi-derelict land is being abandoned; fly-tipping is rife; inappropriate development is taking place; and little consideration is being given to local residents who have vigorously explored their environment's wildlife and landscape. Parts, such as the Warren Ridge and the Sheepcote Valley, may possibly be included into the boundary of the proposed National Park but much new initiative will be required of the City Council. In recent years much has been written of the need to revitalize the City of Brighton and Hove and to make changes in the townscape, but next to nothing is being proposed for the downland setting of the resort. Urban-fringe downland poses special problems (Plate 15). The continuation of farming, for example, is itself problematic. Nevertheless there is a unique opportunity for policies which address the needs of the urban population. Here the urban fringe should be a special target for landscape restoration, the designation of country parks, the extension of more public ownership, farmland diversity, the removal of eyesores and the prevention of intrusive development in the interest of improved public access and quiet enjoyment. An imaginative project of this kind, democratically planned, would command national interest, and hopefully attract external funding. It would also be a contribution to the rejuvenation of Brighton and Hove and a way of bringing potentially beautiful heritage into the twenty-first century, thereby permitting an urban public to regain their old custom of wandering over the Downs. Let us hope that Bangs's fellow citizens take up arms in the battle he invites them to join, and that Brighton's Downs become the focus of civic pride, civic activism and civic enterprise.

The Western Downs

The Downs change character as they begin to strike obliquely inland away from the white cliffs and rise higher and wider as they extend westwards towards Butser. In several respects these Western Downs are radically different from the downland in the east. Entering the Western Downs one is conscious of visiting a different country. The eye is not set free along curves and hollows spread like an ocean without check. Mantling its surface is a remarkable extent of woodland which somewhat cloaks the curvature of the hills, reduces the sense of spaciousness, limits vistas to the horizon and, on account of fencing, the rambler and horse-rider is more confined than in the Eastern Downs. The greater part of the surface shows little sign of Kipling's 'blunt, bow-headed, whale-backed hills', for there are extensive plateaux resulting from a less mature dissection by former springs and streams. In short the pre-war connoisseur of chalk hills tended to regard the Western Downs as less glamorous than the grassy downland further east thought of as archetypal. Those devoted to the austere downland were inclined to regard the Western Downs as 'downless' downs and so hardly proper downland at all. To enjoy them one has to learn a 'special language' and then they are invested with a special charm and significance, and have a cryptic and compelling fascination of their own.

Although traditionally grazed by sheep, they were too leafy to have had the extensive spreads of that springy green turf which was regarded as the glory of the South Downs from the seventeenth century, though Levin Down and Harting Down (Plates 16 & 93) are examples of well-managed chalk grassland. They have experienced less change since the last war, and thus the individual human scale of many features remains small. Because most of it was not so intensively farmed as further east, the 'wilder' landscape elements mix with the cultivated land, both types of landscape being present in turns and melting into another at almost every place. The woodland beauty of the Western Downs has also risen in public estimation. Woodland is being looked upon with keener observation and pleasure than ever before. Its beauty at all seasons is attracting more visitors but there are other pleasurable sensations. Although there is not to be found any 'natural wildness' on account of the successive replantings of trees, there are plenty of places which one can feel to be 'wild' and offer an experience of solitude. Many of these valuable woods were in medieval deer parks and other areas zoned for hunting.

Woodland has always been the permanent background to the Western Downs. From the tops of farms the wood spreads almost continuously along, and the farms have lain in its black shadow. The sustained tending and harvesting of trees is one of its most ancient and cherished traditions, which has added its own rhythm to local life. Coppicing hazel and sweet chestnut (Plates 124 & 125) and the growing of mature trees were customary at Graffham, for instance, which had pottery works and a strong wood-products industry. Today, hardly any mechanical noise is audible in these muffled woods. This is partly because although this is woodcutter's traditional country, his axe, hatchet and hook resound less frequently through the woods, little blue smoke filters through the clearings, and the timber dray bearing great oaks and beech, one of the most familiar sights on the Downs since colonization began, is hardly ever seen now that the

market for wood-products has collapsed. The decline began from the 1880s with imports of timber from overseas, and in recent decades the loss of the pulping mill at Sittingbourne and the end of sales of pit-props and railway-wagon timbers, together with the products of sundry turneries and saw-mills, means that wood-products are on sale only to a very limited degree and at no real profit. Apart from mature trees, the Western Downs have one of the highest percentages of land planted to sweet chestnut and hazel in Britain. Their quick growth, abundance, flexibility and thinness made them among the most valuable of all timber crops, since they could be twisted so easily to make fences and hurdles, or into hop-poles, barrels or pit-props, and their tributary twigs were excellent for bean-stakes. At present coppice is largely abandoned and in danger of becoming impenetrable of access, and deteriorating both in timber quality and biodiversity. The problem of economic viability is exacerbated by the small size of many private woodlands, but the total acreage makes too big an impact on the landscape to ignore.

It is only recently that sustainable woodland management has been widely desirable from an ecological, and thus, also from a recreational point of view. Each cutting of coppice or thinning of mature trees is beneficial to wildlife. The canopy of leaves is opened up, encouraging wildflowers that need light and water and cannot grow under trees. These in turn attract insects to feed on the pollen and nectar, and birds to feed on the insects. As coppicing moved forward from compartment to compartment in rotation there were always areas which provided food, cover and nesting sites for birds and mammals in the light, space and orderliness introduced. A remunerative outlet for wood-products is thus the first step both in the rejuvenation of the rural economy, for the enrichment of the wildlife for public enjoyment and for the preservation of the distinctive landscape. The search for new markets for wood-products has begun, but it is too recent and modest in its targets to be reassuring about the future, and it must be said that progress in this direction appears to have been more successful in the east than in the west.

It is only just that for economic and environmental reasons, every inhabitant of the valleys should receive more benefits from their woods. Anyone conscious of the Downs' traditional place in national forestry and woodsmanship is filled with a sense of shame and disbelief at the waste of indigenous resources, whereas, in the Weald's continuation into France in the Pays de Bray exemplary forestry is pursued, providing much rural employment and wildlife and recreational benefits. As Donald MacDonald remarks in Chapter 8, English woods could never be expected to compete with overseas imports, but government policy and conservation groups, such as the Woodland Trust, are now contributing financial support where

Plate 15 *(right)*
Urban encroachment; post-war housing on the Downs at North Lancing, West Sussex, following the contour, June 1992.
Photo: Phil Belden.

Plate 16 *(centre)*
The view from Harting Down looking towards Tower Hill, West Sussex, showing the more wooded nature of the Western Downs.
Photo: Mike Read.

Plate 17 *(bottom left)*
Old Winchester Hill, Hampshire; a most important archaeological site and National Nature Reserve. The photo shows the Iron Age ramparts (for an aerial photo see Plate 41); the NNR includes the largest colony of juniper in south-east England, and attracts a variety of invertebrates including the Duke of Burgundy fritillary.
Photo: Nick Heasman, courtesy of SDJC.

Plate 18 *(bottom right)*
The River Meon in east Hampshire, less affected by water extraction than other chalk streams.
Photo: Mike McGoran, courtesy of Natural England/SDJC

Plate 19 (*left*)
Amberley Wildbrooks, West Sussex, taken from the South Downs Way looking north, January 1991.
Photo: Phil Belden.

Plate 20 (*below*)
Amberley Wildbrooks showing the drainage ditches that are important for wildlife.
Photo: Cris Brunnen, courtesy of SDJC.

Plate 21 (*left*)
The Adur Valley looking south to the sea from the edge of Upper Beeding, West Sussex.
Photo: Cris Brunnen, courtesy of SDJC.

Plate 22 (*below*)
The Arundel skyline (left and centre) looking westwards over the River Arun with the Downs to the right.
Photo: SDJC.

there is a perceived public benefit, such as providing recreational opportunities or encouraging biodiversity. Let us hope that these measures, together with the search for new markets for wood products, give grounds for optimism for the future of woodland on the Western Downs.

Another distinctive element in the character of the Western Downs is **the great estates** of magnates with locally sporting and farming traditions evolved over centuries. Although sheep and corn have always figured in the economy, neither has been as prominent as further east. A good deal of land has been preserved traditionally for sport, and much of this was not suitable for anything else, given the state of farming art in the past. Early sporting landscapes include the deer parks which were especially prominent on the western Downs. The vanished glories of the Charlton Hunt are still imprinted on the landscape in the form of widely planted fox coverts. Moreover, the woodland and farmland which embellishes the present scene reflects the great landowner's desire to make his home good to live in and to look at, and to provide his incidental sport and leisure. This has involved the visual remodelling of the land surfaces of entire estates, and this lends a tranquil, serene, spacious sense of grandeur and ease which is lacking in the stark landscape of the Eastern Downs, the traditional preserve of the peasant and yeoman. As H. G. Wells noted of these Western Downs 'In no other country in the world has such a continuous effort been made to elevate leisure, or the appearance of it, as a finely judged art'. This *grande luxe* landscape of, for example, Arundel, Cowdray, Goodwood and West Dean, is of course, essentially private, but the grandiloquence is a national asset, and it is heartening to note the present conservation being undertaken on these estates. Game-shooting is now an important source of revenue on many estates and farms. It is also responsible for the appearance of the countryside, for its requirements dictate where and what crops are sown. Deciduous woods are planted specifically for shooting and in addition much game-cover is planted annually.

The Western Downs were the spiritual home of Hilaire Belloc. He always wrote of Sussex as if it were the crown of England, and the downland bordering the river Arun as the jewel of that crown. His milieu is centred on Slindon, his childhood home, and he wrote with great gusto of the high woods, 'noisy in the loud October', through which he rode on horseback, tramped on foot or viewed from the deck of his sailing-boat in the English Channel. He tended to write about a number of specific, real places one of which is Barlavington Down near Duncton Hill, which figures in the closing chapter of his *Four Men* (1912). Belloc perceived this downland as a mysterious landscape of ancient boundary dykes, lynchetted fields and rough woods. Its character was

totally transformed in 1979 by ploughing, which became a national issue (Shoard, 1980), destroying one of the few remaining areas of chalk grassland, damaging scheduled archaeological monuments, diverting rights of way and virtually clearing scrub – a fine habitat of warblers – at a time when the need to bring any more land into cereal production was being widely questioned. A rewarding future project would be to restore, where necessary, Belloc's enchanting places to something like their character of a century ago.

East Hampshire Downs

Beyond Butser Hill the South Downs change again. The East Hampshire Downs are bereft of the formidable north-facing escarpment which has proved the hypnotic feature that captured the imagination of generations, and they become so low that one cannot savour the solemn grandeur and sublimity which some have felt as 'a sort of delectable mountain feeling'. Yet it has an individuality of its own. The old trackway between West Meon and Warnford offers views across serene country, as does the Wayfarers' Way, the long-distance path between Emsworth and Inkpen Beacon, which takes to the higher country between Hinton Ampner and Droxford. Old Winchester Hill (Plate 17) commands the best views. Standing on the ramparts of the great Iron-Age fortress, with skylarks singing overhead, is to find an oasis of the green mantle which once clothed the high chalkland and to enjoy a remote, still and empty landscape amidst rows of regimented winter wheat, where once similar rich habitats have been ploughed and sprayed out of existence. The magnificent views are in a full circle of the horizon towards Salisbury Plain, the Berkshire Downs, Hindhead, the Vale of Fernhurst, the Western Downs, the Isle of Wight, the Solent, the New Forest and the Dorset Downs. It is impossible to believe that this is the immediate hinterland of the large towns of Portsmouth, Eastleigh, Fareham and Southampton, and that fine fragments of lynchetted downland survive on the edge of the built-up areas such as Catherington. The Meon is an exquisite stream which has not suffered the same degree of decline through water abstraction as is the plight of many other chalk streams (Plate 18).

The scarp-foot

The land immediately below the north-facing escarpment, the scarp-foot, extends from East Hampshire eastwards into Sussex and is distinguished by its chain of villages, hamlets and isolated farms standing on **the 'spring-line'**, where hundreds of deliciously clear-running springs emerge more or less exactly at the junction of the permeable Chalk and Upper Greensand formation with the impermeable

Gault Clay. These springs ran mills grinding corn and fulling cloth, watered meadows and orchards, spread into teeming fishponds, and provided pure water for drinking and farm use at no cost. Each of the spring-line villages is linked by deeply worn trackways to the crest of the chalk (locally called 'bostals') and to each other by a narrow byway, which so winds and twists that it is best enjoyed by cycle, or on horseback or by beetling along in an old Morris Minor. The novelist Ernest Raymond (1932) thought the lane between Edburton and Poynings the finest of them all. Certainly this affords magnificent views of the escarpment and other delights. The underhill lane near Ditchling, the Old Coach Road below Firle Beacon, and further west as at West Burton, Bignor, Sutton, Barlavington, Bepton, Treyford and Didling, the road has a special magic of its own, being invariably a hollow way up to twelve feet below the surrounding fields as a result of age-long traffic and periodic heavy rain. In this district the motorist must be prepared to be held up by the regular passage of dairy cows, or to be distracted by extravagantly beautiful downland. This scarp-foot terrain in West Sussex is very special, being made up of very different types of scenery in a shorter distance than is usual in Britain. Patrick Heron (1955), the artist, explaining the sources of the inspiration of the distinguished landscape painter Ivon Hitchens, of Lavington Common near Petworth, noted the variegated, overgrown beauty where miniature hills and valleys run through wooded heaths, flat meadows, marshes and fields, conceal small lakes, hammer-ponds, waterfalls and streams amidst rhododendron tunnels, massive oaks and chestnuts lapping against the smooth chalk-grass-woodland rampart of the Downs. He described it as a lush force of nature regulating itself into a disordered order, a fertile wildness. Eleanor Farjeon in *Martin Pippin in the Apple Orchard* (1921) evokes it as a 'secret' country' where everything was so intricate that it might be 'Eden grown tiny'. This landscape is so brim-full of unregarded landscape features that one thinks of an over-packed suitcase bursting at the seams. Repeated house-building, as in the Stor valley at Storrington, now threatens to destroy it irretrievably.

The river valleys

The river valleys by which the South Downs are divided were integrated into the sheep-and-corn farms on their flanks because they offered rich summer pastures. There are few more beautiful places in England than these valleys. Several of the waterside villages were little ports engaged in sea fishing and salt-making before farmers embanked the rivers to reclaim farmland in the early middle ages. The rivers sweep hard in places against almost precipitous cliffs, relics of former river-cliffs of great age, and the white scars on these hillsides, marking abandoned quarries,

add greatly to the interest of the scene. The quiet reaches of brookland are cut by formerly interconnecting, but now choked channels, and remnants of abandoned control hatches, signs of traditional skills of 'drowning' and draining the meadows for pasture, now largely lost, but for centuries matter of fact and seasonal. In the 1960s and 1970s the rivers have been confined into massive embankments to permit an extension of arable and improved pasture which has greatly reduced flora and wildlife. The current trend is to reverse this in favour of conservation.

The regeneration of wetland originated with the *cause célèbre* over the proposed pump drainage of the Amberley Wildbrooks (Plate 19), long regarded as one of the great natural heritages of Sussex, when two government bodies simultaneously pursued contradictory policies for these wetlands at a time of agricultural over-production. The Nature Conservancy Council (later English Nature, and now to form part of 'Natural England') wanted to preserve them for the nation, and was intending to classify them as a Grade I Site of Special Scientific Interest, whereas the Ministry of Agriculture was examining whether public money should be used to help pay for their destruction. It was argued convincingly to a Public Inquiry by David Streeter, a distinguished ecologist of Sussex University, that the taxpayer was expected to pay a substantial sum for negligible agricultural benefit at the cost of a major conservation loss. As noted in Chapters 5 and 9, the Minister for Agriculture accepted the recommendation of his inspector not to provide grant-aid towards the scheme. This famous battle, which could not have been more timely and important, was a landmark in the regeneration of wetland nationally and turned the tide in their favour in Sussex.

One of the first influences was on the Pulborough Brooks Nature Reserve of the Royal Society for the Protection of Birds, which opened in 1992 as an excellent example of what management can do to restore damaged wetland for conservation. Like the Amberley Wildbrooks and similar low-lying lands, these were traditionally managed as flood meadows (brookland is the local name), that is, grazed and mown in summer, and left to flood in winter (Plate 20). The intensive agriculture of the 1960s and 1970s had damaging effects on wildlife in general and on the wintering and breeding of water-birds in particular. The effects of reverting to traditional practices on the reserve has raised bird populations substantially and also that of species of plants and nationally-important invertebrates.

The overall aim is to make the Reserve a focus for the restoration of wetland in the Arun valley, and for the restitution of reedbeds along streams (for the bittern, hen harrier and reed bunting). It has also had a profound effect on the other river valleys crossing the chalk. In the Adur valley, Church Farm, Coombes, already has converted part of the floodplain into a fishing lake and is proposing to extend wetland upstream into an area of arable land created during the 1960s (Plate 21). In the Ouse valley, a Reserve has already been created and more developments are planned. The Cuckmere valley is the scene of the most controversial wetland proposal (Plate 122). The river meandering down to the shingle beach at the break in the chalk cliffs is one of the most memorable in Sussex. The meanders are more aesthetic than functional because almost the entire water is carried by a relief channel whose banks are reckoned to have reached the end of their working lives. The proposal of the Environment Agency is to breach the aged banks of the river's relief channel, so that the grazing meadows will be flooded and become a tidal estuary supporting myriads of waders and wildfowl. The cost of maintaining the cut is put at £3 million; the fate of the meanders is still an unresolved matter (and see Chapter 9).

This proposal has encountered considerable opposition, and a public inquiry is planned. As Clive Aslet has argued in *Country Life*, the defence of the status quo is similar to the one put forward in another context by John Ruskin and William Morris. They advocated the sort of repair of old churches which would keep them in the state in which they happened to have been found. These principles were those on which the Society for the Protection of Ancient Buildings was founded, and they underlie the modern philosophy of architectural conservation. Aslet argues that they have yet to permeate the world of nature conservation. The Environment Agency has countered by arguing that inter-tidal habitats are declining particularly in the South East. 'Salt marsh, mudflats and saline lagoons are important wildlife habitats, and the Government has international obligations to protect and enhance them' (English Nature, 2004). A great difficulty of the scheme is that it is unclear what the valley would look like if the defensive banks were removed. Would tides cover the ground to create salt marsh? Would the valley be broad enough to draw the species envisaged? What effect would the scheme have on the meanders? Would Alfriston (see Frontispiece) suffer from floods? It is clear that answers to these questions are needed before one can make a decision on the future of the Cuckmere valley.

Paul Millmore and a team of campaigners (2004) drawn from environmental bodies, such as the Campaign to Protect Rural England, Friends of the Earth and the Wildlife Trusts, suggested to the Public Inquiry, as noted in Chapter 13, that the boundaries of the proposed South Downs National Park should be extended by 1.2 miles out to sea at the point where the Downs meet the sea. 'The sea is our last pristine wilderness but its protection is a mess at the moment,' says Millmore. 'Beyond the low-water mark you have a mish-mash of different interests with virtually no real protection and almost no money to enforce what little there is. If you have a National Park Authority extending out to sea, you would have a body whose one purpose is conservation and enhancement, with proper funds and resources.' The Countryside Agency claims that National Park boundaries stop at the low-water mark, but Millmore contests this. He has usefully exposed how very few existing mechanisms protect marine areas of National Parks, whereas in the USA and Australia local seashores have been protected by setting up marine national parks.

The small towns

An important element of the South Downs is the small towns that lie within or on the edge of them. A fascinating form of rural settlement is the decayed market town, of which Alfriston and Hambledon are examples. The latter is now a large, compact downland village, but with its greatly enlarged thirteenth-century church above an agreeable mixture of half-timbered, flint and Georgian brick houses and former shops, it still retains the air of a small-scale town, as does Alfriston. Midhurst, another small town, has been nominated by *Country Life* as the second most attractive town in the country (Alnwick was rated first). Arundel is a charming town with steep streets above the River Arun and a backdrop crowned by a huge French Gothic cathedral and a still larger castle backed by a dramatically wooded park (Plate 22). As an overall landscape composition it is generally considered to be among the grandest and most wonderful creations of the Romantic imagination. The woodland scenery is as inspiring as when John Constable discovered it in 1831. 'The woods hang from excessive steeps and precipices,' he wrote, 'and the trees are beyond everything beautiful. I never saw such beauty in natural landscape before.'

If the special place of the South Downs in our culture lies in its recognition as a 'quintessentially English landscape', then Lewes is a quintessential English town (Plate 23), with its castle, former markets, a coaching inn and merchants' houses in their superb downland setting. In many respects it can be regarded as 'the capital of the South Downs'. It is not a town just like any other. The New Economics Foundation considers that it has not been 'cloned' by the relentless spread of chain-stores as have most larger towns, and thus its degree of loss of aesthetic, architectural and civic diversity is small. It has plenty of independent shops in the High Street, but a great many locals would like to see more useful outlets in this town of unique characteristics than charity shops, antique shops and the like. Petersfield contains a pleasant mix of brick, rendered and timber-framed houses.

The Downs have long been famous for their attractive villages and hamlets. Working villages with farmsteads in the village street no longer exist, though Stanmer, Alciston and Telscombe continue to have a farm in the village. Amberley (Plate 24) is characteristic of the new breed of 'chocolate box' village that has been taken over by immigrants from the towns. At the time of the Tithe Map (1841) numerous farmsteads continued to lie in the village street, and the Census of 1891 reveals that most of its houses were the homes of farm-workers. East Meon, Warnford, Droxford, Selborne, South Harting, East Dean and Singleton, Slindon, Findon, Coombes, Ditchling and West Firle are among the most attractive.

BEYOND THE CHALK

The north-west part of Sussex and Hampshire beyond the Chalk which is within the bounds of the proposed National Park is comparatively unknown countryside, and yet it has been lavishly praised for its rare, distinguished beauty. Disraeli was overcome by its surprising intimacy and variety and more recent admirers have been Dr Cyril Joad (1947), for whom its beauty so surpassed anywhere else in southern England that it was beyond his powers of description. John Rickman has recently written *The Land of Lod* (1998) based on it.

The essence of this landscape is its remarkable variety. It is a muddled, small-scale country in which ridge and hollow, copses, woods, fields, commons, twiddly lanes and small scattered farms all crowd together in the course of a short walk (Plate 25). One gains the impression of a remarkable profusion of trees, shrubs and wild plants that few other parts of Britain can match. The sound of running water fed by springs, where the sandstone meets the clay, enhances the landscape. There is a network of clear-running and tree-lined rivulets, of which one is the Lod, which rises near Linchmere church and reaches the larger river Rother at Selham.

The enemy of this landscape in the strip of Greensand is the invasive spread of rhododendron, which has coalesced in many places into an impenetrable jungle. The grower Harry Mangles began the hybridization of plants from Sikkim in the late nineteenth century at his home below Blackdown. Between the late 1880s and the 1930s immigrants built country houses on unlikely hill-tops – even to the point of having them undermined on steep slopes by land-slipping – as at Fernhurst, and planted up their properties with monkey puzzles, firs, Portuguese laurels, azaleas and, above all, with rhododendrons, which once produced flower-clusters of various hues but have now reverted mainly to their pinkish-mauve prototype. The latter have run riot over the former heathery commons and 'waste'

places. Another ecological problem is the spread of birch and other trees on commons, which has resulted from the cessation of grazing since the First World War.

These problems are being vigorously tackled by the West Sussex County Council, the National Trust and other organizations. Marley Heights and Blackdown are examples of concerted action. Tennyson (Lang & Shannon, 1982) knew the latter as heather-covered heathland dotted with pines and grazed by sheep and cattle, and was charmed by it. He refers to 'heather blossom' and 'wild heather' in his letters and other writings. As grazing declined from the end of the nineteenth century, and the traditional cutting of 'brakes' (bracken and heather) for littering barns on farms short of straw ceased, trees seeded and grew eventually into woods. Blackdown acquired a new 'forest' feeling of close-growing Scots pines with beeches on its flanks; rowans and rhododendrons also multiplied and grasslands were invaded by bracken. The clock is now being turned back. Pines have been felled, rhododendron cut out and birches pulled up to permit heather to regenerate (Plate 26) and to conserve bogs, rarely found on such high ground. The aim of the modern landscape architect is a mosaic which will create new viewpoints lost in a maze of trees, and a habitat for warblers, woodlarks, siskins, stonechats, and rare species of butterfly. Already long-dormant heather seeds are pushing new shoots through earth flattened by contractors' machinery. Blackdown is now becoming once more as Tennyson knew it, and commons such as at Stedham, Iping, Woolbeding and Milland will eventually look again like the scenes painted by Birket Foster, Helen Allingham and other late Victorian artists. A special feature of an ambitious new project is the creation of the Serpent Trail, a 40-mile footpath that snakes its way through the woodland and regenerated heathland north of Midhurst and Petworth (see Chapter 10, Fig.10.1). This could be a prototype for similar schemes in the future.

THE IMPLICATIONS FOR THE FUTURE

Studying the pre-war Downs does not imply a return to 'the old days', which are now distant and irrecoverable. We should not plan an ersatz museum or simply look back to the landscapes of the past for any part of the Downs or its neighbouring hills and vales. We must take advantage of the current crisis in farming to conceive, design, create and maintain new landscapes which would do better for the land degraded by intensively worked arable and 'fit for the social, economic and environmental needs of the twenty-first century' (Green, 2002). Yet it would be wrong to overlook the landscape features most admired by those who led English landscape

Plate 23 (*above*)
The view from Lewes Castle keep – a thousand years of history in the town's roofscape below.
Photo: Harry Montgomery.

Plate 24 (*above right*)
Houses at Amberley, West Sussex; formerly a street village inhabited by small farmers, which from the 1920s was invaded by writers, artists and retired folk so that it has now become a 'chocolate box' type of settlement.
Photo: Peter Brandon.

Plate 26 (*right*)
Scrub clearance of a heathland environment, Forest Mere.
Photo: Keith Fryer, courtesy of SDJC.

Plate 25 (*below*)
The Wealden countryside below Linchmere, West Sussex, in late afternoon, autumn 2006, looking south towards the chalk Downs in the distance. The first line of (blue) hills is part of the sandy ridge between Fernhurst and Midhurst; the highest hill on the horizon is Harting Down.
Photo: Michael Packard.

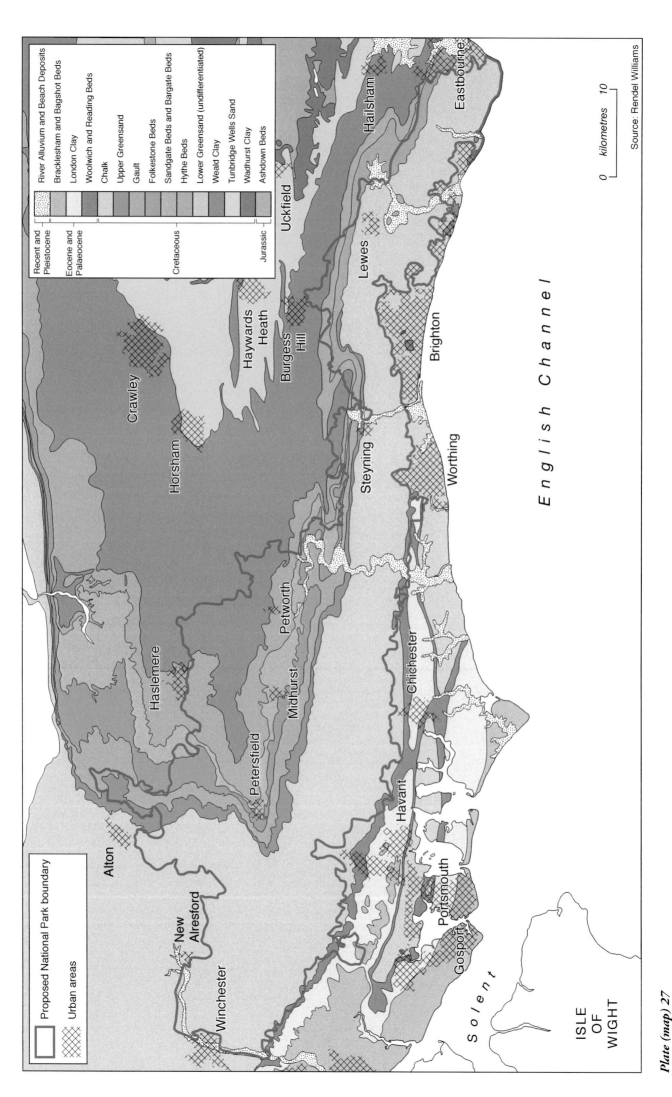

Plate (map) 27

Geological map of the South Downs area.
Produced by Rendel Williams & University of Southampton Cartographic Unit.

Legend:

Proposed National Park boundary
Urban areas

Recent and Pleistocene
- River Alluvium and Beach Deposits

Eocene and Palaeocene
- Bracklesham and Bagshot Beds
- London Clay
- Woolwich and Reading Beds

Cretaceous
- Chalk
- Upper Greensand
- Gault
- Folkestone Beds
- Sandgate Beds and Bargate Beds
- Hythe Beds
- Lower Greensand (undifferentiated)
- Weald Clay
- Tunbridge Wells Sand

Jurassic
- Wadhurst Clay
- Ashdown Beds

Source: Rendel Williams

0 kilometres 10

Winchester
New Alresford
Alton
Petersfield
Haslemere
Midhurst
Petworth
Horsham
Crawley
Haywards Heath
Burgess Hill
Uckfield
Lewes
Hailsham
Eastbourne
Steyning
Brighton
Worthing
Chichester
Havant
Portsmouth
Gosport

Solent
ISLE OF WIGHT

English Channel

taste over the past one hundred years. High in priority was the evidence of age in landscape as expressed in historical associations and a dislike of the present day, in particular anything obviously functional. There is no reason to believe that these conclusions do not remain valid (Lowenthal & Price, 1965). A sense of continuity with the 'Old Downs' should therefore be one of the objectives in any Master Plan for the Downs. A number of projects can be envisaged which could draw upon the 'quintessential Englishness' which was the inspiration of the Downs for Englishmen before the Second World War.

REFERENCES

Allcroft, A.H. (1924) *Downland Pathways.* London. pp. 1–2.

Bangs, D. (2004) *Whitehawk Hill.* Brighton.

Bates, H.E. (1938) in Williams-Ellis, C. (ed) *Britain and the Beast.* London.

Beckett, R.B. (ed) (1952) *John Constable and the Fishers.* London. pp. 183–4.

Belloc, H. (1964) *Collected Verse.* London.

Boardman, J. (2003) Soil erosion and flooding on the eastern South Downs. *Journal of the Institute of British Geographers*, **28**, 2, 176–196.

Bogarde, Sir D. (1992) *Great Meadow.* London.

Brandon, P. (1998) *The South Downs.* Chichester. This section is a revised version of Chapters 11 and 12.

Brooke, S. (1865) *A Life and Letters of F.W. Robertson.* London.

Cole, G.D. and M. (eds) (1930*) The Rural Rides of William Cobbett.* Vol.3. London. pp. 702–3.

Constable, J. *see* **Becket, R.B.** and **Leslie, P.**

Copper, B. (1971) *A Song for Every Season.* London. p. 185.

Davidson, J. (1898) *The Speaker.* London.

English Nature (2004) *English Nature Magazine.* June. 31–2.

Farjeon, E. (1921) *Martin Pippin in the Apple Orchard.* London.

Gill, E. (1940) *Autobiography.* London. pp. 75–7.

Gilpin, W. (1792) *Picturesque Beauty.* London.
 (1804) *Observations on the Coasts of Hampshire, Sussex and Kent.* London.

Godfrey, J. (2002) Land ownership and farming on the South Downs in West Sussex, 1840 to 1940. *Sussex Archaeological Collections* **140**, 113–123.

Granville, A.B. (1841) *Spas of England: The Midlands and the South.* London. pp. 580–1.

Green, B. (2002) The farmed landscape. In: Jenkins, J. (ed), *Remaking the Landscape.* London. p. 210.

Haggard, H.R. (1902) *Rural England.* Vol.1. London.

Hare, A. (1894) *A Guide to Sussex.* London.

Heron, P. (1955) *Ivon Hitchens.* London. pp. 12–3.

Hudson, W.H. (1900) *Nature in Downland.* London. p. 32.

Joad, C.E.M. (1947) *The Untutored Townsman's Invasion of the Countryside.* London.

Johnson, Dr S. *see* **Piozzi, Mrs**

Kipling, R. (1990) *Complete Verse.* (Ed. M.M. Kaye.) London.

Lang, C.W. and Shannon, E.F. (eds) (1982) *Letters of Alfred Lord Tennyson.* London.

Lankester, E. (1948) *The Correspondence of John Ray.* London

Lawrence, D.H. (1912) *England My England.* London. p. 14.

Leslie, P. (ed) (1931) *Letters of John Constable to C.R. Leslie.* London. pp. 117–8.

Lowenthal, D. and Prince, H. (1965) Evaluating Landscapes. *Geographical Review* **2**, 185–222.

Mais, S.P.B. (n.d.) *Listen to the Country.* London.

Meacher, M. (1999) Statement made on the occasion of the Government's proposal to create a National Park of the South Downs.

Merrifield, Mrs. (1864) *A Sketch of the Natural History of Brighton.* Brighton.

Meynell, A. (1899) *The Spirit of Place.* London. p. 210.

Millmore, P. (2004) Statement to the Public Inquiry on the proposed South Downs National Park.

Moore, G. (1911) *AVE.* London. pp. 307–11.

Piozzi, Mrs. (1984) *Anecdotes of the Late Samuel Johnson., LLD.* Ed. R. Napner. London.

Pull, J.H. (1932) *The Flint Mines of Blackpatch.* London.

Ray, J. *see* **Lankester, E.**

Raymond, E. (1932) *Once in England.* London. p. 89.

Shoard, M. (1980) *The Theft of the Countryside.* London.

Tennyson, A. Lord *see* **Lang, C.W. and Shannon, E.F.**

Thomas, H. and M. (1988) *Under Storm's Wing.* London. p. 50.

Wells, H.G. (1915) *The Research Magnificent.* London. p. 151.
 (1909) *Tono-Bungay.* London. p. 231.

Wills, B. (1938) *Shepherds of Sussex.* London. p. 1.

Woolf, V. (1947) *The Death of the Moth.* London. p. 12.

Further reading

Beckett, A. (1909) *The Spirit of the Downs.* London.

Belloc, H. (1906) *Hills and the Sea.* London.
 (1906) *Sussex.* London.
 (1912) *The Four Men.* London
 (1936) *The County of Sussex.* London.

Cobbett, W. (1821-26) *Political Register.* London.

Copper, B. (1997) *Bob Copper's Sussex.* Seaford.

Curwen, E.C. (1929) *Prehistoric Sussex.* London.
 (1936) *The Archaeology of Sussex.* London

Hopkins, G.T. (1927) *Sussex Pilgrimages.* London.

Lower, M.A. (1870) *A Compendious History of Sussex.* London.

Powys, J.C. (1967) *Autobiography.* London.

BOXGROVE CHURCH FROM THE SOUTH-EAST.

CHAPTER 2
Rocks and Relief

RENDEL WILLIAMS

The South Downs and Western Weald are a key part of Britain's geological heritage. The rocks and relief have been intensively studied by researchers for over two centuries, and continue to arouse keen scientific interest. It is beyond the scope of this chapter to provide more than a brief overview, starting with the formation of the Chalk and later rocks. Attention then focuses on the landforms of the Chalk. Finally, a brief account is given of the Western Weald with its alternating series of clays and sandstones that predate the Chalk. As other chapters will demonstrate, the rocks and relief of the South Downs and Western Weald have profoundly affected both the natural vegetation of the region and the human landscape.

THE GEOLOGICAL SUCCESSION FROM LATE CRETACEOUS TIMES ONWARDS

Chalk and its origin

The chalk hills of the South Downs cross Sussex in a west-east direction, forming the southern boundary of the Low Weald (Plate (map) 27). In the east the Downs end abruptly in the sea at Beachy Head, near Eastbourne, but where they start in the west is a matter of opinion. It is often said that they begin near the Sussex-Hampshire border, in line with the western end of the Weald, but this book takes Winchester as the starting point, in the heart of the area often called the Hampshire Downs.

The South Downs owe much of their distinctive landscape-character to the special properties of the underlying chalk bedrock. Chalk is an unusually soft, fine-grained and porous limestone formed by marine organisms. The whiter varieties of Chalk are particularly pure, containing at least 95 per cent calcium carbonate or calcite.

In north-west Europe, the Chalk started forming about 100 million years ago, at the start of the Late Cretaceous Period. The atmosphere contained four times as much carbon dioxide as now, the climate was everywhere tropical or sub-tropical, and there were no polar ice caps. Rising sea levels flooded most of Britain and large parts of the European mainland. Living in the sun-lit, surface waters of the Cretaceous sea were myriads of minute unicellular algae called coccolithophores. These algae are widely distributed in modern oceans, but were particularly abundant in Chalk times. Within their cells, the coccolithophores secreted tiny crystals of calcite arranged in rings called coccoliths, up to 20 microns in diameter. The coccoliths migrated to the surface of the cells, and became detached, sinking very slowly to the sea bed, where they accumulated in sufficient quantities to form a calcitic mud. In addition, minute planktonic crustacea called copepods appear to have feasted on the living algae, expelling the calcite in their faeces which, being relatively heavy, descended quite rapidly to the sea bed, adding to the mud (Hancock, 1993).

When the purer forms of Chalk are examined under the electron microscope, they are found to be very largely composed of coccolithic debris. The remaining eight to 20 per cent of the rock is mostly made up of foraminiferal tests, tiny fragments of seashells, and other finely comminuted debris of biological origin.

The coccolithic debris that accumulated on the Cretaceous sea bed may initially have formed a very soft, watery mud but, as the mud increased in thickness, its lower layers became compressed, losing much of their water (Hancock, 1993). The tiny calcite crystals were pushed together to form an interlocking mass, with much reduced porosity and increased strength. Some of the calcite dissolved, especially where crystals pressed against each other, and was then re-precipitated as cement between the crystals. It was this cementation combined with compaction that transformed the mud into more solid Chalk.

From time to time, deposition of mud on the sea bed slowed or even ceased, allowing the surface layers more time to consolidate and harden. Sponges, sea urchins, molluscs and other animals favouring a firm substrate became more abundant. Chalk beds that represent periods of reduced or arrested sedimentation are called 'hard grounds'. They have varied fossil faunas and often a distinct nodular structure, with glauconitic and phosphatic coatings.

In contrast, when mud was accumulating more rapidly, its softness and wetness favoured crustaceans and other burrowers, but discouraged animals requiring a firm substrate. The burrowers rarely became fossilized because their mostly soft bodies easily decomposed on death. They were very effective, however, in reworking the carbonate mud and obscuring any layering. The resulting chalk has a more uniform and less nodular structure than the hard grounds.

Some areas of the sea bed accumulated large quantities of mud, and now have thick sequences of chalk while others have unusually thin, condensed sequences. Factors that may have influenced local rates of sedimentation include bottom currents and slumps that periodically redistributed the mud and reshaped the sea-floor topography. In addition, recent research has shown that condensed sequences in the South Downs generally represent areas where the sea floor became raised during Chalk times into upfolds or anticlines, whereas the expanded sequences typically accumulated in downfolds or synclines (Mortimore *et al.*, 2001).

A maximum thickness of about 300 m of Chalk is preserved in the eastern South Downs and about 400 m near Winchester. The oldest beds of the Chalk, known as the 'Lower Chalk', contain up to about 35 per cent clay. The clay particles combine with the coccolithic debris to form grey, so-called 'marly chalk'. At times, discrete clay-rich layers ('marl seams') were laid down. Much of the clay in the Chalk was probably weathered from rock outcrops in distant land-areas and washed into the sea by rivers. Some marl seams, however, consist of decomposed volcanic ash, and record the eruptions of distant volcanoes that sent clouds of ash high into the atmosphere. The ash eventually settled on the Chalk sea bed and became converted into clay.

As Chalk sea-levels rose, less and less land was left, and amounts of clay entering the sea greatly diminished. The resulting 'Middle Chalk' and 'Upper Chalk' contain less than two per cent clay on average, and are much whiter than the more clayey Lower Chalk.

Chalk in the South Downs was much quarried in the past to make lime, mortar and cement, but is now only sparingly worked. Crushed chalk or lime was also spread on fields to reduce soil acidity and improve soil structure. In addition, Chalk was used in a few areas as a building stone, particularly for interior masonry. Only a few varieties of Chalk are sufficiently durable for use on exterior walls (Plate 28).

Origin of flint

The Middle and Upper Chalk contain conspicuous layers of flint nodules and sheet flint. The Lower Chalk, by contrast, is virtually flintless. Fresh flint from the Chalk is normally dark grey or black, with a white surface-coating.

Flint is composed of silica combined in some instances with small amounts of water (Clayton, 1986). Electron microscopy suggests that flint formation in the Chalk started with the precipitation of innumerable, closely packed, ultra-small spheres of opal, which is a hydrated, non-crystalline form of silica ($SiO_2.nH_2O$, where $n \cong 10$). These spheres quickly became cemented together with more opal and minutely crystalline ('cryptocrystalline') silica or quartz (SiO_2). Over time, the opal has tended to dehydrate, turning into cryptocrystalline quartz.

The silica in flints is thought to be biogenic in origin. To support their soft, cellular mass, glass sponges living on the sea bed secrete needle-like spicules of silica, which are released when the sponges die and decay. Sponges on the floor of the Chalk sea are believed to have shed great numbers of spicules into the calcitic mud. Diatoms and radiolaria living in the surface waters of the sea doubtless contributed additional silica. Over time the silica accumulating in the mud dissolved, remaining in solution until it was deposited as flint, typically in layers parallel to the sea floor.

Many flint nodules have finger, arm or antler-like forms, and appear to be casts of the burrows of bottom-feeding animals. One suggestion is that anaerobic bacteria in the burrows oxidized organic matter such as faecal wastes, using sulphate dissolved in the pore water. This released sulphide, which lowered the pH, inducing simultaneous carbonate

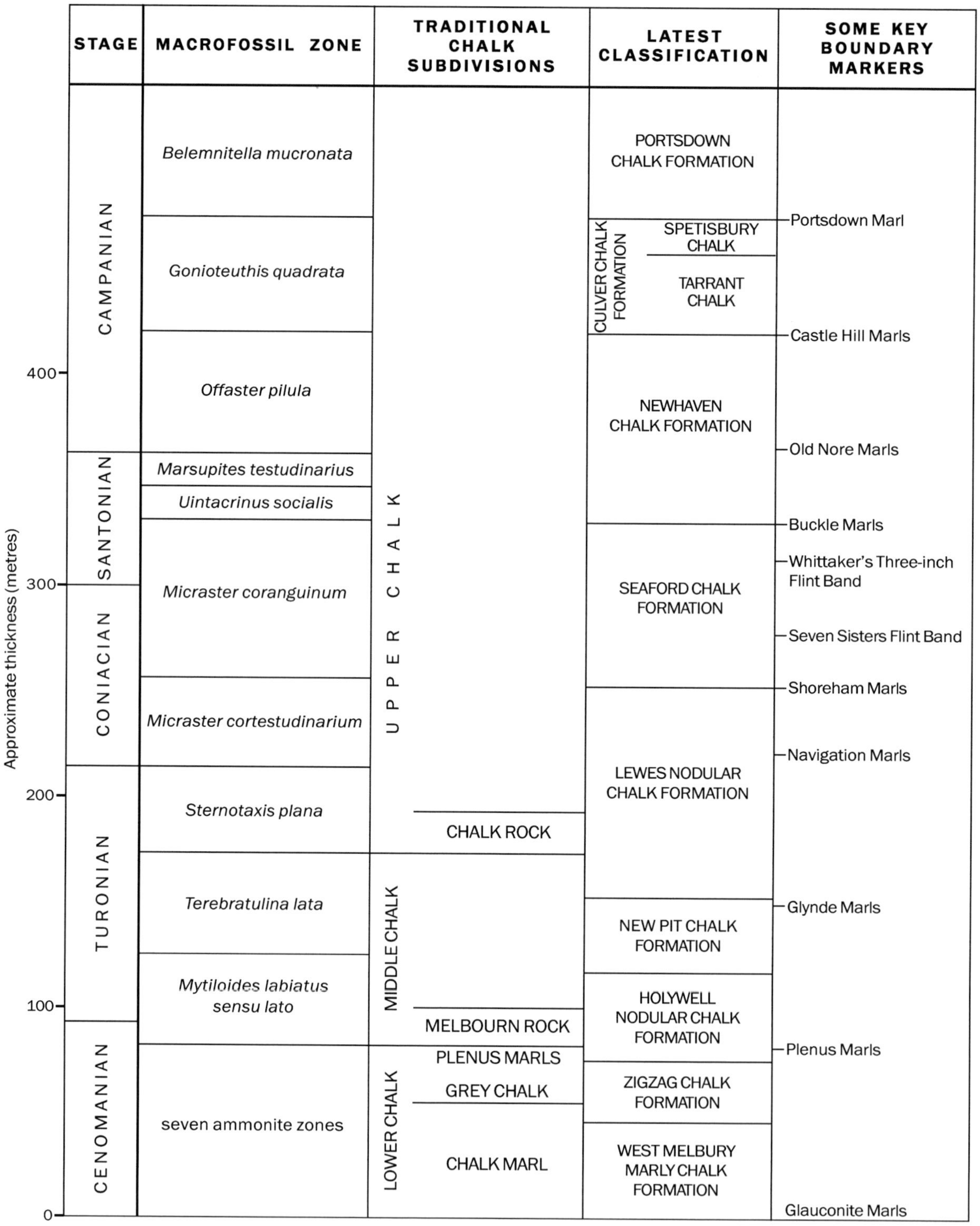

STAGE	MACROFOSSIL ZONE	TRADITIONAL CHALK SUBDIVISIONS		LATEST CLASSIFICATION		SOME KEY BOUNDARY MARKERS
CAMPANIAN	*Belemnitella mucronata*			PORTSDOWN CHALK FORMATION		
	Gonioteuthis quadrata			CULVER CHALK FORMATION	SPETISBURY CHALK	—Portsdown Marl
					TARRANT CHALK	
	Offaster pilula			NEWHAVEN CHALK FORMATION		—Castle Hill Marls
						—Old Nore Marls
SANTONIAN	*Marsupites testudinarius*	UPPER CHALK				
	Uintacrinus socialis					—Buckle Marls
	Micraster coranguinum			SEAFORD CHALK FORMATION		—Whittaker's Three-inch Flint Band
CONIACIAN						—Seven Sisters Flint Band
	Micraster cortestudinarium					—Shoreham Marls
				LEWES NODULAR CHALK FORMATION		—Navigation Marls
TURONIAN	*Sternotaxis plana*		CHALK ROCK			
	Terebratulina lata	MIDDLE CHALK		NEW PIT CHALK FORMATION		—Glynde Marls
	Mytiloides labiatus sensu lato		MELBOURN ROCK	HOLYWELL NODULAR CHALK FORMATION		
CENOMANIAN	seven ammonite zones	LOWER CHALK	PLENUS MARLS			—Plenus Marls
			GREY CHALK	ZIGZAG CHALK FORMATION		
			CHALK MARL	WEST MELBURY MARLY CHALK FORMATION		
						Glauconite Marls

Approximate thickness (metres): 0, 100, 200, 300, 400

Figure 2.1   Chalk fossil zones and lithostratigraphic units (after Mortimore *et al.*, 2001; Mortimore and Duperret, 2004).

Plate 28 (right)
Chalk blocks, known as 'clunch', used as building material in the outside walls of this recently restored tied cottage at Cocking, West Sussex, 2006.
Photo: Jane Bowden, courtesy of SDJC.

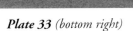

Plate 29 (centre left)
A sea urchin (*Echinocorys*) chalk fossil, dia. 8.5 cm; fossils such as this were often found on the Downs and known as 'shepherds' crowns'.
Photo: Gerald Legg, © The Booth Museum of Natural History, Brighton.

Plate 30 (centre right)
A fossilized prehistoric cockle shell (*Spondylus spinosus*) on flint (19 cm including the flint), found at Telscombe Cliffs, East Sussex.
Photo: Gerald Legg, © The Booth Museum of Natural History, Brighton.

Plate 31 (bottom left)
A fossilized fish (*Holopterix lewesiensis*) in chalk, 15 cm in length, found at Southeram, Lewes.
Photo: Gerald Legg, © The Booth Museum of Natural History, Brighton.

Plate 33 (bottom right)
A Neolithic flaked flint axe-head 14.5 cm long, with evidence of cortex close to one end, where it could have been attached to a wooden shaft; found at Portslade, East Sussex, in 1885.
Photo: Gerald Legg, © The Booth Museum of Natural History, Brighton.

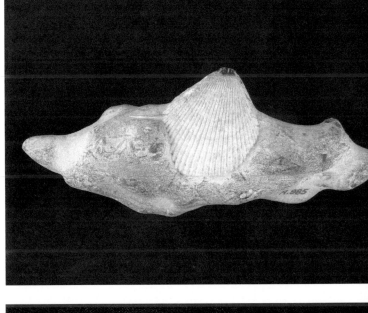

a)

b)

c)

d)

Plate 32 (*a,b,c,d*)
Flint used respectively as
a) randomly-placed, knapped building material set in lime mortar in a 19th century wall; b) elegant 18th century squared knapped flint in the porch of St. Andrew's church, Steyning; c) partially knapped and galleted (use of the small chippings for additional decoration) at West Dean farm buildings; and d) less imaginatively, though pleasantly, set in cement with brick courses today.
Photos: a) Peter Greenhalf, courtesy of Natural England; b) Brian Dawson, courtesy of West Sussex County Council; c) Michael Packard; d) Tina Stallard, courtesy of Natural England.

Plate 34
Erosion at Beachy Head, East Sussex; a headland such as this impedes the longshore movement of flint shingle, creating deficits further along the coast.
Photo: Rendel Williams.

solution and deposition of silica as flint infillings within the burrows (Clayton, 1986). Where sufficient iron was present, the sulphide tended to become fixed as nodules of pyrite or marcasite (iron sulphide). Such nodules are particularly common in the Lower Chalk. They invariably have a rusty exterior, but when broken open often reveal a radiating mass of elongated, shiny yellow crystals. When found on the surface of ploughed fields they are often mistaken by members of the public for meteorites or 'thunderbolts'.

Not all flints are burrow casts. Sheet flints, for example, seem to have developed along discontinuities in the Chalk, such as bedding planes and joints. Other flints are 'body fossils'. Some of the more spherical forms are recognizably casts of sponges. Particularly interesting are flint fossils of sea urchins. The living urchins had calcite exoskeletons, and calcite fossils of urchins often occur in chalk, but sometimes silica was able to replace the calcite molecule by molecule, creating replica fossils in flint (Plates 29, 30 & 31).

Most flints seem to have formed within the top 5 to 10 m of mud on the sea floor, while it was still quite soft (Clayton, 1986). However, some flints seem to have developed in steeply-inclined joints after the Chalk was more or less consolidated.

Many flint bands are remarkably rhythmically spaced. In the sea cliff at the Seven Sisters, for example, the bands average about 0.7 m apart. Another kind of repetition occurs in the flintless Lower Chalk, where bands of greyer marlier chalk alternate with bands of whiter, purer chalk at roughly one-metre intervals. It is widely believed that these Chalk rhythms are due to the variations in the Earth's orbit known as the Milankovitch cycles, which affected the climate (Insole, Daley and Gale, 1998). Each repetition may represent an interval of 20,000 to 40,000 years, implying an average rate of chalk deposition of 2.5 to 3.5 cm per thousand years.

Until approximately a century ago, flints were much used as building stone, greatly adding to the character of Downland villages and towns. Most of the flints were gathered from ploughed fields, but some were a by-product of chalk quarries, and, in addition, large quantities of rounded flint cobbles were collected from beaches. To build walls, the flints were set in mortar, either in a more or less random fashion or in regular 'courses' (Plates 32a, b & c). Usually, they were left in their natural state, but sometimes they were 'knapped' to expose their shiny interiors. For maximum decorative effect, they could be expertly square-knapped to resemble bricks (Dawson, 1998).

Zonation of the Chalk

In the past it was customary to subdivide the Chalk into stratigraphical units or time-zones largely on the basis of the fossils that were found. Many species living in the Chalk sea were replaced over time by more advanced forms, and their fossils serve as convenient markers for the particular periods when they existed (Fig. 2.1). For example, fossils of the distinctive, heart-shaped sea urchin, *Micraster coranguinum*, which Downland shepherds used to collect as good-luck charms, are restricted to the middle part of the Upper Chalk and help to identify Chalk of this age. Modern geologists, however, seek to study Chalk stratigraphy using all available evidence, not just fossils. Some flint bands and marl seams are now known to extend great distances across southern England, and these form valuable 'marker horizons' that can be used to subdivide the Chalk into 'lithostratigraphic units', as shown in Fig. 2.1 (Mortimore, 1997; Mortimore *et al.*, 2001). The Seven Sisters Flint Band, for example, is present in many parts of the South Downs and can be traced as far west as Dorset.

The Middle Chalk in Sussex and Hampshire consists mainly of the Holywell Nodular Chalk and overlying New Pit Chalk, which outcrop on the lower slopes of the escarpment of the South Downs. The Upper Chalk is divided into five units: the Lewes Nodular Chalk (main part), Seaford Chalk, Newhaven Chalk, Culver Chalk and Portsdown Chalk.

The Seaford and Newhaven Chalks have the greatest area of outcrop within the South Downs, and in Sussex the youngest chalk that is preserved is the Culver Chalk. However, the succeeding Portsdown Chalk underlies the Sussex Coastal Plain and outcrops on the foreshore at Dell Quay and Felpham. Further west it forms the Portsdown ridge. Almost certainly, still younger beds of chalk were laid down in Sussex and Hampshire, but have since been removed by erosion.

Chalk deposition ended in southern England when world sea levels started falling and the area began to experience major uplift. The uplift appears to have been particularly marked in the central Weald, where the Chalk, which has now disappeared, was arched up into an elongated dome, called the Wealden Anticline. This dome extended in an east-west direction into the Boulonnais of northern France. Superimposed on the dome were a series of minor anticlines and synclines, which were also aligned east-west. In the South Downs area (Fig. 2.2) these subsidiary folds often represented a renewal of the folding that occurred while the Chalk was being deposited.

During the uplift and folding there was much erosion in southern England. By the end of the Cretaceous, 65 million years ago, erosion had succeeded in cutting through most or all of the chalk folds, leaving an undulating plain or surface of low relief, called the Sub-Palaeogene (or Sub-Tertiary) Surface. It was at this time that a large meteorite slammed into Mexico, destroying much life on Earth. Shortly after this cataclysmic event the dinosaurs went

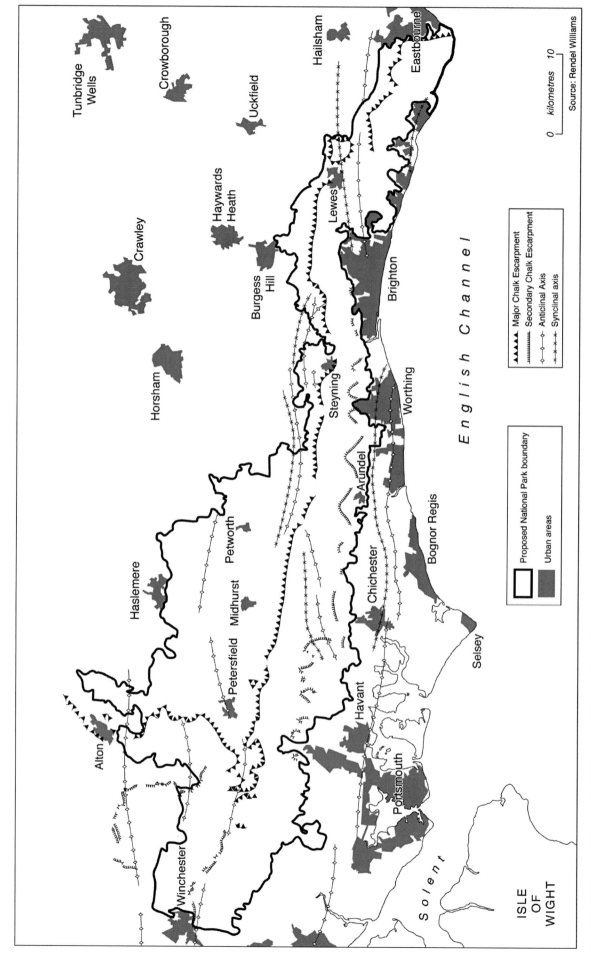

Fig 2.2   Fold lines within the South Downs and the position of the main and secondary escarpments.

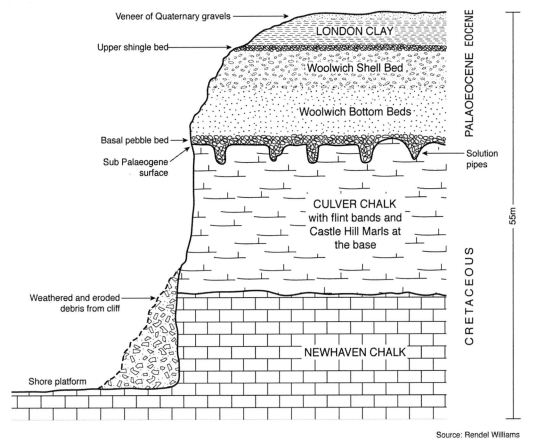

Figure 2.3   The cliff section at Castle Hill, Newhaven.

extinct, allowing mammals to take over as the dominant land animals. Plant communities began to assume a distinctly modern aspect.

The Tertiary

The Tertiary is divided into five periods: the Palaeocene (from 65 to 56 million years ago), Eocene (56 to 34 million years ago), Oligocene (34 to 23 million years ago), Miocene (23 to 5 million years ago) and Pliocene (5 to 1.8 million years ago). The first three periods are known as the Palaeogene (or Early and Middle Tertiary) and the last two as the Neogene (Late Tertiary).

During the Palaeogene, southern England experienced repeated episodes of uplift and erosion. Palaeocene and Eocene sediments were laid down on the Sub-Palaeogene Surface in many areas during periods when sea levels were high. More and more Chalk was eroded, and in the Weald the underlying rocks began to be exposed. Chert pebbles from Lower Greensand rocks beneath the Chalk have been found in mid-Eocene deposits in Surrey, indicating that erosion had already breached the Chalk cover somewhere in the Weald by about 45 million years ago.

The sea cliffs west of Newhaven Harbour provide excellent exposures of Palaeocene and Eocene deposits overlying the Sub-Palaeogene Surface, which

at this site is cut in Culver Chalk (Fig. 2.3). Resting directly on the Sub-Palaeogene Surface is a shingle-beach deposit, known as the Woolwich Basal Bed, which consists of black and green-coated flint pebbles set in a sandy matrix. Above the Basal Bed are marine and estuarine sands and sandy clays, known as the Woolwich Bottom Bed, which turn yellow and orange as they weather. The overlying Woolwich Shell Beds consist of grey clays with subsidiary sand and shell beds. Lignite fragments and gypsum crystals (hydrated calcium sulphate) are found in the clays, together with yellowish masses of an unusual iron sulphate called jarosite. Another bed of beach shingle on top of the Shell Beds marks the start of the Eocene, when a sea advanced across much of southern England, depositing the overlying London Clay, which is poorly exposed in the Newhaven cliffs because of landslipping.

Water percolating through the Tertiary deposits has dissolved some of the Chalk beneath the Sub-Palaeogene Surface, creating deep cylindrical holes, called solution pipes, into which the basal Woolwich Beds have collapsed. In some of the pipes, rare aluminous minerals have been precipitated (Wilmot and Young, 1985).

Palaeocene and Eocene deposits are preserved in few places on the Downs in East Sussex, but become rather more extensive westwards. They must originally have had a much greater area of outcrop. In many parts of the Downs, reddish brown clays with numerous broken flints form a shallow covering on the Chalk, often directly overlying the Sub-Palaeogene Surface. Known as 'Clay-with-flints', these superficial deposits represent the remains of eroded Palaeocene and Eocene Beds often combined with flints and other material released by dissolution of the Chalk (Quesnel *et al.*, 2003).

The sedimentary record in the South Downs area stops well before the end of the Palaeogene. Early Oligocene deposits outcrop in the Isle of Wight and on the south side of the New Forest, but not within the area of the present South Downs where uplift and erosion is thought to have dominated, continuing perhaps until well into the Miocene. Any deposits that may have been laid down within this area of uplift, for example on river floodplains, can be assumed to have been removed by later erosion. A possible exception is provided by the enigmatic sarsen stones, which occur in widely-scattered areas on the Chalk in southern and eastern England. In the South Downs, they are most frequent around Falmer and Stanmer, near Brighton. Sarsens are boulders of strongly silicified sandstone or, more rarely, pebble conglomerates that are believed to have formed when surface sands or pebble beds overlying the Chalk became indurated, perhaps under humid tropical conditions in the Palaeogene, or later in the Tertiary when the climate became more temperate (Ullyot *et al.*, 2004). They closely resemble the silcretes that are presently forming in some low latitude areas, such as Botswana. Few, if any, remain in their original positions. Many have been moved downhill by natural slope processes, cleared from fields by farmers or removed for use as building stone.

Opinions differ as to the scale and significance of the Palaeogene and early Neogene uplift of southern England. Some writers, notably Wooldridge and Linton (1955), have argued that the uplift was much more massive than its Late Cretaceous predecessor, and that the Wealden Anticline was reborn in a rapid and dramatic way, particularly in the Oligocene and Miocene, triggering a period of vigorous erosion. Others, such as Small (1980) and Jones (1981 & 1999 a and b), are more cautious, suggesting that the Wealden Anticline and its subsidiary folds underwent repeated episodes of renewed but relatively modest growth with concomitant erosion throughout the Palaeogene and early Neogene. At Alum Bay in the Isle of Wight, the Upper Chalk and overlying Palaeocene and Eocene strata, including the famous, multi-coloured Alum Bay Sands, dip at a near vertical angle on the northern limb of the Brighstone Anticline. Early Oligocene deposits capping Headon Hill are also deformed. It is hard to escape the conclusion that much of the folding in this area is Late Oligocene or Miocene in age, though it may have started in the Eocene (Insole, Daley and Gale, 1998). What is less clear, however, is whether the Isle of Wight story has relevance for other areas, such as the South Downs, where the folding may have occurred at different times (Jones, 1999a).

No Pliocene deposits have been found in Sussex apart from a few blocks of shelly marine sandstone near Beachy Head (Edmunds, 1927), which have been rather insecurely dated. More extensive deposits of ferruginous sand and shelly ironstone were discovered in the 1850s on the crest of the North Downs near Lenham in Kent. Known as the Lenham Beds, they are often referred to the late Pliocene, but may actually date from the late Miocene. There can be no doubt that they are shallow-water marine deposits, and sea level at the time seems to have been around 265–270 m OD (Jones, 1981). Unfossiliferous sands on the Downs near Folkestone may be the same age.

The eastern North Downs have a remarkably level top at 190–200 m. Wooldridge and Linton (1955) thought that the sea that deposited the Lenham Beds, which they dated as late Pliocene, advanced over the Chalk outcrop and bevelled the area that is now the top of the Downs, creating a marine plain or platform (the 'Pliocene marine bench'). They claimed to find traces of the same platform in the South Downs and western North Downs, and interpreted the higher summits in both areas as former islands that escaped inundation. However, further research has shown that the Pliocene marine bench is almost certainly imaginary (Jones, 1999a and b). The Pliocene (or Miocene) sea submerged most, if not all, of south-east England, but it did not achieve any significant planation. The bench that it supposedly cut is very probably the Sub-Palaeogene Surface transformed by uplift and warping.

The Quaternary

A marine incursion during the Red Crag stage at the end of the Pliocene (around 2.5 million years ago) deposited fossiliferous sands and gravels at places in the North Downs and Chilterns that now lie up to 190 m above sea level (Jones, 1999a). Whether this was merely a continuation of the earlier Lenham Beds incursion or a wholly separate event is uncertain, but in any case it seems to have caused minimal erosion of the Chalk. World sea levels were not especially high at this time, and the conclusion must be that the Chilterns and North Downs have risen considerably since the Pliocene, that is, during the Quaternary. In the Weald and the South Downs the uplift is likely to have exceeded 200 m (Jones, 1999a), but there are no marine deposits of Red Crag age to act as a marker.

During the Quaternary cold stages or glacial periods, global sea levels fell dramatically as ice sheets built up on land, storing water that under temperate conditions would have been quickly returned to the oceans. In the last glacial period, for example, sea level fell 100 m or more, exposing the bed of the

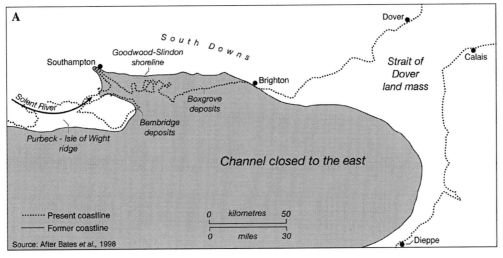

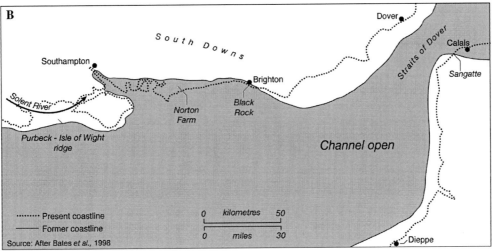

Figure 2.4 Palaeogeography of the English Channel before (A) and after (B) the opening of the Straits of Dover (after Bates *et al.*, 1998).

English Channel. The nearest sea to the South Downs was off the Scilly Isles. In the temperate stages or interglacials, the ice sheets disappeared and global sea levels recovered.

Most researchers are agreed that south-east England escaped glaciation during the Quaternary cold stages, but experienced periods of extreme frost-climate when permafrost developed and tundra-steppe vegetation replaced the temperate stage forests. Under these periglacial conditions, the chalk bedrock of the South Downs became very fractured near the surface due to either frost-weathering in the seasonally thawed layer above the permafrost (Williams, 1987) or, more probably, ice-segregation within the permafrost (Murton, 1996).

Wind-blown silt or loess was deposited across large areas of Britain during the last cold stage. On chalk outcrops the loess and other surface deposits often became churned into the frost-fractured bedrock, forming distinctive cellular structures called involutions (Williams, 1986). Good examples can be seen at the top of the sea cliffs between Brighton and Peacehaven.

The South Downs underwent considerable erosion during the Quaternary cold stages, as described in detail later. Large quantities of chalky rubble and mud, mixed with flints, were transported down hillsides and along valley floors by sheetwash, solifluction and other processes. Known as Coombe Rock, this material accumulated within some of the valleys and on the Coastal Plain, particularly around Chichester.

During the cold stages, the Rivers Arun, Adur, Ouse and Cuckmere excavated their valleys through the Downs to depths far below present sea level, and extended their valleys across the exposed Channel sea bed. During the last 10,000 years, they have infilled their valleys as sea level has risen, and they now flow over thick deposits of alluvial silt and other materials. At Newhaven, for example, the Ouse valley is infilled to a depth of 30 m (Jones, 1981). Sands and gravels, presumably deposited by the Ouse under periglacial conditions, overlie Chalk bedrock, and pass upwards into swamp peat, estuarine mud and, finally, alluvium.

A marine bench of Middle Quaternary age bevels the base of the Downs north and east of Chichester, reaching a maximum height of 30–35 m OD. Backed by a degraded sea cliff, it is overlain by beach sands and gravels, forming the so-called Slindon or Goodwood raised beach, which pass upwards into estuarine and terrestrial silts, termed the Slindon Silts (Bates *et. al.*, 1997 & 1998; Roberts, 1998). All these deposits and the ancient cliff are buried beneath flint gravels that were eroded off the Downs during later cold stages, but commercial gravel extraction and archaeological excavations at Boxgrove have provided useful temporary sections. The silts have yielded fossil mammal remains, including fragments of a hominid ('Boxgrove Man'), and also *in situ* ovate flint hand-axes (Plate 33). The mammals suggest that the silts date from an early interglacial known as the Cromerian (Roberts, 1998), but amino-acid dates suggest a correlation with the succeeding Hoxnian interglacial (Bates *et. al.*, 1997). Boxgrove Man is tentatively ascribed to the species *Homo heidelbergensis* (Roberts and Parfitt, 1999).

The Slindon beach deposits imply a former sea level of about 40 m OD and appear to be equivalent in age to the Steyne Wood Clay at Bembridge in the Isle of Wight, which records a similar high sea level (Preece *et al.*, 1990). At this stage, the English Channel may not have extended much further east than Beachy Head, and a wide land bridge may have connected both Kent and Sussex with France (Fig. 2.4). The Straits of Dover may have been excavated by overflow waters from a glacial lake during the Anglian cold stage, allowing the North Sea to connect with the English Channel in the subsequent Hoxnian interglacial (Gibbard, 1995).

During the Middle Quaternary, world sea levels were probably never more than 10 m higher than now, so the Slindon beach deposits must have been uplifted by at least 30 m. This suggests a mean uplift rate for the South Downs of at least 0.06 mm per year over the 500,000 years that are thought to have elapsed since the Slindon deposits were laid down (Roberts, 1998).

Younger raised beach deposits of possible Hoxnian age are found at Aldingbourne south of Slindon, resting on a marine bench and banked against a former cliff, up to a height of 22 m OD (Bates *et. al.*, 1997). Still younger raised-beach deposits reaching heights of 13.5 m OD underlie the Sussex coastal plain and are exposed in the cliff at Black Rock, Brighton. They seem to date from at least two interglacials.

LANDFORMS OF THE SOUTH DOWNS

The dry valleys

The landforms of the South Downs are as distinctive as the geology, and equally interesting. It is a paradox that a rock as soft as Chalk should form relatively high ground, and also a paradox that such a relatively uniform rock should produce such varied scenery. The steep, northward-facing escarpment contrasts with the gently inclined, south-facing dip-slope, which is interrupted by a much dissected secondary escarpment (Fig. 2.5). Also present is an extensive network of dry valleys whose origin is controversial (Fig. 2.6). The permeability of the Chalk ensures that rain is normally absorbed without surface runoff, so the fact that the valleys lack streams is unsurprising, but how did they come to be eroded in the first place?

Some researchers, following Reid (1887), believe that the dry valleys were created during the Quaternary cold stages. Permafrost rendered the Chalk impermeable, causing summer rain and meltwater to flow off the Downs, collecting into streams and rivers of considerable erosive power. It was this seasonal runoff under periglacial conditions that supposedly excavated the now dry valleys.

Other researchers, influenced by Wooldridge and Linton (1955), refuse to accept this explanation, and claim that the valleys were excavated under temperate conditions when the water table in the Chalk was higher than now, allowing surface-water flow. Various explanations have been advanced as to why the water table could have dropped since the valleys were formed, including the southward retreat of the Chalk escarpment, erosional lowering of the Weald plain, and downcutting of the river valleys through the Downs. The most plausible explanation, however, is provided by the Quaternary uplift of the Downs, which may have exceeded 200 m. This must have triggered a large fall in the water table, and could well be the main reason why the valleys dried out.

The dry valleys vary greatly in form, and unusual examples have provoked more discussion than the commonplace, which deserve greater attention. Near Eastbourne strange, corrie-like embayments in the escarpment may have been created by snow patch erosion and solifluction (Williams, 1986). Further west, the escarpment is trenched in places by remarkably steep-sided valleys, such as the Coombe at Lewes, the Devil's Dyke near Brighton, and Rake Bottom at Butser Hill. Studies of the similarly chasm-like Devil's Kneadingtrough in the North Downs in Kent have demonstrated that periglacial processes excavated at least a third of the valley in a period of less than 1000 years at the end of the last cold stage (Kerney *et al.*, 1964). There is no evidence, however, that any of the steep-sided South Downs valleys formed so quickly. Headwater sapping by springs, meltwater torrents and other erosive processes have been invoked to explain the curious form of the valleys, but no consensus has been reached.

Many dip-slope dry valleys are asymmetrical, with short, steep slopes facing north-west and longer, gentler slopes facing south-east. Good examples are provided by the valleys of the Seven Sisters, which

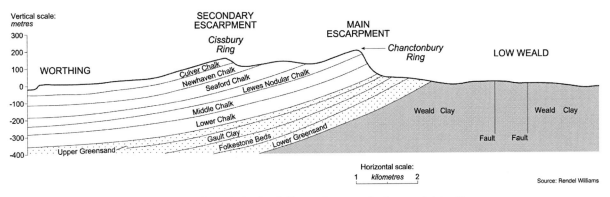

Figure 2.5   Diagrammatic cross-section through the South Downs between the Arun and Adur Gaps.

have been left hanging above the sea by continuing cliff erosion. The short slopes are excavated in bare, frost-shattered chalk, but the longer slopes are veneered with loess, which has been churned into the shattered chalk, forming a layer of involutions. The asymmetry of the valleys does not seem to be due to geological factors, such as the dip of the chalk beds, and probably results from aspect-controlled differences in amounts of periglacial erosion on opposing slopes (Williams, 1986).

Water-gaps and wind-gaps

Another major puzzle is how the Arun, Adur, Ouse and diminutive Cuckmere have managed to carve deep valleys or 'water-gaps' through the Downs. All four rivers rise in the Weald and flow south to the sea, cutting straight through the Chalk hills instead of skirting round, as might be expected. Other rivers have cut similar water-gaps through the North Downs. Wooldridge and Linton (1955) thought that the river courses were initiated on the bench or platform that the Pliocene sea had supposedly carved across the folded beds of chalk. As the sea withdrew and the land became uplifted, the rivers cut down through the platform into the underlying Chalk, maintaining their courses undeflected by the east-west trending folds. This explanation is now generally rejected because the Pliocene (or Miocene) sea is thought unlikely to have ever cut a platform of sufficient width to allow the rivers to superimpose their courses on the rocks beneath. The modern view is that the rivers developed on the Sub-Palaeogene Surface soon after it formed and were able to maintain their courses despite the uplift of the Wealden Anticline and its subsidiary folds (Jones, 1999a). This 'antecedence hypothesis', though impossible to prove, at least has the virtue of simplicity.

Less deep, riverless valleys that cut through the Downs from the Weald are known as 'wind-gaps' (Fig. 2.6). Particularly impressive are the Findon valley, utilized by the Worthing to London road, and the Pyecombe valley, which carries the Brighton to London A23 road. At least some of these wind-gaps are likely to be failed water-gaps (Williams and Robinson, 1983). Minor rivers draining the Weald may have cut the valleys and then disappeared because they could not deepen their beds fast enough to keep pace with falling water tables in the Chalk, or because other Wealden rivers captured their drainage water.

The evolution of the Meon and Itchen drainage systems in Hampshire provokes continuing discussion. The Meon rises in the south-west corner of the Weald, near Petersfield, and runs north-westwards through the chalk, away from the sea, before making a great bend at Warnford to flow southwards to the Solent. Although some disagree, it appears likely that the upper Meon once drained north-westwards into the New Alresford valley, now occupied by the upper Itchen (Small, 1980). The lower Meon, benefiting from a steeper gradient to the sea, cut headwards across the Winchester anticline, capturing the upper Meon and diverting its flow away from New Alresford. The old route of the upper Meon just beyond the point of capture is marked by a low col or wind-gap at Wheely Farm, Warnford. The lower Itchen also seems to have eroded headwards through the Winchester anticline, capturing the 'Alresford River' (the present upper Itchen) at Winchester. Originally the Alresford River may have drained westwards into the Test.

The main and secondary escarpment

The main escarpment of the South Downs forms a continuous barrier along the southern edge of the Weald, except where it is broken by water-gaps and wind-gaps. It is undoubtedly retreating southwards, but it has beheaded relatively few dip-slope valleys, and retains a remarkably even crest line, with only occasional notches or sags. Most dip-slope valleys begin just behind the escarpment, and, if the escarpment were to retreat by only another kilometre, the number of notches in its crest would be trebled. Walking the South Downs Way is presently quite easy, but, a million years hence, any replacement route would need to make repeated ascents and descents into a host of dip-slope valleys beheaded by scarp retreat.

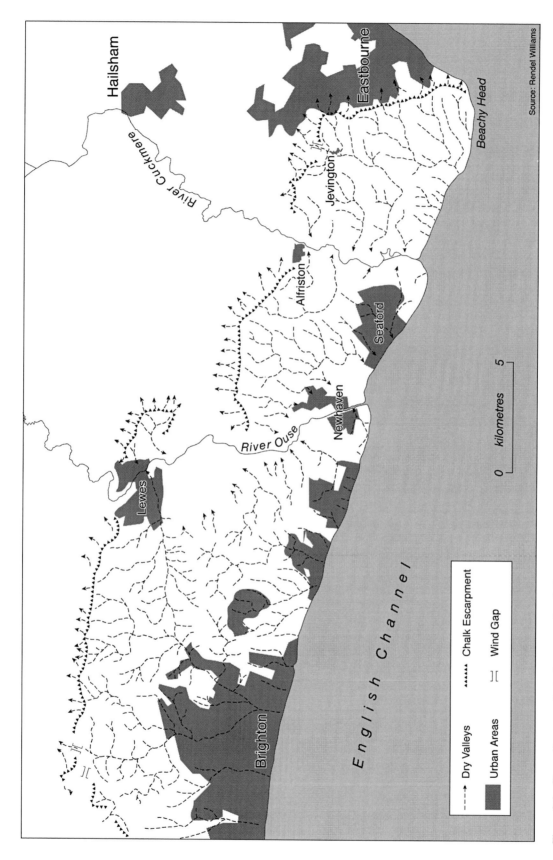

Figure 2.6   Dry valley networks in the eastern South Downs.

Williams and Robinson (1983) suggested that the escarpment has a relatively level crest because most dip-slope valleys formed after it reached more or less its present position, and regarded this as evidence that the valleys are periglacial in origin. Although the valleys may indeed be of no great age, it seems more likely that they formed under a variety of climatic conditions and that the Quaternary uplift of perhaps 200 m has robbed the valleys of their streams.

The steepness of the South Downs escarpment has proved difficult to explain, but is probably due to a combination of factors. Erosion is demonstrably lowering the Weald Plain in front of the escarpment, and this almost certainly contributes to scarp-foot steepening. Springs at the foot of the scarp are eroding headwards, but they are widely spaced, and create only very localized steepening. Lower Chalk outcrops towards the base of the scarp, and being clayey probably allows more surface runoff and erosion. The upper slopes of the escarpment are mostly developed in the relatively hard Lewes Nodular Chalk, which probably functions as a protective cap rock. The Seaford Chalk that outcrops on the upper dip-slope is much softer.

As already explained, the Chalk originally extended across the whole of the Weald, but has been stripped off by erosion. The South Downs scarp now lies 20 to 25 km south of the axis of the Wealden Anticline. If it began its southward migration near the start of the Neogene, around 23 million years ago, it has retreated at an average rate of about 10 cm per century. If the scarp began moving south early in the Palaeogene, say 40 to 50 million years ago, its rate of retreat will have been about 5 cm per century. Although very crude, these estimates are likely to be of the correct order of magnitude, and appear plausible when matched against field evidence. Many of the steeper escarpment slopes are covered in terracettes (popularly known as 'sheeps' tracks'), which indicate that the soil cover is moving gently downhill. On the lower slopes of the escarpment, colluvial deposits or hillwashes have accumulated in places as a result of erosion of the slopes above. Under periglacial conditions, the escarpments may have retreated more rapidly than at present because of frost weathering of the Chalk and meltwater erosion, combined perhaps with solifluction and snow avalanching (Williams, 1980, 1986). The importance of periglaciation is indicated by the flint gravels and scattered flints that are spread across the Weald plain north of the escarpment, for example at Piltdown. They cannot have reached their present positions by river transport, as the rivers flow southwards through the Downs, not northwards. The flints, together with much fine chalky waste, which has since been washed away, must have been carried off the Downs by solifluction when the escarpment lay somewhat further north than today.

Half-way down the dip-slope of the South Downs is a prominent secondary escarpment, which extends from Hampshire through West Sussex towards Brighton, where it disappears (Figs. 2.3 & 2.6). In contrast with the main escarpment, it is much dissected by dry valleys, and consists of a series of more or less isolated hills, each roughly triangular in plan with a pointed northern end. The hills are mainly developed in Newhaven Chalk, but are capped by Culver Chalk. The disappearance of the secondary escarpment near Brighton may relate to the fact that the outcrop of Culver Chalk is very restricted in East Sussex.

In many places the top of the secondary escarpment coincides with the Sub Palaeogene Surface. The former Palaeogene strata have been mostly eroded away, but a covering of impermeable Clay-with-flints often remains, which Hodgson *et al.* (1974) suggested protects the underlying Chalk from weathering and erosion, thus creating the secondary escarpment. It is more probable, however, that the reverse is true and that existence of the scarp explains the preservation of the Sub-Palaeogene Surface and the Clay-with-flints. No secondary escarpment is present in the North Downs even though Palaeogene strata and residual Clay-with-flints cover many hilltops.

Most researchers have sought to explain the secondary escarpment in terms of lithological differences, but the precise nature of these differences is open to debate. The Newhaven Chalk possesses more marl seams and insoluble matter than the Culver Chalk and may have been subject to more surface runoff and erosion in the past (Sparks, 1949; Mortimore *et al.*, 2001). Both chalks contain similar amounts of flint. The Newhaven Chalk tends to be better jointed and harder than the Culver Chalk (Mortimore *et al.*, 2001). Nevertheless, laboratory tests suggest that the Culver Chalk may be more resistant to frost weathering and could perhaps have acted as a cap rock under periglacial conditions (Williams, 1980).

Clearly, much more research will need to be carried out if the important question of the origin of the secondary escarpment is to be satisfactorily resolved.

Solution of the Chalk

The rounded outlines and swelling contours of the Downs have long caught the attention of observers, but the cause of the roundness has not been firmly established. As already mentioned, rain falling on the Downs soon disappears underground, yielding little or no surface runoff. The soil tends to move away down slope very slowly, mainly as a result of soil creep. Sparks (1971) attributed the rounded profiles of downland summits to the dominance of soil creep over runoff. He rejected solution as an explanation, claiming that it always creates uneven relief by selectively enlarging major joints. This may be true of sparsely jointed, hard limestones, but Chalk possesses so many joints and fractures that it probably dissolves in a relatively even manner. Although direct evidence is lacking, the rounded summits of the Downs can be quite plausibly attributed to solutional weathering. Yet another possibility is that periglacial processes, such as solifluction, have created the roundness (Williams, 1986). Hills with similar convexities to those of the Downs occur in areas of soft limestone in the Arctic.

Few caves have been discovered in the South Downs, although the Chalk is undoubtedly undergoing solution. It seems that the rock is generally too closely jointed and too weak to permit caves to form. None of the rivers that pass through the South Downs disappears underground, unlike the River Mole in the North Downs, which loses all its water during droughts to swallow holes in its bed. However, a few minor streams draining off Tertiary clays in West Sussex disappear into tiny swallow holes on reaching the Chalk.

Solution pipes provide the most obvious evidence for chalk solution. Fine examples, up to 20 m long, filled with sand and clay, can be seen in vertical section in the top of the cliffs at Seaford Head. At Hope Gap near Cuckmere Haven, pipes are exposed in cross-section on the shore platform, forming circular pools resembling wellheads. Solution pipes are most common near outcrops of Tertiary sands and clays and also remnant patches of Clay-with-flints. Water draining off these deposits tends to be quite acidic, which has doubtless increased the rate of solution of the underlying Chalk.

Water issuing from Chalk springs and pumped from boreholes in the Downs is more or less saturated with calcium carbonate. In the Brighton and Worthing area, for example, the carbonate hardness of groundwater averages about 190 mg/l (Young and Lake, 1988). The average annual rainfall in this part of the Downs is around 800 mm, and about half is lost through evapotranspiration, leaving around 400 mm to percolate into the Chalk. The density of chalk is about 1.6 mg/l. The volume of chalk dissolved annually in each square kilometre can be estimated to be $(400 \times 190)/(1.6 \times 1000) = 48$ cubic metres. This is a sizeable loss, and the difficult question to answer is whether it mostly occurs near the ground surface or near the water table.

Common sense suggests that amounts of solution ought to decrease with depth below the soil/rock interface. The percolating rainwater is charged with dissolved carbon dioxide, acquired through contact with the atmosphere and soil, and also with humic acids derived from decomposing plant material. On entering the Chalk the percolating water ought to have maximum acidity, and, as it descends through the maze of joints, and is absorbed into the rock pores, it ought to become progressively neutralized. If all

the solution occurs within a few metres of the ground surface, the annual loss of chalk, calculated above, would equate to a surface-lowering of 48 mm per 1000 years. This may not sound much, but the implication is that the Downs have been lowered by 240 m since the start of the Pliocene, 5 million years ago. This is only eight metres less than the present height of Ditchling Beacon!

A counter-argument can be put forward, however, suggesting that much more solution occurs at depth than near the surface. Chalk under the dip-slope dry valleys yields water to wells and boreholes much more readily than the Chalk under the intervening ridges. In the Brighton and Worthing area, for example, the transmissivity of the Chalk is commonly five times greater under valleys than under ridges (Young and Lake, 1988). Some valleys have developed along lines of structural weakness where there is a high density of joints, and it is also possible that erosion of the valleys has caused stress relief and the development of additional joints. Nevertheless, the most plausible and generally accepted explanation for the increased groundwater flow under valleys is that the joints in the Chalk have become solutionally enlarged (Jones and Robbins, 1999). Enlargement is greatest in a zone near the water table, which may reflect seasonal fluctuations and longer-term changes in the height of the water table.

At the moment, it is not possible to reach a firm conclusion about how rapidly solution is lowering Downland surfaces and removing Chalk at depth, but it would seem to be much the most active process operating under temperate conditions, except at the coast, where marine processes obviously dominate.

The Downland coast

The Chalk outcrops over a 25 km stretch of the Sussex coast between Brighton and Eastbourne, giving rise to some of the grandest sea cliffs anywhere in Britain. The cliffs rise in height from 30-40 m near Brighton to a full 160 m at Beachy Head. The stretch of coast from Seaford Head to Beachy Head, which is of exceptional natural beauty, was the first in Britain to be designated a Heritage Coast by the Countryside Commission.

Sea walls and an undercliff walk protect the base of the cliffs for much of their length between Brighton and Newhaven, but nearly everywhere else the cliffs are unprotected and are retreating rapidly because of undercutting by the sea and weathering of the cliff faces (Plate 34). The cliffs at the Seven Sisters (Plate 14) are exposed to the full force of gales advancing up the Channel and are eroding at an average rate of around 46 cm a year (BAR, 2005). By contrast, the equally famous, but more sheltered, White Cliffs of Dover are retreating at an average of about seven centimetres a year.

These averages conceal the fact that Chalk cliff-erosion tends to be very episodic. Small, weathered pieces of chalk fall from the cliffs quite regularly, especially in winter, but cliff falls, in which sections of cliff fall *en masse*, occur less frequently and at irregular intervals, temporarily protecting the base of the cliff from further undercutting. Most falls yield only a few thousand cubic metres of debris, which can be quickly removed by the sea, but occasionally much bigger falls occur, creating so much debris that the waves are unable to sweep it all away for many years. The massive fall just west of Beachy Head on 12 January, 1999, may have had a volume of 100,000 cubic metres (Mortimore *et al.*, 2004), and much of the debris from this fall still litters the foreshore despite five years of wave attack. The fall occurred at a place where the cliff is around 125 m high, and the debris ran outwards from the base of the cliff for about the same distance, stopping just short of the lighthouse. Most chalk falls, in contrast, come to rest quite close to the base of the cliffs.

A fall that exhibited a remarkable degree of mobility relative to the height of the cliff took place on Easter Monday, 1914, at Went Hill, west of Birling Gap (Williams *et al.*, 2004) (Plate 9). About 12,500 cubic metres of debris travelled outwards over the shore for a distance of up to 75 m, or 1.6 times the height of the cliff, forming a long, tongue-like promontory.

As chalk cliffs retreat, they leave a shore platform behind at their base. This platform can exceed 150 m in width, and often extends well beyond the low water mark. At the top of the platform, next to the cliff, there is usually a narrow shingle beach, composed of flints supplied by the weathering and erosion of the cliffs. In many places, parallel runnels dissect the shore platform; water flows up and down these runnels depending on whether the tide is rising or falling. The runnels tend to follow joints and are quite evenly spaced.

The shore platforms are being worn down and worn back by wave attack, weathering processes and the erosive effects of limpets and other organisms. The overall mean rate of lowering of the platform surfaces between runnels is about 2.3 mm a year (Andrews and Williams, 2000). In stormy weather pounding waves pulverize the surface of the platform and remove joint blocks. They also move beach shingle up and down the upper parts of the platforms, eroding the chalk beneath. In very cold winters, frosts shatter the platform surfaces, detaching numerous platey fragments. Throughout the year, limpets ingest chalk as they graze surface algae; they also excavate hollows to which they return after grazing when the tide falls. It is estimated that limpets are responsible for an average of about 12 per cent of platform downwearing in areas that they frequent (Andrews and Williams, 2000). Boring

molluscs, such as the common piddock, also cause significant erosion.

The sea walls between Brighton and Newhaven have reduced the supply of flints to Sussex beaches. This is unfortunate because beaches provide a natural defence against the sea, causing waves to lose energy before they reach the land behind. If beach sand or shingle is lost, the coastline becomes more vulnerable to wave attack. Many sections of coast are now suffering from shortages of beach sediment, mainly because ill-planned coastal defence structures have interfered with the natural movement of shingle along the coast, but also because the walling up of the cliffs has reduced fresh supplies of flints. Many beaches along the Sussex coast now have to be recharged artificially at considerable expense, using shingle dredged from the sea floor. To add to the difficulties it has been discovered that flint shingle is not nearly as durable as previously assumed (Dornbusch *et al.*, 2002). Even in a single tidal cycle a flint pebble can experience a measurable amount of wear. Securing adequate supplies of shingle has become a major coastal management issue in Sussex (BAR, 2005).

THE WESTERN WEALD

The South Downs as a geological and geomorphological entity share the same area and borders as the Chalk outcrop, but administratively, as the Sussex Downs and East Hampshire AONBs and as a candidate National Park, they cover a much larger area, including much of the western Weald. This Wealden 'borderland' includes outcrops of sands, sandstones and clays that predate the Chalk and give rise to very different landforms (Plate 23).

Immediately underlying the Chalk are two shallow-water marine deposits: the Upper Greensand and Gault Clay. The Upper Greensand is a soft, yellowish, often calcareous, silty sandstone ('malmstone') interbedded with silty sand ('malm') and clay. It is quite thin near Storrington and Amberley, where it forms a low bench in front of the Downs, but it thickens markedly westwards, developing into a prominent escarpment, which reaches a height of 150 m at Selborne. Though not very durable, the sandstone was much used in the past as a local building stone, for example at Amberley Castle. The Gault forms a narrow strip of mostly low-lying ground to the north of the Upper Greensand outcrop. Its poorly draining soils are exceedingly sticky when wet and difficult to plough. During droughts it shrinks badly and in wet weather it expands, disrupting road and building foundations.

Still further north is the outcrop of the Lower Greensand. This marine formation is divided into four members: the basal Atherfield Clay, Hythe Beds, Sandgate Beds and topmost Folkestone Beds. The Hythe Beds sands and sandstones give rise to a bold escarpment, which reaches a height of 280 m at Blackdown and 290 m at Leith Hill in Surrey. In places the sands contain numerous nodules of chert, which is chemically the same as flint, but paler in colour. Soils on the Hythe Beds are generally acid, sandy, and very free draining. Many dip-slope valleys have streamless upper sections, recalling chalk dry valleys. The sandstones are generally rather rubbly and poorly cemented, but have been used locally as building stone and for road foundations.

The succeeding Sandgate Beds are very variable in character. In some places they are quite clayey and form low ground, for example in the valley of the River Rother, but they also include sands and sandstones, such as the iron-cemented Pulborough Sandrock and the usually calcitic, but sometimes silica-cemented, sandstones of the basal Bargate Beds.

The unconsolidated, yellow and orange, current bedded sands of the Folkestone Beds form low ridges covered in heath and woodland. The soils are exceptionally free draining, infertile and acidic.

The Lower Greensand is underlain by up to 400 m of Weald Clay, which was deposited under freshwater and sometimes brackish conditions. Together with the overlying and relatively thin Atherfield Clay it forms an extensive area of lowland. Within the Weald Clay are thin beds of sandstone, such as the Horsham Stone, which was much used in the past for roofing 'slates' and paving material. There are also occasional limestone beds, known as '*Paludina* limestone' or 'Sussex marble', which are crowded with the fossilized shells of water snails, belonging to the genus *Viviparus*. Descendent species live in Sussex rivers today. The limestone was formerly much prized as an ornamental building stone.

Local folding of the rock layers in the western Weald produces richly varied scenery. The Vale of Fernhurst, for example, is a classic example of an eroded anticline, much studied by geology students. The small Hammer Stream and somewhat larger River Lod have excavated the floor of the Vale in the Atherfield and Weald Clays. The Hythe Beds form the escarpment of Older Hill and Bexleyhill on the south side of the Vale and the corresponding escarpment of Blackdown Hill on the north. They have been bent ('cambered') down the scarps in several places, perhaps as a result of freezing and thawing during the Quaternary cold stages, and in addition massive rotational landslips have developed in the clays just below the scarps. Some landslipping still occurs, but on a much reduced scale. That erosion of the area is continuing is demonstrated by the River Lod, which carries much suspended sediment when in flood. Looking out over the Vale of Fernhurst from the Hythe Beds escarpment, one cannot fail to be impressed by the many changes that the area has undergone. The pace of landform evolution appears much more rapid than in the chalk country to the south where the landforms seem in many cases to be a legacy of erosional processes that have now vanished.

CONCLUSION

Few other parts of lowland Britain match the South Downs in offering such great diversity of geology and scenery within a relatively confined area. The chalk stratigraphy of the South Downs continues to be a focus of intensive geological research, and is providing many valuable insights into the events that shaped north-west Europe during nearly 30 million years of Earth history. In addition, the landforms of the Downs are of key importance, not only because they are scenically very attractive but also because they are of great scientific interest. The bold escarpment, chasm-like Devil's Dyke and sister valleys, the shapely meanders of the Cuckmere and precipitous cliffs of the Seven Sisters, are often chosen as illustrations in scientific textbooks.

None of the existing National Parks in Britain contains Chalk within its boundaries. The designated South Downs National Park includes the most geologically interesting area of Chalk in Britain, with its key exposures and splendid array of classic landforms. In the Western Weald the boundaries of the Designated Park extend across a range of sands, sandstones and clays that predate the Chalk. This area is also of major geological and geomorphological interest, and well deserves National Park status, with the opportunities this brings for protection and better understanding of its geological and scenic heritage.

REFERENCES

Andrews, C. and Williams, R.B.G. (2000) Limpet erosion of Chalk shore platforms in Southeast England. *Earth Surface Processes and Landforms*, **25**, 1371–81.

BAR (2005) *Beach sustainability and biodiversity on eastern Channel coasts*. Interim Report of the BAR Project, University of Sussex.

Bates, M.R., Parfitt, S.A. and Roberts, M.B. (1997) The chronology, palaeogeography and archaeological significance of the marine Quaternary record of the West Sussex coastal plain, Southern England, UK. *Quaternary Science Reviews*, **16**, 1227–1252.

Bates, M.R., Parfitt, S.A. and Roberts, M.B. (1998) Later Middle and Upper Pleistocene marine sediments of the West Sussex coastal plain: a brief review. In: Murton, J.B., Whiteman, C.A., Bates, M.R., Bridgland, D.R., Long, A.J., Roberts, M.B. and Waller, M.P. (eds) *The Quaternary of Kent and Sussex: Field guide*. Quaternary Research Association, London. pp. 151–165.

Clayton, C.J. (1986) The chemical environment of flint formation in Upper Cretaceous chalks. In: Sieveking, G. De C. and Hart, M.B. (eds) *The scientific study of flint and chert*. Cambridge University Press, Cambridge. pp.3–54.

Dawson, B. (1998) *Flint Buildings in West Sussex*. West Sussex County Council, Chichester.

Dornbusch, U., Williams, R.B.G., Moses, C. and Robinson, D.A. (2002) Life expectancy of shingle beaches: measuring *in situ* abrasion. *Journal of Coastal Research*, Special Issue, 36, 249–255.

Edmunds, F.H. (1927) Pliocene deposits on the South Downs. *Geological Magazine*, 64, 287.

Gibbard, P.L. (1995) The formation of the Strait of Dover. In: Preece, R.C. (ed) *Island Britain: a Quaternary perspective*. Geological Society Special Publication No. 96. London. pp.15–26.

Hancock, J.M. (1993) The formation and diagenesis of chalk. In: Downing, R.A., Price,M. and Jones, G.P. (eds) *The hydrogeology of the Chalk of North-West Europe*. Clarendon Press, Oxford. pp. 14–34.

Hodgson, J.M., Rayner, J.H. and Catt, J.A. (1974) The geomorphological significance of Clay-with-Flints on the South Downs. *Transactions of the Institute of British Geographers*, 61, 119–129.

Insole, A., Daley, B. and Gale, A. (1998) *The Isle of Wight*. Guide No. 60. Geologists' Association, London.

Jones, D.K.C. (1981) *Southeast and Southern England*. Methuen, London.

Jones, D.K.C. (1999a) Tertiary evolution of southern England. In: Smith, B.J., Whalley, W.B. and Warke, P.A. (eds) *Uplift, erosion and stability: perspectives on long-term landscape development*. Special Publication 162. Geological Society, London. pp. 1–23.

Jones, D.K.C. (1999b) On the uplift and denudation of the Weald. In: Smith, B.J., Whalley, W.B. and Warke, P.A. (eds) *Uplift, erosion and stability: perspectives on long-term landscape development*. Special Publication 162. Geological Society, London. pp. 25–43.

Jones, H.K and Robins, N.S. (1999) *The chalk aquifer of the South Downs*. Hydrogeological Report Series. British Geological Survey, Keyworth.

Kerney, M.P, Brown, E.H. and Chandler, T.J. (1964) The Late-glacial and Post-glacial history of the Chalk escarpment near Brook, Kent. *Philosophical Transactions of the Royal Society of London*, B248, 135–204.

Mortimore, R.N. (1997) *The Chalk of Sussex and Kent*. Guide No. 57. Geologists' Association, London.

Mortimore, R.N., Wood, C.J. and Gallois, R.W. (2001) *British Upper Cretaceous Stratigraphy*. Geological Conservation Review Series No. 23. Joint Nature Conservation Committee, Peterborough.

Mortimore, R.N., Lawrence, J., Pope, D., Duperret, A. and Genter, A. (2004) Coastal cliff geohazards in weak rocks: the UK Chalk cliffs of Sussex. In: Mortimore, R.N. and Duperret, A. (eds) *Coastal chalk cliff instability*. Geological Society Engineering Geology Special Publication No. 20. London. pp. 3–31.

Mortimore, R.N. and Duperret, A. (eds) (2004) *Coastal chalk cliff instability*. Engineering Geology Special Publication No. 20. Geological Society, London. pp. 3-31.

Murton, J.B. (1996) Near-surface brecciation of Chalk, Isle of Thanet, southeast England: a comparison with ice-rich brecciated bedrocks in Canada and Spitzbergen. *Permafrost and Periglacial Processes*, 7, 153–164.

Preece, R.C., Scourse, J.D., Houghton, S.D., Knudsen, K.L. and Penney, D.N. (1990) The Pleistocene sea-level and neotectonic history of the eastern Solent, southern England. *Philosophical Transactions of the Royal Society of London*, B328, 425–477.

Quesnel, F., Catt, J., Laignel, B., Bourdillon, C. and Meyer, R. (2003) The Neogene and Quaternary Clay-with-flints north and south of the English Channel: comparisons of distribution, age, genetic processes and geodynamics. *Journal of Quaternary Science*, 18, 283–294.

Reid, C. (1887) On the origin of dry chalk valleys and of coombe rock. *Quarterly Journal of the Geological Society of London*, 43, 364–373.

Roberts, M.B. (1998) Middle Pleistocene sediments and archaeology at ARC Eartham Quarry, Boxgrove, West Sussex. In: Murton, J.B., Whiteman, C.A., Bates, M.R., Bridgland, D.R., Long, A.J., Roberts, M.B. and Waller, M.P. (eds) *The Quaternary of Kent and Sussex: Field guide*. Quaternary Research Association, London. pp. 187–213.

Roberts, M.B. and Parfitt, S.A. (1999) *Boxgrove. A Middle Pleistocene hominid site at Eartham Quarry, Boxgrove, West Sussex*. English Heritage, London.

Small, R.J. (1980) The Tertiary geomorphological evolution of south-east England: an alternative interpretation. In: Jones, D.K.C. (ed) *The shaping of southern England*. Institute of British Geographers Special Publication 11. Academic Press, London. pp. 49–70.

Sparks, B.W. (1949) Denudation chronology of the dip slope of the South Downs. *Proceedings of the Geologists' Association*, 60, 165–215.

Sparks, B.W. (1971) *Rocks and relief*. Longman, London.

Ullyott, J.S., Nash, D.J., Whiteman, C.A. and Mortimore, R.N. (2004) Distribution, petrology and mode of development of silcretes (sarsens and puddingstones) on the eastern South Downs. *Earth Surface Processes and Landforms*, 29, 1509–1539.

Williams, R.B.G. (1980) The weathering and erosion of Chalk under periglacial conditions. In: Jones, D.K.C. (ed) *The shaping of southern England*.Institute of British Geographers Special Publication 11. Academic Press, London. pp. 225–248.

Williams, R.B.G. (1986) Periglacial phenomena in the South Downs. In: Sieveking, G. De C. and Hart, M.B. (eds) *The scientific study of flint and chert*. Cambridge University Press, Cambridge. pp. 61–167.

Williams, R.B.G. (1987) Frost weathered mantles on the Chalk. In: Boardman, J. (ed) Periglacial processes and landforms in *Britain and Ireland*. Cambridge University Press, Cambridge. pp. 127–133.

Williams, R.B.G. and Robinson, D.A. (1983) The landforms of Sussex. In: Geography Editorial Committee, *Sussex: environment, landscape and society*. Sutton, Gloucester. pp. 33–49.

Williams, R.B.G., Robinson, D.A., Dornbusch, U., Foote, Y.L.M., Moses, C.A. and Saddleton, P.R. (2004) A sturzstrom-like cliff fall on the Chalk coast of Sussex, UK. In: Mortimore, R.N. and Duperret, A. (eds) *Coastal chalk cliff instability*. Engineering Geology Special Publication No. 20. Geological Society, London. pp. 89–97.

Wilmot, R.D. and Young, B. (1985) Aluminite and other aluminium minerals from Newhaven, Sussex: the first occurrence of Nordstrandite in Great Britain. *Proceedings of the Geologists' Association*, 96, 47–52.

Wooldridge, S.W. and Linton, D.L. (1955) *Structure, surface and drainage in South-East England*. Philip, London.

Young, B. and Lake, R.D. (1988) *Geology of the country around Brighton and Worthing*. British Geological Survey Memoir. HMSO, London.

CHAPTER 3
The Archaeology of the South Downs

DAVID MCOMISH AND PETER TOPPING

The variety and extent of the archaeological remains on the South Downs typify one of the richest cultural landscapes in England (Plate (map) 35). The current environment masks a landscape of stunning complexity and intensity of use and hosts an unparalleled inventory of sites and monuments of all periods. These sites are among the rarest and most fragile known in the British Isles, notably the Palaeolithic deposits close to Chichester as well as the Neolithic flint mines and causewayed enclosures. The significance of the historic fabric of the area, however, is as clear to those living and working here as it is for those simply travelling through. This chapter will look only at fragments of what is none the less a remarkably subtle, distinctive and diverse history of human endeavour on the Downs.

THE PALAEOLITHIC ON THE SOUTH DOWNS

The work at Boxgrove has made a significant impact on our understanding of the oldest archaeology of Sussex and Hampshire. These excavations have provided evidence of the early hominid occupation of the British Isles and generated enormous public interest too. The pre-Holocene ice sheets, of course, never reached the South Downs, but their effects would have induced the large-scale flow of soils and other debris. This resulted in not only the movement of artefacts around the landscape but also in deeply burying older material. Distribution maps of Palaeolithic finds, for instance, clearly reference zones

that may have accumulated redeposited artefacts or contain buried ground-surfaces. Other findspots are revealed when sites are disturbed, during gravel extraction or quarrying, for example. Recent research in the area has concentrated on investigations along the coastal plain targeting buried Pleistocene deposits. In contrast, little work has been undertaken in the river valleys or on the Downs. Two significant pieces of work have charted the general range of Palaeolithic material in Sussex: Woodcock (1981) and Wymer's Southern Rivers Project (Wymer, 1994). These detail all the major findspots of artefacts from river valleys and raised-beach deposits. Indeed, much work has been undertaken in mapping the course and morphology of the main raised-beach deposits (see Pope, 2003), notably the Goodwood-Slindon series. The focus of investigation has centred on the ARC quarries at Eartham and been brought to public attention by the discovery of human remains there in the early 1990s (Roberts and Parfitt, 1999). The landscape half-a-million years ago was unrecognizable but it is clear that what drew those early humans to the site included good supplies of flint. This flint was a central part of the prehistoric toolkit and its procurement was of crucial importance. The degree of occupation uncovered at Eartham does suggest that further investigation of the Goodwood-Slindon deposits to the east and west along the coastal plain would produce similar levels of intensive land use. Other later raised-beach deposits, including the Aldingbourne, Brighton-Norton and Pagham series, reflect fluctuations in sea levels as well as the impact

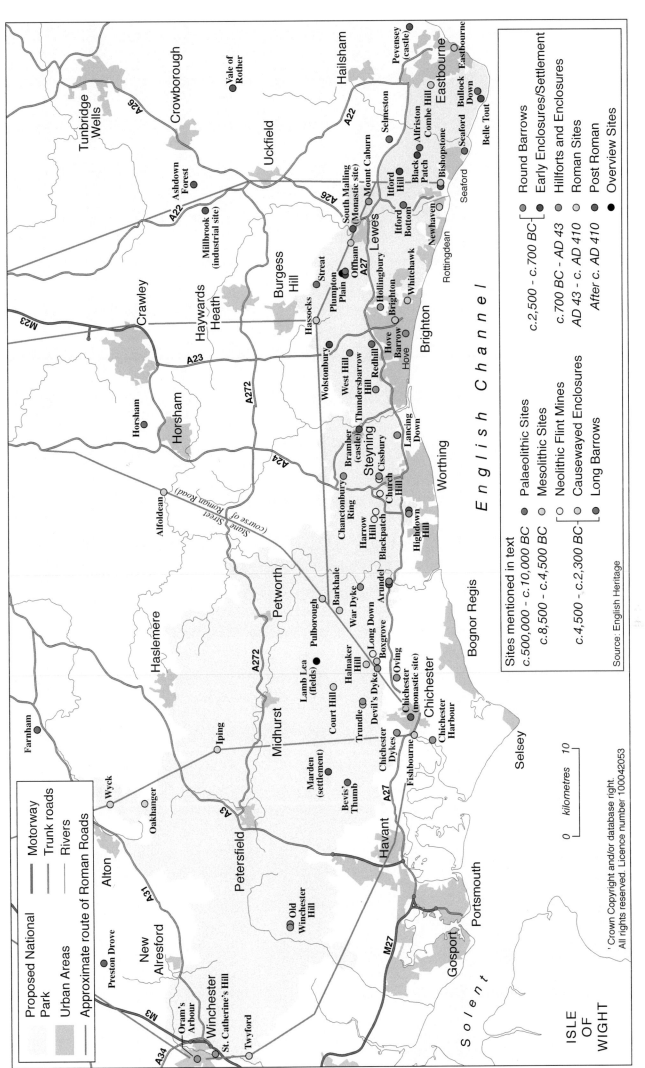

Plate (map) 35

Archaeological sites in the South Downs area.

Source: English Heritage; map produced by the University of Southampton Cartographic Unit.

Plate 36 *(top left)*
The flint mines at Harrow Hill, West Sussex, are located on a prominent downland spur opposite those at Black Patch. A later prehistoric enclosure overlies the mines, as at Cissbury.
Photo: English Heritage.

Plate 38 *(centre left)*
The Early Neolithic enclosure at Barkhale, West Sussex, which subsequently became a focus for later Bronze Age round barrows.
Photo: English Heritage.

Plate 37 *(top right)*
The flint mines at Cissbury, West Sussex, now partly enclosed by later Iron Age hill-fort defences.
Photo: English Heritage.

Plate 39 *(centre right)*
St Roche's Hill (The Trundle) at Goodwood, West Sussex. The circuit of the Middle Iron Age enclosure is clearly visible, and within it a number of Neolithic enclosures can be seen (and see Plate 151).
Photo: English Heritage.

Plate 40 *(far left)*
A bell barrow on Kingley Vale, near Chichester, West Sussex.
Photo: Mark Bowden, courtesy of English Heritage.

Plate 43 *(left)*
Chanctonbury Ring, West Sussex; the hill fort can be seen top centre, and a medieval or later pond at bottom right. Between the two are the remains of a cross-ridge boundary.
Photo: English Heritage.

of isostatic uplift during the past 500,000 years. All contain excellent evidence of archaeological and palaeo-environmental data, and 'distinguish(es) the Sussex Coastal Plain as an area of worldwide archaeological importance' (Pope, 2003, 24). This presents something of a dilemma since it is obvious that this zone is being actively destroyed through gravel extraction, road building and house construction.

POST-GLACIAL ACTIVITY ON THE SOUTH DOWNS

The importance of the South Downs and the Weald have long been recognized and especially since the pioneering work of Clark in the 1930s (Clark, 1932) and, more recently, Jacobi (1978). Principally, we are concerned with communities which exploited the resources of the study area from the end of the last glaciation some 12,000 years ago and the subsequent 7500 years; clearly a long period of time when much of the evidence found is confined to flint tools and, infrequently, indications of settlements. These communities are characterized as hunter-gatherer groups living a fairly mobile lifestyle but within increasingly fixed territories. The Mesolithic toolkit comprised a number of highly distinctive implements, such as microliths, small finely-worked blades employed as projectile points, scrapers and axe-like pieces. Clark's work at Seaford, Farnham and Horsham, amongst many others, helped frame an understanding of this early cultural landscape. His work at Selmeston is especially pivotal as, alongside lithic remains, it uncovered evidence for some sort of rudimentary structure – one of the earliest discoveries of such features in the British Isles. This work illustrated that many of these early sites were located close to springlines on well-drained soils, and that there was an intense focus of activity in the Weald. Here, a range of open sites as well as a number of rock shelters have been found contrasting with the lower densities of finds from the chalk ridge. Curwen (1954, 54) noted this, rather dramatically suggesting that 'nothing better could illustrate Mesolithic man's preference for sand and his abhorrence of chalk'. More recent fieldwork has redressed the imbalance but there does seem to be a real tendency for the earliest Mesolithic sites to be found on the Lower Greensand in the Weald and that the widespread activity now apparent on the Downs is almost certainly post-6500 BC in date. However, as Drewett (1999) suggests, this polarity in distribution may be due to the destructive impact of later communities on the Downs. The Coastal Plain is also under-represented and this, likewise, is in all likelihood due to site destruction or burial beneath later development. The shell-middens close to Hastings do suggest that this was a heavily exploited zone; other contemporary sites should be expected along the coast and off-shore. At this time the first major alterations to the natural vegetational cover occurred. The Weald and chalk ridge presented two very different landscapes with good evidence now emerging that the former was being periodically cleared of tree cover by at least the ninth millennium BC. The chalk ridge in contrast, retained a more complete tree canopy, apart from one or two instances such as Itford Bottom, where clearance of sorts has an early ninth millennium BC date (Bell, 1983, 132–42).

Recent work stresses the ubiquity of Mesolithic activity across the various topographical and geological zones. Frequently those sites uncovered are characterized by massive numbers of artefacts and, increasingly, by an association with probable settlement structures, either stakeholes for slight timber structures or quarry pits, as found at Streat (Butler, 1998) or at Oakhanger in the Weald (Rankine and Dimbleby, 1960). The nature of these deposits is difficult to characterize. They are unlikely to represent long-lived and permanent settlements; instead they are best viewed as temporary staging-camps for small social groups moving around the landscape – perhaps they were hunting camps? More intensive evidence of activity is found on the Downs in the late eighth to fifth millennia BC particularly on sites located on or close to clay-with-flints deposits such as Bullock Down (Drewett, 1982). Holgate (2003) summarizes the most recent discoveries at Redhill and West Hill, Pyecombe, and more recently English Heritage fieldwork close to the Plumpton Plain Bronze Age settlements uncovered a dense scatter of flint debris, some of it Later Mesolithic in date (McOmish and Tuck, 2004).

CEREMONIAL LANDSCAPES – THE NEOLITHIC AND EARLY BRONZE AGES

The South Downs preserve the remains of some of the earliest archaeological sites surviving in the modern countryside. Flint mines, causewayed enclosures and earthen burial mounds indicate that this period was one of considerable change; new technologies were adopted, particularly pottery-making, mining for flint, constructing monuments, but perhaps most symbolically there was a move away from hunting and gathering to farming. However, this change took a considerable time to make an impact upon the landscape with farms and settlements appearing only at the end of the third millennium BC.

Flint mines

The Sussex flint mines appear to be the earliest in England, beginning around 4000 BC at Harrow Hill (Plate 36), Blackpatch, Church Hill and

Long Down. Those at Cissbury were sunk a century or two later (Plate 37). The mines were finally abandoned around 2800 BC, although they continued to be a focus for later activity. For example, at Blackpatch and Church Hill, later burial monuments containing Beaker pottery and Collared Urns were built. However, some burials also took place while mining continued, as in Shaft 1 at Church Hill, Shaft VI at Cissbury or Barrow 12 at Blackpatch. A female skeleton was discovered in Shaft 27 at Cissbury, raising interesting questions concerning gender, miners and mining.

Excavations at flint mines have uncovered unusual deposits: human remains in shafts or at gallery entrances; pottery in the shafts, on chalk platforms or at gallery entrances; carved chalk objects near gallery entrances; imported stone axes in some mines; hearths on shaft floors or in shaft fills; and graffiti are positioned near gallery entrances. Much of this appears to be connected to ritualized behaviour. Such a 'ritualization' of mining would have embedded a symbolic value into the hard-won nodules, which would have been enhanced when they were 'transformed' into special artefacts such as axes (cf. Whittle, 1995).

Furthermore, analysis of flintwork from non-mining sites on the South Downs indicates that only a small proportion was demonstrably of mined flint – surface flint was used for functional types of tool. Flint from the mines was reserved for specific artefacts such as axes (Gardiner, 1990; Holgate, 1995). The origin of the raw material, the methods of production and its subsequent use created the social value for the artefact.

The choice of the flint-mining locations may have been influenced by mythologies or rituals rather than geological considerations. The mines at Harrow Hill and Blackpatch were intentionally located upon poorer-quality flint (cf. Barber et al., 1999, 73). Such preferences suggest that it was cultural importance rather than the quality of the raw material that was the most significant factor.

The apparent lack of settlement evidence at flint mines (cf. Barber et al., 1999, 58–61) adds to the speculation that they were special places with sacred space surrounding the mines. Such an area may have existed between the Rivers Adur and Arun where Cissbury, Church Hill, Blackpatch and Harrow Hill are located on a block of downland which does not appear to contain any other contemporary monument (cf. Oswald et al., 2001, 117–118; Kinnes, 1992, 167, Fig 1A.11).

Causewayed enclosures

Causewayed enclosures, constructed between c. 4000 and 3300 BC, are the earliest surviving enclosures built in the British Isles and are characterized by perimeters with multiple entrances. The South Downs hosts at least six causewayed enclosures, with another possible site on Halnaker Hill overlooking the Long Down flint mines. These enclosures occur west of the River Arun and east of the River Adur, avoiding the main concentration of flint mines.

The scale of the enclosures varies, ranges from 1ha in area to 5.5ha. Structurally, these enclosures show some variety: Court Hill, Barkhale Camp (Plate 38) and Halnaker Hill all have single circuits; Offham has two closely-spaced circuits; Combe Hill has widely-spaced circuits; and Whitehawk Camp and The Trundle (Plate 39) feature both closely and widely-spaced circuits (Oswald et al., 2001).

The function of causewayed enclosures is enigmatic. They are not permanent settlements, although pits and groups of postholes suggest the presence of some form of structures. Debris, such as pottery and animal bones, indicative of periodic feasting has been found in the ditches of downland enclosures. Likewise, imported stone tools have been found alongside evidence for tool manufacture, bone and leather-working and pottery-making. Some ditches produced human skeletal evidence, implying that the enclosures had a role in processing the dead or were the depositories for the (possibly partial) remains of significant ancestors.

Both Whitehawk Camp and The Trundle were remodelled and enlarged, creating more complex multiple circuits, and demonstrating that some enclosures had a continuing importance. Once the enclosures were abandoned, the earthworks still attracted the attention of later communities. Over 1000 years later, Early Bronze Age groups built round barrows at both Barkhale Camp and Combe Hill; perhaps oral histories attached some importance to the enclosures, or it may be that the locations retained a deep significance.

Long barrows

Earth-built long barrows (linear burial mounds) date to between c. 4000 BC and 3500 BC (Kinnes, 1992, 120). Most vary from 55 m to 25 m in length, with occasional exceptions such as Preston Drove (79 m) and Bevis' Thumb (61m); the mounds vary in width between 19m and 11m. Long barrows were normally constructed from soil, dug from parallel flanking ditches, and many are aligned roughly east to west, with some variations, and are located on both north and south-facing downland slopes. Multiple burials have been discovered suggesting that these were communal monuments, the burial places of groups or extended families. Certainly they would have taken a communal effort to build and maintain.

Most recent excavations have focused upon sampling barrows. The only extensive excavation occurred at Alfriston in East Sussex on a 'short' long barrow. The ditches produced plain pottery-sherds

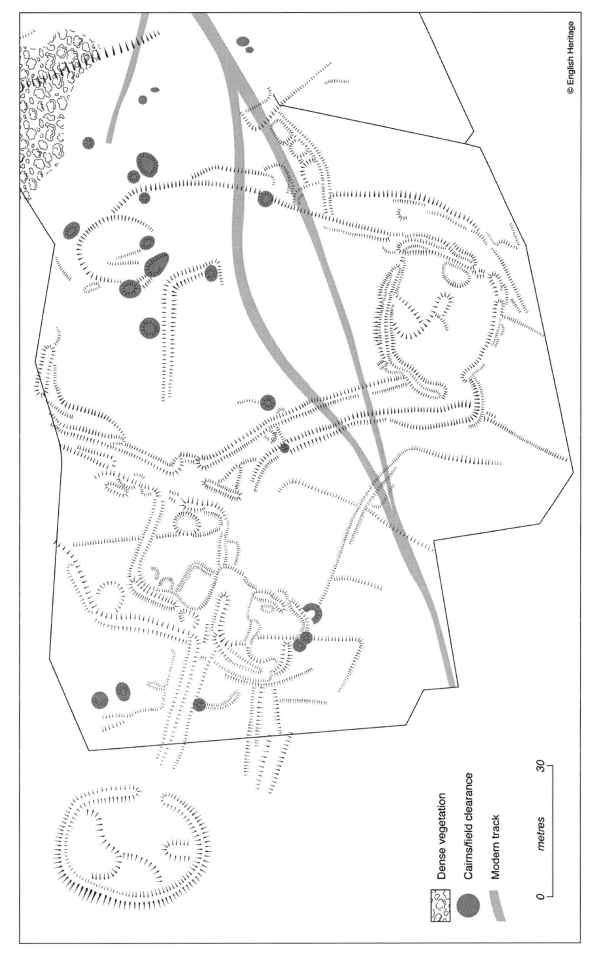

Figure 3.1   English Heritage survey of the Middle Bronze Age settlement complex at Plumpton Plain. The enclosures overlie the remains of a pre-existing field system.

Dense vegetation

Cairns/field clearance

Modern track

0   metres   30

and flint-knapping debris, and the mound covered two small pits, one containing a single crouched female burial (Drewett, 1975), suggesting it may have been a late barrow.

Round barrows

Round barrows, or circular burial mounds (Plate 40), are located along the full extent of the South Downs. Originating in the Later Neolithic period they reached their apogee during the Early Bronze Age, *c.* 2300 BC to 1500 BC. Not only are round barrows more numerous than the long mounds but they also illustrate a shift in burial rite from 'communal' burials in the long barrows to individuals in round barrows. Occasionally, these round barrows cluster together in tight-knit groups or cemeteries. This can be seen clearly within the later Iron Age enclosure at Old Winchester Hill, Hampshire (Plate 41). Here the barrows, including bowl and pond variants, have been built side by side in a linear arrangement and form an impressive, eye-catching feature from all viewpoints (McOmish, 1994). Many burials were accompanied by grave goods; a particularly rich group of burials was located around the Hove area. At Hove itself, a large round barrow covered an oak coffin which held human bones, and grave goods included a perforated stone axe, a bronze dagger, a whetstone and an amber cup. Most other rich graves are located within 20 km of the Hove barrow (Drewett *et al.*, 1988, 84), suggesting an important grouping which has implications for the interpretation of social dynamics on the South Downs.

Late enclosures

Enclosures constructed after the causewayed examples are extremely rare on the South Downs. One of the few is at Belle Tout on Beachy Head, which produced primary evidence of quarrying activities in the Earlier Neolithic period, followed by working areas, flint-knapping, several hearths, a midden and structural evidence all surrounded by earthen banks dated by Beaker or Food Vessel pottery to the Late Neolithic to Early Bronze Age period (Bradley, 1970; 1982). Clearly this location had some local importance over this period of time.

FIELDS, FORTS AND FARMS – THE DOMESTICATED LANDSCAPE

Throughout much of the preceding fourth and third millennia BC there is little physical trace of established settlement and certainly no surviving evidence for cultivation in the area. However, one of the more profound transformations in the South Downs landscape took place between *c.* 1600 BC and 900 BC when the first sedentary agricultural communities became established.

The environmental evidence for vegetational change on the South Downs is outlined by Somerville (2003, 241–2) who identifies widespread woodland clearance in the second millennium BC intensifying until the early first millennium BC. Generally, it is perceived that by the Middle Bronze Age deforestation of the chalk was extensive (Robinson and Williams, 1983). Pollen spectra are dominated by cereal and weeds of disturbed ground and much of the colluvial build-up is directly related to the occupation of settlements and the use of the land around them for arable cultivation. This is seen clearly at sites such as Highdown Hill and at Itford Hill (Bell, 1983) where pottery fragments contemporary with the settlements were found in colluvial soils nearby.

There are at least 26 Middle Bronze Age settlements identified across the South Downs (Hamilton, 2003, 70). A number of these, including Plumpton Plain Site A (Fig. 3.1), Itford Hill and Black Patch, show evidence of settlement-shift over time and for extended occupational sequences (Needham, 1996).

Later prehistoric activity across the South Downs is profuse with an enormous range of settlement forms, land use and craft activities. Perhaps the best known components of this landscape are the hill forts – though more usefully termed 'prominent enclosures' by Hamilton and Manley (1997; 2000). Many of the large hillforts have their origins in the Middle Iron Age (*c.* 450 – 75 BC) and this is true of sites such as Cissbury, The Trundle, Mount Caburn, and St. Catherine's Hill (Plate 42) amongst many others, but this form of monument has its origin in the closing centuries of the second millennium BC. At Wolstonbury, the unusual enclosure has been dated to *c.* 1000 BC and is among the earliest prominent enclosures so far dated in southern England. These enclosures, long thought of as defensive constructions, could equally have played a significant role in a symbolic fashion, demarcating special places. This is obvious at Cissbury (Donachie and Field, 1994; Barber *et al.*, 1999) and The Trundle (St. Roche's Hill), and Old Winchester Hill (McOmish, 1994), where the impressive ramparts of the Iron Age enclosures overlie earlier monuments; a deliberate juxtaposition of the 'ancient' and the 'new'. A number of the earliest hill forts enclose very large areas within single banks and ditches and show a preference for the edges of the main chalk escarpments as at Thundersbarrow Hill and Hollingbury. These sites are curious as they rarely contain evidence for settlement in contrast with the later sites such as Mount Caburn.

There is a wide variety of settlement forms, ranging from lightly enclosed sites to those that are completely open, and these extend across a wide topographical range showing that all parts of the landscape were being exploited. In addition to these farmsteads, the

Plate 41

Old Winchester Hill, near East Meon, Hampshire, August 1995. This aerial photo taken from the east shows the outline of the hill fort very clearly, its circuit punctured by two entrances; that at the foot of the picture is the main one. What is not so clear is the dramatic ridge-top location (but see Plate 17), evidently significant long before the construction of the Iron Age boundary; within the site there are several Bronze Age burial mounds, now scarred by footpaths, and other round barrows underlie the bank to the east and south. The slight remains of prehistoric constructions can be seen inside the hill fort, as well as other later features, including a pond, close to the east entrance, and smaller hollows probably dating from World War II.
Photo: English Heritage

Plate 42

St. Catherine's Hill, near Winchester, Hampshire, July 1987. The oval outline of this large hill fort is picked out by the erosion caused by walkers, though the defences remain in good condition. The large internal rampart is flanked by a ditch and a further bank outside this, so it must have presented a formidable barrier. The remains of a medieval chapel, built before the middle of the 12th century, lie in the circular copse at the highest point of the site. Beside this are the remains of a small mizmaze originally cut between 1647 and 1710. To the north, remains of medieval strip cultivation encroach on the Iron Age boundary.
Photo: English Heritage.

Plate 44

An aerial view of Arundel Castle. Originating in the late Norman Period (AD 1066–1154), the castle has survived over the centuries, latterly preserved by the Fitzalan-Howard family headed by the Dukes of Norfolk.
Photo: English Heritage.

Plate 45 *(left)*
Reconstruction of an Iron Age house, formerly at Butser but now sited at Chalton, Hampshire, based on studies by Peter Reynolds.
Photo: Peter Brandon.

Plate 46 *(below)*
The Great Barn at Alciston, East Sussex, with 13th century foundations; built by the monks of Battle Abbey for the storage of the produce of their farms.
Photo: Peter Brandon.

Plate 47 *(left)*
A medieval cottage, originating from Hangleton, East Sussex, rebuilt at the Weald and Downland Museum at Singleton, West Sussex.
Photo: Peter Brandon.

Plate 48 *(below left)*
The Clergy House at Alfriston, East Sussex, before restoration. Built in *c*.1350, this timber-framed 'Wealden' house was partially rebuilt in the 17th century. It was bought by The National Trust in 1896 for £10.00.
Photo: © The National Trust Photographic Library.

Plate 49 *(below right)*
A view of the west front of the restored Clergy House at Alfriston taken from the graveyard.
Photo: Andrew Butler
© The National Trust Photographic Library.

landscape is further sub-divided by a series of linear earthworks known as cross-ridge boundaries. Typically, these are found on the summit of the chalk ridge and were built to cut off small promontories or spur projections. They are notoriously difficult to date; some might be Late Neolithic in date, others, such as that close to Chanctonbury Ring (Plate 43), are Roman, but there is a close association between hill forts and these earthworks. They may have been used to demarcate specific zones or to act as visual markers for boundaries. In all instances they would have interrupted free movement along the ridge-top.

Environmental sequences show that there was a mix of arable and pastoral concerns and that other quasi-industrial activity, such as pottery manufacture, was well established. As Hamilton and Manley (1999) have pointed out there is a greatly reduced incidence of Middle Iron Age material, suggesting possibly, that there was a fall in population between the fifth and second centuries BC.

The final centuries of the Iron Age witnessed the development of new forms of settlement and the seeming collapse of older traditional ways of life. Many of the hillforts ceased to be maintained, and there was an expansion in the areas of settlement to include the whole coastal plain. Enclosed farmsteads, such as that at Oving, continued to be occupied and ritual centres were also established. That at Lancing Down (Bedwin, 1981) consisted of small wooden rectangular buildings associated with the deposition of metalwork and pottery – a larger temple was constructed adjacently in the Romano-British period. Other innovations of this period include the introduction of rudimentary coinage with a marked concentration of finds coming from the coastal plain and the Chichester area in particular (Bedwin and Place, 1995). Perhaps the most important development in the South Downs landscape at this time, however, takes place to the east of Chichester harbour, where a series of massive linear earthworks were constructed in the early first century AD. The earthworks, referred to as *oppida*, define large enclosed areas and cover several square kilometres of the coastal plain, and are generally taken to be of a defensive nature, although a wide range of social and economic activities took place within their boundaries. Similar developments may have taken place, though on a much smaller scale, at Oram's Arbour, near Winchester. Here a univallate (single bank and ditch) enclosure of indeterminate size and shape produced evidence of Late Iron Age to Early Roman activity contemporary with that at Chichester (Qualmann and Whinney, 2004).

Recently, fieldwork by English Heritage has shed light on another important '*oppida*-like' area immediately surrounding the town of Arundel. Here, there has long been speculation about a prehistoric origin for the earthwork associated with the Norman castle. In particular, attention has focused on the massive enclosing boundary surrounding Castle Park, but recent work there would suggest that the earthwork enclosure is late Saxon in date at the earliest. What is apparent from survey is that this enclosure overlies a less well-preserved earlier bank and ditch, the line of which extends to the south-west from the north-western corner of the larger enclosure towards the sharp break of slope above a now dry valley. This slighter earthwork is undated, but finds of Middle Iron Age pottery from the larger embanked perimeter may well be residual and relate to this earlier phase of enclosure. If correct, this earlier bank and ditch may well have cut off the southern extent of a chalk spur that extended roughly north-westwards.

Other earthworks in the wider landscape are reminiscent of the Chichester Dykes, to which they are connected by the Devil's Dyke, and it may well be that they are of the same date. The War Dyke, 3km to the north of Arundel, is a massive and, in places, multiple linear earthwork. This extends in a shallow arc from the banks of the River Arun, westwards for a distance of at least 2km. Other intermittent lengths of complex linear boundary extend the line south-west towards the edge of escarpment above Slindon. Further linear ditch elements extend to the south, and lead ultimately to a point on the River Arun midway between Ford and Tortington. The earthwork boundary, therefore, encloses close on to 22 sq km in area. Within the enclosed area a number of earthwork complexes, long thought to be medieval in date, are more likely to belong to the Late Iron Age and Early Roman period. Finds of high-status imported pottery underline the importance of the Arundel area at the time of the Roman Conquest, and it is plausible that a settlement contemporary with the Late Iron Age activity at Chichester existed here.

THE ROMANO-BRITISH PERIOD

Recent work at Fishbourne is radically altering our view of the early stages of the Roman Conquest, and it is now apparent that the Chichester area played a significant part in events during AD 43 and AD 44. Debate still rages about the reasons for the invasion and its social impact, but its manifestation in the archaeological record is clear with new forms of public building, the development of urban centres, a formal communications network, as well as a revolution in the politico-economic world.

Much current research has focused on the 'palace' at Fishbourne and its role in the Roman invasions of AD 43. It seems plausible that there may be an early military focus to activity here, but the villa complex that developed and lasted into the third century AD was a grander version of a number of similar building complexes that were constructed in the area during the centuries following the Claudian Conquest. Villas have been uncovered at a number of locations across the South Downs, such as at Pulborough, Eastbourne, Newhaven, Brighton, Wyck and Twyford (for a fuller resumé see Rudling, 2003). Their general distribution is noteworthy in that there is a bias towards the lower edges of the chalk ridge often close to river valleys or on the coastal plain. This may well reflect the fact that these complexes were used as centres for estates that extended for considerable distances into the chalk hinterland. They are high-status centres, and it is likely that this wealth was founded upon the agricultural produce of the area. This prosperity is reflected in the range of smaller farmsteads and field systems that proliferate on the Downs as well as the coastal plain. Some of these, including those at Bishopstone and on Bullock Down, are long-lived farms and have produced evidence for an organized landscape of arable and pasture with integrated trackways punctuated by settlements of a form relatively unchanged since prehistoric times. They may well be the equivalent to tied or tenanted farms of more modern times and were, presumably, responsible for the richness so clearly illustrated at the villa complexes.

Rural industry flourished during the Romano-British period (again see Rudling, 2003 for fuller analysis). Iron-making, particularly in areas on the Weald, was established, as were centres of pottery-manufacture, stone-quarrying, forestry and salt-making.

Another feature of this era is the development of urban centres. That at Chichester was the *civitas* capital – part of a local government system introduced by the Romans. As well as this, other, lesser, usually roadside settlements were established as at Hassocks, Alfoldean and Iping. The roads themselves comprised well-built and maintained major routes connecting the larger urban centres, as well as a series of inter-connecting routes feeding into the wider landscape and which (alongside rivers and the sea) provided an arterial service route for the agricultural villages scattered across the area.

Temples and shrines, signs, perhaps, of more organized religion can be seen at a number of locations across the South Downs. Frequently they take the form of substantial buildings, either circular or square in layout and often located close to important pre-existing sites. At Lancing, the Roman temple was built adjacent to an earlier shrine, and at Chanctonbury Ring two small temple buildings were constructed within the interior of an earlier hill fort (Plate 43).

THE POST-ROMAN LANDSCAPE

The impact of the ending of Roman rule sometime early in the fifth century AD is being hotly debated at present, but it is clear that in the centuries leading up to *c.* AD 900, regardless of any manipulation in the socio-political sphere, there was a massive alteration in the form of settlement, the nature of landscape exploitation and a reconfiguration of the local economy (Gardiner, 2003). Against a declining population, the South Downs reverted to a prehistoric way of life, in many respects, after the collapse in the Roman economy. Notably, the vast carpets of fields and settlements seen on the Downs, for instance, went into terminal decline in the fifth century AD. This is evidenced further by the development of wooded landscapes on the ridge-tops and associated coombes. Some of the longer-established stands of forestry may have developed at this time, and it is tempting to suggest that the Ashdown Forest to the north of Lewes is the remnant of a once much larger post-Roman forest that extended to the west; likewise, the heavily wooded landscapes to the west of the Arun. Clearance in both cases took place in more recent historic times and is reflected in the good survival of archaeological monuments in these bands of woodland.

The scale of change must have been massive. Drewett has suggested (1982, 213) that at Bishopstone cultivation did not take place between the end of the Roman period and the thirteenth century – a picture repeated at a number of locations, not only on the South Downs but further afield throughout southern England. In general, settlement shifted into the river valleys and coastal plain, and the slopes of the Downs were used as pasture for stock, mainly cattle and sheep but also pigs, which would have found pannage in the woodland glades much to their liking. Alongside the more established settlements a range of temporary homesteads was used, probably in response to a pattern of seasonal transhumance, or as part of wider resource exploitation, including metalworking as at Millbrook in Ashdown Forest. On the South Downs the temporary sites of woodland pasture are often referenced by the place-name 'den' suffix, such as at Playden or Marden.

Very few settlements of this date have been found. None was placed within a defended enclosure, and the use of timber as a building material ensured that houses and other structures disappeared quickly after abandonment. Much the best evidence for Anglo-Saxon activity comes from burials within cemeteries with finds including pottery and glass as well as metalwork. At Highdown Hill, rare fifth to seventh century evidence of an early Saxon re-use of a Roman cemetery was uncovered and, in general, the distribution of cemeteries of this date indicates a real bias to the east of the Arun valley. This valley clearly marks a cultural watershed evident, too, in settlement intensity with lower levels of occupation apparent to the west of the river. The most notable density of cemeteries lies on the chalk ridge and related coombes in the area immediately to the north of Lewes underlining the importance of the pre-Norman Conquest settlement here.

In the tenth century, the South Downs appear to have been in the process of a significant transformation. Increases in population levels are evident as are intensifications in industrial development and the re-emergence of urban centres. The current pattern of parish boundaries was established in the tenth and eleventh centuries, and there was an expansion in the areas of settlement with newly-established farms created on the Downs, possibly replacing pre-existing sites. A standard method of land division, the strip parish, established at this time, is with us today and afforded access to a wide variety of resources, ranging from low-lying meadow through arable fields and on to pasture and woodland areas on the higher slopes. In many instances, such as the Vale of Rother, for example, land was apportioned between a number of manors so that there was shared access to meadow, arable and pasture (Gardiner, 2003). Iron-making and stone-quarrying for milling stone had been re-established by the end of the tenth century. Indeed, iron was being forged at a number of sites in the Western Weald, and the Lower Greensand flanking the northern chalk ridge was producing stone employed in the milling process. This story of a flourishing economy is enhanced by the intensity of salt-making evident along the coast and on tidal river stretches, as well as the founding of pottery kilns at places such as Chichester (Down, 1981).

Castle sites also feature prominently in the medieval landscapes of the South Downs, and offered clear symbols of authority, power and wealth. Sussex, of course, at Pevensey, hosts the earliest documented castle in the country, and in this study area there are at least 26 other similar fortifications by the end of the twelfth century. This number increases dramatically when moated sites are included as well as fortified monastic houses (Jones, 2003). The distribution of castle sites is very heavily biased towards low-lying zones, especially the river valleys and other natural routes that cut through the chalk, connecting Weald with coast. Those castles at Arundel (Plate 44) and Bramber are excellent examples of this strategic choice, but each of the Sussex rapes was provided with a fortified focus. These served as the foci for lordly control of the area, and provided a suitable framework for continued economic development and facilitated easy cross-channel communication and trade. Other notable influences are exercised by the monastic orders. Until the Dissolution in 1536 these wealthy landowners played an important role in shaping society and events across the South Downs, and their legacy is still apparent in earthwork remains and, occasionally, standing buildings. The relatively small number of pre-Conquest religious communities, for example, those at South Malling or Chichester, expanded in the eleventh century.

OVERVIEW OF THE SCOPE AND IMPACT OF LANDSCAPE CHANGE

As Brandon points out (1998), much of the downland during the medieval and late medieval periods is confined to sheepwalk with the majority of arable cultivation taking place on the lower slopes or closer to the contemporary settlements. It would seem reasonable to conjecture that the higher downland plateaux, as well as hosting substantial flocks of sheep and housing their shepherds, contained good stretches of managed woodland – the remains of ancient coppicing are still evident – and these, in turn, have helped preserve more ancient archaeological features, destroyed elsewhere by recent cultivation. Monument survival is poor on the exposed and open downs, a survival rate that is sadly matched on the enfolding slopes and flanking river valleys. In these zones important, early, landscape features are only retrievable through excavation, field collection strategies or via aerial photographs. Woodland is clearly an important element in the preservation of archaeological features, even more so if the block of woodland is long-lived. In general, monument density across the ploughed chalk landscapes of the South Downs is low with an average of less than two archaeological sites per square kilometre. This is not unexpected and fits a national pattern identified and quantified during the Monuments at Risk project (Darvill and Fulton, 1998), which pinpointed the disastrous impact of cultivation, especially twentieth century agriculture, on the landscapes of England. What is perhaps more surprising is that monument-density in woodland on the South Downs is lower, with an average of 0.5 monuments per km^2 – an inaccurate statistic, the reasons for which lie in the fact that relatively little fieldwork has taken place in areas of established woodland. In reality, the situation is different and recent fieldwork in the area of Lambs Lea, West Sussex, illustrates this well. Here, in an open stretch of downland there are substantial traces of ancient fields consisting of lyncheted boundaries that survive to a height of *c.* 0.2m. Part of this layout has been erased by cultivation, but a more substantial element extends southwards into a block of mixed deciduous woodland. The range of tree species, as well as their age, makes it clear that this is a long-established forest, and so it is no surprise that archaeological survival in the woodland is exceptional with field boundaries standing to a height of 2m in places. A detailed survey here would, undoubtedly, find evidence for discrete phasing of this ancient cultivation as well as traces of associated settlement. Local archaeology projects are targeting woodland, and so biases in discovery and distribution will be addressed. This will be particularly productive to the west of the Arun valley, where the clay-with-flints-capped summits of the Downs are commonly cloaked in woodland.

The deleterious impact of cultivation in the last two centuries and, particularly the middle decades of the twentieth century, cannot be understated. Earlier land use with a focus on pasture and woodland, especially on the upper slopes and chalk plateaux, ensured good archaeological survival. Changes to these regimes meant that the chalk soils were ploughed with some intensity, destroying relict landscape components such as fields and settlements. This is seen clearly in the area around the Bronze Age settlements at Plumpton Plain. Today the small enclave at Plumpton Plain provides an important habitat for a range of flora and fauna long lost on other, extensively damaged, areas of the South Downs chalk ridge. The scale of this loss can be illustrated by the work of the Brighton and Hove Archaeological Club on the site in the early 1930s at a time when much of the downland surrounding Plumpton Plain was still in pasture. Their area plan shows the wider context of the settlement set within a landscape that includes extensive early fields and other contemporary sites, both enclosed and open. It is especially noteworthy that arable cultivation close to the site is confined to a small paddock to the south-west of the enclosures. Another parcel of enclosed arable was established to the south lying across the valley floor of Faulkner's Bottom, but the largest extent of early twentieth century arable lay to the west of Streathill Farm 500m to the west of the Plumpton settlements. More recent land use is dominated by arable cultivation, so much so that the enclosures and a small portion of the associated field system survive only because of their location within a small fenced-off area of pasture. The pasture is partly wooded with mixed deciduous species, and scrub and bracken coverage is extensive and growing despite the grazing of cattle, occasionally herded within the penning. This is a surviving fragment of what must once have been a more extensive expanse of undisturbed chalk grassland; after the Second World War large areas of chalk grassland were ploughed up for arable farming, and it has been estimated that up to 25 per cent of the chalk grassland of the South Downs was lost between 1945 and 1980.

The cultural value of the archaeological sites and landscapes on the South Downs cannot be underestimated. At various locations across the area there is good surviving evidence for many of the most remarkable transformations apparent in the archaeological record of southern England. The rise in new forms of settlement, fields and a change in the associated material culture was allied to the development of intensive agriculture, territorial land divisions and long-lived nucleated settlements. The

area affords an excellent amenity value too. Change in the countryside is part of a dynamic process – many of the most significant features are themselves the results of more ancient changes in land use – but there has to be a degree of moderation and sympathetic adjustment so that economic and environmental concerns mesh together. A diverse constituency of people use the Downs and many are unaware of the significance of the monuments, their setting and their role in the development of the South Downs landscape. It is suggested here that better awareness would raise its value to the community and add to the enjoyment and understanding of those visiting the area. It will be essential that any new curatorial agency given the task of protecting and enhancing the South Downs and their historical environment should have a number of tightly focused aims, including:

- Providing information and understanding for continued good management of archaeological sites at farm, area and AONB/National Park level;
- Promoting aspects of sustainable tourism across the area, related to the appreciation of the historic heritage;
- Adding value to public enjoyment of the gateway sites and raising the profile of other, less well-known, places;
- Stimulating the local economy through access to and management of archaeological sites;
- Providing leadership for the comprehensive recording of archaeological sites, and monitoring of their condition.

REFERENCES

Austen, B. (1999) Industrial Sussex. In: Leslie, K. and Short, B. (eds) *An Historical Atlas of Sussex*. Phillimore, Chichester. pp. 104–105.

Barber, L. (2003) The Archaeology of Post-Medieval Sussex: a Review. In: Rudling, D. (ed) *The Archaeology of Sussex to AD 2000*. University of Sussex, Brighton. pp. 203–216.

Barber, M., Field, D., and Topping, P. (1999) *The Neolithic Flint Mines of England*. Royal Commission on the Historical Monuments of England. English Heritage, Swindon.

Bedwin, O. (1981) Excavations at Lancing Down, West Sussex, 1980. *Sussex Archaeol. Coll.* **119,** 37–55.

Bedwin, O. and Place, C. (1995) Late Iron Age and Romano-British occupation at Ounces Barn, Boxgrove, West Sussex; excavations, 1982–83. *Sussex Archaeol. Coll.* **133,** 45–101.

Bell, M. (1983) Valley Sediments as evidence of prehistoric land use on the South Downs. *Proceedings of the Prehistoric Society* **49,** 119–150.

Bradley, R. (1970) The excavation of a beaker settlement at Belle Tout, East Sussex, England. *Proceedings of the Prehistoric Society* **36,** 312–379.

Bradley, R. (1982) Belle Tout – Revision and Reassessment. In: Drewett, P. (ed) *The Archaeology of Bullock Down, Eastbourne,*

East Sussex: The Development of a Landscape. Sussex Archaeological Society Monograph 1. pp. 62–71. SAS, Lewes.

Brandon, P. (1974) *The Sussex Landscape.* Hodder, London.

Brandon, P. (1998) *The South Downs.* Phillimore, Chichester.

Brandon, P. (1999) Countryside Conservation. In: Leslie, K. and Short, B. (eds) *An Historical Atlas of Sussex.* Phillimore, Chichester. pp. 140–141.

Butler, C. (1998) Mesolithic Streat. Ancient Hunters: cooking, knapping and camping. *Sussex Past and Present* **84**, 6. Sussex Archaeological Society, Lewes.

Clark, J.G.D. (1932) *The Mesolithic Age in Britain.* Cambridge University Press, Cambridge.

Cleere, H. and Crossley, D. (1995) *The Iron Industry of the Weald*, 2nd edition. Merton Priory Press, Cardiff.

Curwen, E.C. (1930) Wolstonbury. *Sussex Archaeol. Coll.* **71**, 237–245.

Curwen, E.C. (1954) *The Archaeology of Sussex*, 2nd edition. Methuen, London.

Darvill, T. and Fulton, A. (1998) *MARS: The Monuments at Risk Survey of England, 1995*: Summary Report. Bournemouth University, Bournemouth, and English Heritage, London.

Donachie, J.D. and Field, D.J. (1994) Cissbury Ring: a Survey by the RCHME. *Sussex Archaeol. Coll.* **132**, 25–32.

Down, A. (1981) *Chichester Excavations 5.* Phillimore, Chichester.

Drewett, P.L. (1975) The excavation of an oval burial mound of the third millennium B.C. at Alfriston, East Sussex, 1974. *Proceedings of the Prehistoric Society* **41**, 119–152.

Drewett, P.L. (1982) *The Archaeology of Bullock Down, Eastbourne, East Sussex: the development of a landscape.* Sussex Archaeological Society Monograph 1. SAS, Lewes.

Drewett, P.L. (1999) First Farming Communities and Communal Monuments. In: Leslie, K. and Short, B. (eds) *An Historical Atlas of Sussex.* Phillimore, Chichester. pp. 16–17.

Drewett, P.L, Rudling, D. and Gardiner, M. (1988) *The South East to AD 1000.* Longman, London.

Gardiner, J.P. (1990) Flint procurement and Neolithic axe production on the South Downs: a re-assessment. *Oxford Journal of Archaeology* **9**(2) (July 1990), 119–140.

Gardiner, M. (2003) Economy and Landscape Change in Post-Roman and Early Medieval Sussex, 450–1175. In: Rudling, D. (ed) *The Archaeology of Sussex to AD 2000.* University of Sussex, Brighton. pp. 151–160.

Gardiner, M. (1999) Late Saxon Sussex *c.* 650-1066. In: Leslie, K. and Short, B. (eds) *An Historical Atlas of Sussex.* Phillimore, Chichester. pp. 30–31.

Gould, R.A. (1977) Ethno-archaeology; or, Where Do Models Come From? In: Wright, R.V.S. (ed) *Stone Tools as Cultural Markers.* Australian Institute of Aboriginal Studies, Canberra. pp. 162–177.

Hamilton, S. (2003) Sussex not Wessex: a regional perspective on Southern Britain *c.* 1200-200 BC. In: Rudling, D. (ed) *The Archaeology of Sussex to AD 2000.* University of Sussex, Brighton. pp. 69–88.

Hamilton, S. and Manley, J. (1997) Points of view: prominent enclosures in first millennium BC Sussex. *Sussex Archaeol. Coll.* **135**, 93–112.

Hamilton, S. and Manley, J. (1999) Regional Traditions c. 1000-100 BC. In: Leslie, K. and Short, B. (eds) *An Historical Atlas of Sussex.* Phillimore, Chichester. pp. 20–21.

Hamilton, S. and Manley, J. (2000) Hillforts, monumentality, and place: a chronological and topographic review of first millennium BC hillforts of south-east England. *Journal of European Archaeology* **3**(3), 371–406.

Holgate, R. (1995) Neolithic flint mining in Britain. *Archaeologia Polona* **33**, 133–161.

Holgate, R. (2003) Late Glacial and Post-Glacial Hunter-Gatherers in Sussex. In: Rudling, D. (ed) *The Archaeology of Sussex to AD 2000.* University of Sussex, Brighton. pp. 29–38.

Jacobi, R.M. (1978) The Mesolithic in Sussex. In: Drewett, P.L. (ed) *Archaeology in Sussex to AD 1500.* CBA Research Report 29. Council for British Archaeology, London. pp. 15–22.

Jones. R. (2003) Hastings to Herstmonceux: The Castles of Sussex. In: Rudling, D. (ed), *The Archaeology of Sussex to AD 2000.* University of Sussex, Brighton. pp. 29–38.

Kinnes, I. (1992) *Non-Megalithic Long Barrows and Allied Structures in the British Neolithic.* Occasional Paper 52. British Museum, London.

McOmish, D. (1994) *An Earthwork Survey at Old Winchester Hill.* English Heritage report. Unpublished.

McOmish, D. and Tuck, C. (2004) *Plumpton Plain, East Sussex.* English Heritage Archaeological Investigation Report No. AI/08/2004. English Heritage, Cambridge.

Needham, S. (1996) Chronology and periodisation in the British Bronze Age. *Acta Archaeologica* **67**, 121–140.

Oswald, A., Dyer, C. and Barber, M. (2001) *The Creation of Monuments: Neolithic Causewayed Enclosures in the British Isles.* English Heritage, London.

Pope, M. (2003) The Earliest Occupation of Sussex: Recent Research and Future Objectives. In: Rudling, D. (ed) *The Archaeology of Sussex to AD 2000.* University of Sussex, Brighton. pp. 17–28.

Qualmann, K.E. and Whinney, R.J.B., (2004) *Oram's Arbour: The Iron Age Enclosure at Winchester. Vol.1. Investigations 1950–99.* Winchester Museums Service & English Heritage.

Rankine, W.F. and Dimbleby, W.G. (1960) Further excavations at a Mesolithic site at Oakhanger, Selborne, Hants. *Proceedings of the Prehistoric Society* **26**, 246–62.

Roberts, M.B. and Parfitt, S.A. (1999) *A Middle Pleistocene Hominid Site at Eartham Quarry, Boxgrove, West Sussex. UK.* Archaeological Report 17. English Heritage, London.

Robinson, D.A. and Williams, R.B.G. (1983) The soils and vegetational history of Sussex. In: The Geographical Editorial Committee (ed), *Sussex: Environment, Landscape and Society.* Sutton, Gloucester. pp. 109–126.

Rudling, D. (2003) Roman Rural Settlement in Sussex: Continuity and Change. In: Rudling, D. (ed) *The Archaeology of Sussex to AD 2000.* University of Sussex, Brighton. pp. 111–126.

Somerville, E. (2003) Sussex: from environmental change to landscape history. In: Rudling, D. (ed), *The Archaeology of Sussex to AD 2000.* University of Sussex, Brighton. pp. 235–246.

Whittle, A. (1995) Gifts from the earth: symbolic dimensions of the use and production of Neolithic flint and stone axes. *Archaeologia Polona* **33**, 247–260.

Woodcock, A.G. (1981) *The Lower and Middle Palaeolithic Periods in Sussex.* Brit. Ser. 94. British Archaeological Reports, Oxford.

Wymer, J.J. (1994) *The Sussex Raised Beaches and the Bristol Avon. The Southern Rivers* Palaeolithic Project: Report No. 3, 1993–1994. Wessex Archaeology, Salisbury.

CHAPTER 4

The History of the South Downs Landscape

PETER BRANDON

The history of the South Downs landscape has been different from that of most of England, which has been shaped and reshaped repeatedly over the course of centuries (Brandon, 1998). Change has, of course, occurred on the Downs because landscape and society are always evolving in response to economic and social conditions. Yet continuity in the Downs was more pervasive than change for a thousand years or more up to 1939, when the landscape and ways of life became altered out of all recognition in the space of less than a single generation.

EVOLUTION OF THE LANDSCAPE

Woodland clearance

The greatest change to the landscape of the South Downs occurred in the prehistoric and Roman periods. It is only comparatively recently with the science of environmental archaeology and related techniques that the ancient vegetation of the Downs has been indisputably clarified. As late as the 1930s, the naturalist Harold Peake (1931) argued that old chalk grassland was natural to the thin permeable soils of chalkland, and that the first farmers had taken into cultivation grassland and scrub, not differing much from the vegetation then widespread on the upper parts of the Downs. Since then, as mentioned elsewhere in this book, the new techniques have confirmed that the Downs were initially covered with woodland, and that this became progressively more open with the impact of prehistoric farmers who tore down the trees with stone, bronze and iron axes to graze their animals and plant their crops. It is now considered likely that, with the warming of temperatures from c.10,000 BC after the last Ice Age, the primeval forest (now termed the 'wildwood') on the Downs was a mixed oak and hazel forest where deep loamy soil existed on flatter and gentler slopes, while steep slopes, including the north-facing escarpment with shallower, chalky soil, were probably covered with elm and lime. Beech and yew, so characteristic of semi-natural woodland on the Downs today, do not appear to have been common. Research by Sir Arthur Tansley on the Western Downs in the 1920s and 1930s (Tansley & Adamson, 1925; 1926) led to the acceptance that chalk grassland was the product of man-induced agriculture, though he did not discount the possibility that some grassy patches might have persisted through the forest period, a view held by the late Francis Rose. The latter had suggested that chalk-loving plants of the open grassland, such as yellow-worts, trefoil and orchids may have survived in 'refugia' on the edges of river and sea cliffs, in fact wherever trees could not take root, as relict species. Moreover, it is likely that some natural clearings would always have existed because of the existence of grazing animals such as the bison, wild horse, wild boar and the aurochs, a species of wild cattle, and red and roe deer. These openings in the wildwood of Western Europe made by large herbivores have recently been stressed by F. W. M. Vera, the Dutch ecologist, though the British evidence for this has yet to be tested (Vera, 2000). Of special importance are some 18 ancient woods where the large-leaved lime occurs, notably at the base of the escarpment of the Western Downs, the best example being Rook Clift near Treyford. Rare molluscs, insects and mosses still cling on there on the edge of local extinction. Generally this species of lime grows in elm-sycamore-hazel woodland which was probably the typical downland tree cover before man began farming. In the Eastern Downs, where forest clearance was most intense, only four ancient woodlands possibly survive east of the River Adur – the Holts at Newtimber, Clayton, Glynde and Wilmington (Rose, 1995).

The ancient clearance of forest on the South Downs compared with the North Downs is vividly expressed by the absence of place-names employing the word *wald*, the Saxon name for a place exploited as a forest, which are commonplace on the North Downs where the forest-clearance continued well into historical times. Forest-clearance on the South Downs, which began with the coming of the first herder-farmers *c.* 5–4000 BC, was facilitated by the flint axes produced at the flint mines at Old Winchester Hill, and near Worthing at Black Patch, Harrow Hill and Church Hill, the earliest recorded in Britain. During the Bronze Age (*c.* 1500–500 BC) woodland clearance and farming appear to have spread all over the Downs, and then progressively it was spread during the Iron Age, reaching its zenith during the Roman occupation (AD 43–410), when the process was virtually completed in the Eastern Downs. We can picture considerable woodland and scrub persisting at times earlier than AD 43. On the Western Downs there was probably a denser tree cover because of the appreciable depth of non-calcareous soil, and here woodland clearance was slower and less complete. Dr Rose identified certain woodlands which may never have been cleared. Examples include East Dean Park Wood, Pads Wood near Uppark, Tegleaze Wood and West Dean Woods.

The development of farmed land

By 100 BC the Downs were broadly divided into the three environmental tiers that characterized them for two thousand more years: a hill pasture for sheep on the highest ground; the middle slopes and combes were the sites of farms and villages – and here lay the arable land; finally the water meadows (brookland) used as summer pasture in the valleys cutting through the chalk. There is abundant visual evidence still existing in the form of ploughed-out lynchets in the present-day downland. Again and again the prehistoric and Romano-British arable fields can be seen to have climbed high up on to the Downland slopes where the post-war ploughing up was also to extend. The zenith of early arable farming was

probably in the later Roman period, say *c.* AD 200, when the amount of arable was apparently not exceeded until the post-war period. It is significant that, although the Downs were intensively farmed during the Roman occupation, the stability of the three environmental tiers persisted. Before the last war there was evidence that the South Downs were one of the cradles of civilization in Britain. It may not be wrong to envisage in AD 100 a virtually continuous succession of separate farms with intermixed villages in these now emptied hills. It must not be assumed that Iron Age and Romano-British farmers were 'barbaric'. On the contrary, they had even then learned by experiment and inherited experience how to get the best out of the Downs. The essence of this was sheep-and-corn farming. This agriculture had presumably evolved from Neolithic times, perhaps as early as 4000 BC. With spasmodic shifts in the proportion of arable to sheep pasture this was to be the farming system which continued almost universally on the Downs throughout the historic period until living memory, when it was replaced by an unsustainable system of agriculture. The present author has discussed the research of Dr Peter Reynolds at Butser Hill and Chalton near Horndean of an economy which is surprisingly precocious (Plate 45) and is not devoid of lessons which are relevant today (Brandon, 1998, pp. 45–6).

The establishment of settlements

Professor Barry Cunliffe's research in the Horndean and Catherington area in Hampshire has provided a possible model for Saxon settlement on the Downs in general (Cunliffe, 1972). He discovered a number of substantial village sites of early occupation on the hill-tops of the Downs. Such sites tended to be abandoned about the ninth century and valley settlements adopted instead, although Catherington is an example of continuity. Further east, Up Marden and nearby Compton occupy hill-top sites. These may also have been early sites of occupation which continued despite population being drawn off to the valleys, but no archaeological work has yet been undertaken. In East Sussex Bishopstone is another example of an early hill-top Saxon settlement. It is probable that in the ninth and tenth centuries, when settlement was moving valleywards around Horndean, a shift of population took place from the higher Downs (which were virtually abandoned) to the spring-line villages we know today. These had peasant farmhouses in the village street and expanding common fields below the sheepwalk. The strip parishes then began to evolve, their boundaries possibly inherited from Romanized villa estates which had earlier occupied the fertile malmstone bench. Owslebury, an early Saxon settlement in Hampshire was affected by a similar process. In addition to these villages, a sprinkling of isolated Saxon farms existed on the Downs proper. These typically have Saxon place-name suffixes in -ley, -worth, and so on. These include Chilgrove, Colworth, Downley, Hylter, Locksash, Malecomb, Raughmere, Stapleash and Tegleaze. At Domesday in 1086 these little farms were mainly in the hands of freemen, which suggests that they were not archaic survivals of Romano-British occupation but the result of recent colonization.

Population continued to increase up to the Black Death in 1348. In the stronger light of the thirteenth and fourteenth centuries we find peasants working unfenced strips of common arable and sharing a sheepwalk and brookland, whilst the lord of the manor held similar categories of land separately in his personal demesne for his own use. Although almost all peasant farmers lived in nucleated villages, it appears that population pressure was forcing some young people to reclaim farms out of the downland sheepwalk. There is visual evidence of this on hillsides of lynchetted fieldstrips, where the lynchets are not of the short prehistoric and Romano-British type, but long, curving strips made by a team of plough-oxen. Examples are those visible from the road between Edburton and Poynings; another is a well-preserved set at Catherington, Hampshire. On the face of the escarpment is a field system at Upper Beeding, with prominent lynchets implying long-continued use; another outside Edburton, evidently shorter-lived; and the fine set of strip fields on Newtimber Hill, the work, apparently of the Knights Templar of Saddlescombe. In each case strips have been created out of steep hillsides. This process can be seen throughout the Downs. At nucleated sites the common fields were extended, often on less fertile soils. Small cultivators with family holdings occupying common fields had subsistence in view.

On the other hand the great church estates and those of magnates operated large demesne farms, worked by numerous dependent cultivators, and engaged in the coastwise trade in wool and corn. The segregation of the lord's arable from that of the peasants' common fields, and the distinction between the lord's sheep-pasture and that of the small farmers (which came to be known as the tenantry down), permitted lords to engage in agricultural innovation which resulted in crop-yields and quality of wool greatly superior to the English norm. In particular, the Eastern Downs became celebrated in the thirteenth century for advanced agricultural techniques and fleeces of good fine wool, which contributed to England's staple export.

An excellent village where one can examine these achievements is Alciston between Lewes and Eastbourne. This was the home farm of the monks of Battle Abbey. They built the magnificent barn (Plate 46) to house their vast stocks of hay, corn and wool (mistakenly called a Tithe Barn). The outstanding development was the suppression of fallow on the best or the most easily manured fields, a practice much facilitated by sheep-folding but more particularly by the sowing of legumes in a continuous three-year succession of crops. Barley (or oats), legumes and wheat, combined with a favourable climate and a thick sowing of seed (partly to smother weeds and reduce fallowing) produced cereal yields substantially higher than the medieval norm, that is, harvests of wheat more than double the normal medieval expectation of six to eight bushels per acre. Other cereals yielded in like proportion, so producing a surplus for sale. The surrounding fields have hardly altered in character since. A peasant farmer with his few score sheep could not manure and consolidate his thin soils with these alone. By putting them into a common sheep-flock guarded by a common shepherd, he could command for several days each year up to 500 or more sheep which dunged in rotation each villager's dispersed arable in the common fields.

Farming methods

Without the use of the common sheepfold, peasant farmers would not have survived on the Downs. More than anything else this institution that fed and clothed man and manured and trod his soils was as perfect for the purpose as any that could ever have been invented. It is necessary to stress the importance of arable farming which had a symbiotic relationship with sheep. When Arthur Young and William Marshall praised the agriculture of the Eastern Downs in the eighteenth century they were admiring a district with a tradition of advanced agriculture which dated to the thirteenth century and almost certainly to changes before that. The scarp-foot of the Eastern Downs, in particular, was famed for both corn and sheep. The Elizabethan writer, William Camden, observed that the 'fat chalk or marle' of Sussex yielded corn abundantly, and successive writers have confirmed that in their day this district contained some of the best cereal grounds in England. To this day the largest, most efficient and productive arable farms in England have been on, or at the margins of, the South Downs.

The medieval period

The sharp drop in population resulting from famine and successive recurrences of the Black Death from the early fourteenth century led to a retreat of settlement on the Downs. The most notable visible sign of this is at totally abandoned settlements. Janet Pennington and Pamela Platt have identified 109 deserted settlements, mostly on the Downs and including some lost to the sea (Pennington & Platt, 1999). The only site to have been thoroughly excavated is Hangleton near Brighton (Plate 47) now covered by a housing estate. In some cases a solitary church may suggest vanished homesteads, as at Beddingham, Hamsey and Warminghurst At others vanished chapels tell of decline, as at Balmer near Falmer, Old Erringham, North Marden, Up Marden and Linch. A very common phenomenon is the shrunken village, such as Preshaw in Hampshire. Coombes in the Adur valley is a classic example with a farmhouse and related cottages but the site of the peasants' holdings is now a field. The dwellings of the priests were only a little less humble than those of the villagers of these impoverished settlements (see the Alfriston Clergy House, Plates 48 and 49). Another in the Adur valley is Botolphs which has shrunk to four houses. Berwick near Alfriston is now only a fragment of its former size. The same is true of Glyndebourne, Sutton near Seaford and Winton near Alfriston. Another interesting shrunken site is Alciston; the present village is almost entirely north of the church but the presence of houses southwards is indicated by house platforms above the holloway leading to the Downs. To the inexperienced or untrained eye, the remains of a deserted settlement are vestigial in the extreme. Grass covers a tangle of bumps and hollows, concealing stretches of tumbled-down flint walling, hollowed-out lanes, house platforms, and small farm buildings. Eventually an observer will detect more readily the signs of decay and make a contribution to the subject, for the number of deserted settlements will certainly grow by extra field work and documentary study.

Another medieval setback was the *flooding* from the sea and inland of the brooks in the valley floors. The thirteenth-century coastline of the Adur estuary is marked by a wave-cut edge of raised beaches, marking still earlier coastlines, as at the Sussex Pad inn, North Lancing. An important factor in the evolution of the coastline has been the relative level of land to sea. Throughout the Saxon period the surface of the land was gradually subsiding. Natural conditions, however, were still favourable to the reclamation of marshland until the early thirteenth century, when the overflow of high tides had reached such a frequency and extent that the first sea and river embankments were erected in an attempt to exclude it. The fall in the relative level of land to the sea, particularly marked between the mid-thirteenth and the sixteenth centuries, combined with the increased storminess of this period, and spells of 'foule weder', led to the overwhelming of most of the embankments erected earlier and the long continued submergence of former agricultural land on an extensive scale. Early forerunner-floods, such as that of 1287, were manifestations of this submergence. Major flooding is reported on a number of occasions in the early fourteenth century. Serious floods also occurred towards the end of the fourteenth century and the worst floods of all occurred in the early fifteenth century. The outstanding disaster was the 'St. Elizabeth' flood of 1421 which also wrought much havoc in the Netherlands.

Sixteenth and seventeenth centuries

During the the sixteenth and early seventeenth centuries most of the common fields.were enclosed. In the Western Downs there was less reliance on the sheepfold, and small family farmers were diversifying into cattle-raising, dairying, orchards and timber production so that common fields were restraints. In the Eastern Downs, small occupiers were declining and the larger tenants found the common sheepfold irksome and wanted to sow their crops independently of manorial control. The normal method of enclosure was by piecemeal arrangements between holders. Strips were gathered into bundles and exchanged between lord and tenants. Even on unenclosed systems innovations were taking place which have not been realized formerly. Thus at Jevington in 1584 tenants of arable strips were evidently not keeping to the time-honoured three-field system of cultivation but sowing crops on the fallow as it pleased them. This state of affairs was usually a preliminary to formal enclosure.

Another innovation of the period was the management of *brookland* in the river valleys. Despite the raising of embankments in the Middle Ages floods remained all summer on the lower meadows. The Ouse and Laughton Levels were in 'great rewyn' in 1537. The 6000 acres inundated between Sheffield Park and Seaford were better protected about 1540, when a new scheme for the drainage of the Levels was brought into operation With the advice of Dutch engineers a new channel was cut to the sea to increase river flow. This is still evident and is regarded as the earliest canalization in England. The drainage improvements, however, deteriorated in the seventeenth century and nothing was done effectively to improve the Levels until the end of the eighteenth century. Similar problems arose in the other river valleys.

A seventeenth-century innovation which had important effects on the sheepwalk was the introduction of new *fodder crops* such as sainfoin and clover, which was sown on cultivated land as part of the arable rotation. Such crops were undersown with wheat or barley and 'fed off' for two or three years before being sown again to cereals. This became known as 'ley farming' and formed the basis of downland agriculture up to the 1960s. The increase in fodder crops permitted a heavier stocking of sheep, but this was largely at the expense of parts of the sheepwalk. For centuries little in the way of its breaking up could be undertaken because it would have harmed 'the run of the sheep'. The introduction of the new fodder crops permitted for the first time the breaking up of 'maiden down', the term for the traditional sheepwalk. At this period breaking up was called 'denchering', a Sussex form of 'Devonshire (ing)' from where the practice probably originated. Sometimes the word is rendered as 'denture'. On the 2½-inch maps of the Ordnance Survey the word 'dencher' is repeatedly used. The turf was pared off and ashes ploughed in for extra fertility. At Alfriston part of the sheepwalk had been 'denchered' by 1690, at Telscombe probably *c.* 1701, and at Kingston-by-Lewes in 1705. Similar developments took place all over the downland. Ever since the Downs have been the subject of a periodic campaign to increase arable at all costs, even into the realm of nonsense, for fear of running out of corn, followed by putting the arable back into poor grass.

The eighteenth century

Between 1788 and 1815 **sheep-and-corn farming** was exceptionally prosperous. It was an era of high wool and corn prices, and a lively controversy ensued as to the number of sheep which could be kept on the Downs and what amount of sheepwalk could be broken up. The Revd. Arthur Young estimated in 1813 that 240,000 adult sheep were kept on the Downs, of which 150,000 were in the Eastern Downs (Young, 1813). The vast flock in the Eastern Downs was stocked at the rate of about 1½ ewes per acre, which Young thought was the highest in the United Kingdom and 'one of the singular circumstances of the husbandry of England'. The sheep in the Eastern Downs not only produced the finest wool but the immense flocks led to an increase in corn-yields which, as previously mentioned, was largely related to the number of sheep dunging a fold, which in turn depended on the amount of fodder available in the winter (Plate 50). This was facilitated by the sowing of new grasses and the introduction of turnips and lucerne.

These crops tended to encroach on the sheepwalk. Charles Goring of Wiston (the boy planter of Chanctonbury Ring) urged the intensification of arable on existing land, rather than the breaking up of sheepwalk on account of the extreme length of time the turf needed to restore itself (Goring, 1801). Despite his advice, and that of others, the steep rise in corn prices induced many downland farmers to plough up sheepwalk which had previously been considered unviable to cultivate. In 1816, with the ending of War, cereal prices crashed. Even after thirty years the sward was valued at only half its original price. In 1900 the naturalist W. H. Hudson could identify such areas, described by the old shepherds as 'sickly'. These were covered with a coarse grass called 'gratton grass' (i.e. grass which had grown thorough corn stubbles) and contrasted with the springy, close-matted turf of the untouched sward which remained freshly green and nutritious throughout the summer. Sheep which had a choice of pasture sedulously avoided it. With the recovery of agriculture between the 1840s and the 1870s landowners again broke up sheepwalk. This process is ascertainable from contemporary maps, such as those of William Figg, a notable cartographer in East Sussex. Lord Gage, for example, ploughed up part of his demesne on Alciston, Berwick and Winton Downs, leaving the tenantry downs intact. This was put down again to coarse pasture on the onset of farming depression. One of the best documented of these reclamations of sheep downs is that at Brighton where the common field proprietors from the 1760s broke up a fresh tract of pasture each year and added additional arable strips to their holdings. The extra furlongs in this instance were presumably needed to feed the growing population of the town, which was just entering on its career as a seaside resort. The extension of tillage on to old pasture, and its subsequent abandonment, left many minor features on the ground, such as the widespread imprint of ridge-and-furrow, marks of old ploughing, which have given a corrugated effect, resembling a giant washboard, to the surface of fields. Such features are less common than formerly owing to the widespread ploughing up of the Downs, but they persist on some steep banks which have survived intensification.

Sheep and cattle breeding

Meanwhile the Southdown sheep had been greatly improved by John Ellman, a tenant farmer on the Trevor estate at Glynde. His handsome, boxy, chunky-faced sheep (Plate 51) were to triumph over all other downland breeds in Britain, and became the progenitors of sheep flocks in the USA, Canada, New Zealand, Australia and the Argentine. Before Ellman's achievements, there were apparently two distinct breeds of sheep on the Downs, separated by the Adur valley. A 'wild-looking, base-bred' sort of sheep inhabited the Western Downs, which the eighteenth-century agricultural writer William Marshall (1798) described as having 'the same mongrel appearance as the mountain sheep of the West of England'. He concluded that it was an old native breed dating back centuries. These grazed inferior pasture on the Western Downs, this being an admixture of coarser grassland, scrub and woodland. The lack of brookland was also a disadvantage. East of the Adur valley the South-downs were in exclusive possession. The sheep Ellman improved continued to have a folding function, but they produced a better fleece and mutton.

Not all agriculturists were convinced that Southdowns were the best downland breed. Vancouver (1798) thought that the longer-legged, taller, sheep of the Western Downs, akin to the

Hampshire Down breed, coped better with their poorer pasture than the improved Southdowns, which were shorter and stockier. Marshall argued that it was as fitting to put an Arabian courser into the shafts of a dung-cart as to put a delicate, high-blooded and fashionable 'Southdowner' into a sheepfold.

The breeders of Southdowns were often breeders of Red Sussex Cattle, the native breed of Sussex (Plate 52). This was not successful because the Sussex cattle were a dual-purpose breed which pulled the plough or farm wagons before being fattened by the grazier. There was a revival at the end of the nineteenth century when horse traction had largely replaced oxen, and a number of downland farmers bred Red Sussex. But even this collapsed with the onset of agricultural depression. Nowadays the time is ripe for a revival since consumers are developing a taste for locally-bred meat.

The farming systems appraised

It is appropriate to make some conclusions at this point. The stability of the hill pasture is evident, despite the spasmodic breaking up of part of it, and its fate as coarse pasture that sheep avoided, when bad farming conditions returned, is also significant. In the post-war era artificial fertilizers replaced the traditional sheep-folding as a means of sustaining arable. It is also important to stress that the ley farming which began in the seventeenth century continued until living memory. The ley was the temporary grass undersown with cereals. This grass was fed off by sheep and cattle for two or three years before cereals were sown again. The importance of under-sowing leys was that humus and fertility were restored to the soil, and that the biodiversity created was beneficial to the corn bunting, lapwing, grey partridge, hare, butterfly and bee together with plants and other animals which are now virtually absent (Plate 53). Until the mid-1960s downland farmers mostly followed the traditional mixed-farming economy which had effectively created the landscape of the South Downs, and which was underpinned by ley farming. John Goring of Wiston extolled the system in *The Times* newspaper in 1956 in which spring cereals were the dominant crops and the undersown ley the key element in the low-input traditional agriculture of those days. But from the early 1970s agricultural subsidies encouraged winter-wheat monoculture, and farmers raced each other for higher cereal yields. Fields were sprayed with herbicides and pesticides from the air. In 2006 the picture is totally different from that of 1970.

Environmental effects

The changed pattern of farming has had an adverse effect on wildlife. The most stunning feature of much of the downland is the silences. The heavens are as devoid of life as the waving wheat beneath them. The Game Conservancy has highlighted some of the causes of the problem in the central section of the South Downs with reference to the grey partridge, the only farmland bird which at present is being monitored (Potts, 1996). Most significantly, rotation grass under the ley-farming system has all but vanished from the study area, between the rivers Arun and Adur, being restricted to a single farm (see the case study of Applesham Farm in Chapter 7). This single farm accounts for less than ten per cent of the area monitored but now accounts for 23 per cent of the grey partridge and 21 per cent of the skylarks and corn buntings, and yet the farm has an excellent overall production of cereals and meat. The grey partridge is one of the few species of farmland birds on which the insecticidal effect of herbicides are known. When partridge chicks hatch in mid-to-late June they feed mainly on the caterpillar-like larvae of the sawfly (*Doleros gonager*) and Lepidoptera (moths and butterflies) which over-winter in leys established under cereals.The corn bunting needs the same food for its survival. Moreover, at Applesham care is taken not to spray heavily at the base of grassy-bottomed hedges and fence-lines. This leaves suitable nesting sites in long grass remaining from the previous season's growth. Dick Potts (1996), the former Director of the Game Conservancy, has argued: 'Politicians, scientists, authors and journalists have pleaded for years for new integrated farming-systems for a sustainable future. Meanwhile, traditional leys have been staring them in the face.' The farming system at Applesham Farm, and at several farms in East Hampshire, may thus be models for the future. In several respects their husbandry has resembled what DEFRA is currently promoting.

THE ARCHAEOLOGICAL HERITAGE

Water retention

Much of the heritage of this farming history is still visible on the face of the landscape. Farming the chalk has always raised difficulties with water. The porosity of chalk means that excessive rain is absorbed through the pores of the rock instead of lying on the surface. Thus there may be no visible water for miles around. One ubiquitous feature which overcame this lack of surface drainage was the *dew-pond*. This was constructed with great skill. A saucer-like depression was dug out of the surface and the chalk thus removed was built up around the pan to form a slight lip. The floor was then covered in straw alternately with puddled clay from the Weald or the clay-with-flints surface, each layer being thoroughly beaten down. Two inches of burnt lime followed, to prevent worms puncturing the clay, and another layer of straw followed. Finally, a layer of rough local earth was piled on top. This was thought to aid condensation of dew and mist, although actually the main source of water appears to have been rain. Dew-ponds intended for cattle had a layer of flints to prevent them breaking the lining. Each sheepwalk had several of these dew-ponds, jealously guarded by shepherds from neighbouring flocks. The age of dew-ponds is disputed, but it is probable that the art of making them dates from prehistoric times. In recent years the restoration of dew-ponds as habitats for great crested newts and other rare amphibians has been made. The National Trust at Newtimber was one of the pioneers in restoration, and the Society of Sussex Downsmen (now the South Downs Society) has also been active. Such new ponds usually have a concrete base and they add greatly to the diversity of the Downs.

Another solution to the lack of water on the surface was the **well-house**. The village well-houses of East Marden and Up Waltham still exist, from which water from about 100 feet below was obtained. A donkey wheel was used to bring water up from greater depths. Such a well at Saddlescombe Farm near Brighton has been restored. This raised water from 150 feet below; a similar donkey wheel at Stanmer drew up water 252 feet below. Another example is Milbury's pub near Preshaw in Hampshire.

Quarries

Also frequently met with are the small **chalk quarries** dotted on farmland all over the high downs. Now abandoned, the sites are identifiable from afar by the circular green hollows amidst an ocean of wheat or barley. At Applesham Farm in the Adur valley, and on the Alciston Downs, they are striking phenomena. These old chalk pits were dug for raw chalk which was applied to leached red soils above the chalk. These tended to be acid and had to be mellowed and sweetened by chalk for corn production. The raw chalk took over a year to dissolve before it could be ploughed in. The chalk was raised in buckets by a simple winch operated by a cart wheel. A single small pit would have chalked four to five acres. Gell of Applesham applied 160 cart loads of chalk on 160 acres over a twenty-year period. Most of these old pits date to the Napoleonic Wars or to the 1840s–1870s when sheepwalk was being reclaimed. The effectiveness of the long-term improvement is illustrated at Applesham by recent soil analyses, showing that the beneficial effect of chalking was still apparent in the 1960s.

The constant search for fertilizer has left other vestiges of human action in the landscape. Old **lime pits** and **kilns** are common features. The most spectacular lime-works were on the banks of rivers where water transport was available to convey the lime into the Weald for agricultural use. On the banks of the Ouse near Lewes are more chalk quarries and workings than anywhere in Britain and Europe, including those made famous by Gideon Mantell (1822), the pioneer stratigrapher of the Downs (Plate 54). At Houghton, Amberley and Bury on the river Arun were also major quarries and kilns; part of this complex is now used by the Working Museum. Smaller lime works were sited all along the north-facing escarpment, which is pock-marked by white hollows. The surviving lime-kilns are ruinous and have not been mapped. At the base of Duncton Hill is the unusually large kiln of Lord Egremont of Petworth, in use until his Rother Navigation offered alternative sites. A site of a small kiln can be traced near the Shepherd and Dog inn at Fulking and at Buriton Bank Heritage Centre, and fieldwork would produce many more.

Trackways

The local trackways on the Downs are distinctive. The most interesting are old **droveways** working their way across the Downs towards the Weald. These are deeply worn into the face of the escarpment, but their oblique inclination enabled oxen and horses to draw heavy loads up and down them. These trackways are known as 'bostals', a name probably derived from Saxon *beorg,* a hill and *stig,* a path. Some of these tracks are very ancient, doubtless prehistoric in many cases, and a number lie on long-distance droving routes into the Weald.

Evidence of ploughing

The extension of tillage on to the carpet of grassland has left many minor features on the ground such as the imprint of ridge-and-furrow, marks of old ploughing which have given a corrugated effect resembling a gigantic washboard to the surface of the fields. The ridges are best visible with the aid of long shadows of evening light or when picked out by a thin powdering of drifted snow. Walking across the old ploughlines will reveal not a smooth surface but a series of parallel troughs and ridges. Much of this old sheepwalk has disappeared with modern ploughing but on steep hillsides it has survived into the recent landscape.

A natural feature which is often mistaken for something man-made is the little 'terracettes' on chalk hillsides which result from the slipping of the top-soil. The **terracettes** are held up by flint layers and consolidated by the passage of sheep. They give grassy slopes a striking ribbed appearance.

Barns and other farm buildings

The repeated reclamation of downland sheepwalk has left a remarkable legacy of flint-built barns and other buildings on the remoter parts of the great

Plate 50 (above right)
Southdown sheep in their fold. The animals were kept in such portable enclosures at night; their dung fertilized the valley fields for later planting of corn and oats, and their hooves consolidated the downland soil. From an old postcard, photographer unknown, courtesy of Peter Brandon.

Plate 51 (above left)
A Southdown ram. Photo taken in 1939 by an unknown photographer, which appeared in a national newspaper. Courtesy of Peter Brandon.

Plate 52 (centre)
Sussex red cattle; originally bred from the oxen used for ploughing in the Downs but now being revived for production of beef. Photo: Janina Holubecki, courtesy of High Weald AONB.

Plate 53 (right)
Harvest at Falmer, East Sussex, 1941. Here the emphasis is on growing corn to help feed the nation in wartime. Note the 'land girls' who worked on the farms while most of the men were away at war. Photo by an unknown photographer from a national newspaper, courtesy of Peter Brandon.

Plate 54 *(above left)*
A chalk-pit near Glynde, East Sussex; one of the many quarries associated with Gideon Mantell, whose greatest work was *The Fossils of the South Downs* of 1822, based on studies made of the chalk workings in the Ouse Valley near Lewes.
Photo: Peter Brandon.

Plate 55 *(above right)*
Traditional flint barns near Birling, East Sussex.
Photo: Peter Brandon.

Plate 56 *(left)*
The deserted village of Idsworth, Hampshire, Winter 2000. All that remains is the medieval church, St. Hubert's, with a few scattered houses many metres away built in much later periods or moved in Victorian times to make way for the London to Portsmouth railway.
Photo: SDJC.

Plate 57 *(left)*
The church of St. Andrew, Jevington, East Sussex, with its Saxon tower. It has an effigy of a 'Saxon' Christ in the nave.
Photo: Peter Brandon.

Plate 58 *(below left)*
The church of St. Andrew, Didling , West Sussex, one of the numerous little, 'lost' churches of humble origin.
Photo: Peter Brandon.

Plate 59 *(below right)*
A near-perfect example of a 13th century church, St. Mary, Tarring Neville, East Sussex; such buildings never evolved into the Decorated or Perpendicular styles due to lack of money, the result of population-loss in the 14th century.
Photo: Peter Brandon.

farms (Plate 55). These distantly built barns are little used now and are falling into dereliction. When erected in the late eighteenth or early nineteenth century they were busy places for sheltering cattle, particularly oxen, who worked the reclaimed downland, it being too distant for them to plod to and from the parent farm on the centuries-old arable in the valley below. They also stored the heavy harvests and provided the new lands with a return of their own dung, and saved the carriage of corn to the home barns. They tend to conform to a standard pattern of an enclosed yard where cattle ate barley and oat straw in winter and 'hovels' at the side for shelter. In some cases cottages were also built at these sites. It has been impossible to let these remote buildings since the 1960s, and they also lie empty and dilapidated. Not all the remote barns were built for cattle. Some were erected for 'cotting' sheep in bad weather (practice which improved the fleece) and for lambing, shearing, foot-paring, culling and selecting. A fine example, built in 1845, is New Barn on an outlying part of Housedean Farm near Falmer. It comprises a hay barn for winter feed, two sheep pens with shelters and a stone-built shepherd's hut provided with a chimney. It has recently been excellently restored by the owners, Brighton Council. From these hill-top barns one would have had a good view of a busy working farm, as did William Cobbett in 1832, where in a single field near Shoreham he witnessed four teams of large oxen, six in a team, ploughing for wheat, and several pairs of horses harrowing and rolling in the same field. Formerly every shepherd had a hut on the downs in addition to his cottage at the farm. Sometimes it was merely a kind of cave dug into a bank (a 'link' in shepherds' dialect from the Saxon *hlinc*, meaning bank). Large stones inside were the only furnishings. A hut might also be made of sods of earth, or bark, boughs of hawthorn or straw. This type of hut tended to be replaced by a flint-built structure, as at Cornish Farm near Eastbourne. In turn this was succeeded by the mobile shed in which the shepherd kept his tools and medicine, some feed for the sheep, his own clothing and a bed used at lambing time.

The many ancient farm buildings on the Downs are richly eloquent of old ways of rural life. The oldest are those on medieval foundations, of which that at Alciston is the largest and most complete. Here the Benedictine monks of Battle Abbey created a model farm.in the thirteenth century which attained a rare distinction and was emulated, with varying degrees of success, in the surrounding countryside. The most fascinating complex is at Alciston where several of the grange buildings are documented in medieval records and are still remarkably complete. The most conspicuous is an enormous three-aisled barn with a high pitched roof supported on massive piers and rafters. Its precise age is indeterminable but the basic structure, and some of the wooden piers are almost certainly of the thirteenth century. The beauty of its interior reminds one of D. S. MacColl's observation (1904) that the 'mysterious welling of light amongst the old beams and timbers of a barn is one of the loveliest things upon earth'. The barn forms two sides of a courtyard across which until recently was the ox-stall and probably the sheepcote where ewes were housed in the winter, the shepherds living in lofts above. The unusual double-chambered dovecot is now a picturesque ruin. Fish stews still survive as a chain of artificial ponds along the course of a running spring. Part of the medieval grange at Alciston, now incorporated in a wing of Alciston Court Farm, includes a unique cross-passage extending throughout the building and giving access to former service rooms and the medieval hall, lofted over in the sixteenth century to provide bedrooms above, which has stone-built arches of the thirteenth century on its opposite sides. Wilmington Priory also has a large medieval barn, as does Bishopstone Manor Farm, once an estate of the bishops of Chichester. Numerous examples of seventeenth- and eighteenth-century barns and other farm buildings exist. East Hampshire has fine examples of more modern model farmsteads, for example at Froxfield, Droxford and West Meon.

Farmhouses

A number of downland farms have particularly good groups of old buildings. At one, the further door of the seventeenth-century aisled barn opens out into the old shearing-yard and to an early nineteenth-century round house, originally containing a horse-wheel which was used to drive a chaff-cutter and, later, an early threshing machine. On its side is a long range of purpose-built buildings erected by the Petworth estate, containing a wheelwright's shop, the carpenter's workshop, the smithy and stores for implements, sacks and hurdles. At the far end of this range is a former granary which had a wagon loft below. Opposite was another range of buildings housing the cow-shed, ox-stalls, fattening pens and byres for Red Sussex cattle. The flintstone farmhouse is a fascinating place with stone window surrounds under a centuries-old pitched roof of Horsham stone. Entering by a side entrance we find its former kitchen still largely furnished with plain deal furniture, where smock-frocked farm labourers clumped in with their loud-sounding hobnailed boots and dined cheerily at the tables up to the late nineteenth century, just as their predecessors had for centuries. A brick wing, added to the farmhouse in the late nineteenth century looks southward to the sea, and provided a comfortable home for a well-off tenant farmer in the heyday of farming on the South Downs. Other farmhouses, which give an indication of the standing, prosperity and comfort of the occupying farmer and his family, are Upper Stoneham Farm (painted by

Grimm when it wore a quite different appearance), Newhouse Farm near West Firle and Milton Street Farm, Wilmington. All over downland, in fact, are signs of a great rebuilding of farmsteads on more elegant and comfortable lines in the first half of the nineteenth century. A number of these farms have exceptionally good complexes of farm buildings, including Saddlescombe Farm in the downs north of Brighton and John Ellman's old farm at Glynde.

Churches

Of exceptional interest are the simple, squat little churches characteristic of downland. When their churches were built numerous downland communities were poor, and this poverty and small population is the background to the modest little churches with their austere interiors such as Idsworth (Plate 56) in Hampshire, the three (formerly four) at the Mardens, and Hardham, Didling, Up Waltham and Coombes. Damaging raids by the French also account for the decline in population in the fourteenth century, which was compounded by the effects of pestilence. For these reasons the repeatedly enlarged church notable in the Weald is rarely a feature of downland.

Of particular interest is the substantial proportion of churches containing surviving features of Saxon workmanship. H. M. and J. Taylor's list of Anglo-Saxon churches in England numbers 267 of which 18 and possibly more are in the Downs (1965). E. A. Fisher regarded the 'probables' of Taylor as certainties and added nearly 20 more (Fisher, 1970). The great disparity in numbers between these two lists arises from the difficulty of dating precisely many of the ancient churches. At Jevington (Plate 57), Sullington and Singleton, Saxon west towers survive. Sompting, with its Saxon tower of about the same date, is one of the most famous Anglo-Saxon churches and the only surviving example of a steeple of the 'helm' type, derived from churches in the Rhineland. Bishopstone, one of the early minster churches, had a *porticus* or side-chamber used for special services.

The simplest little churches normally have a single or double chamber. A few existing churches have retained the simple single-cell structure of earliest churches with little change to this day, including Warnford in the East Hampshire Downs, and East Marden, North Marden, Didling (Plate 58), Wiggonholt, Buncton, Denton and West Dean. Tiny, rather later two-cell churches are relatively common and include Chithurst, St Botolph's Hardham, St Peter's Westhampnett, Greatham, Up Marden (with one of the loveliest interiors in England), Selham, and Idsworth and Corhampton in the East Hampshire Downs. Several of these ancient churches are on burial mounds raised imposingly by pre-Christian Saxons to guard the bones or ashes and

preserve the memory of heroes, as for example at Hamsey, Piddinghoe, Southease, Tarring Neville (Plate 59) and Berwick.

A considerable number of churches were rebuilt in the thirteenth century. These, like the simple churches mentioned earlier, are also basically modest and have always had small congregations. Barlavington is a good example of the utter simplicity of these later village churches. Its aisles were blocked up after the Middle Ages, the north aisle being unblocked in 1874. The exterior has been thoroughly restored but the interior is surprisingly unaltered and is virtually devoid of monuments. Litlington is even simpler, and has hardly changed over centuries until restored in 1863, when the original rood screen and stone tympanum in the chancel arch were removed.

A number of the modest downland churches have remarkable works of art in the form of medieval wall-paintings. These comprise the most famous in Britain, and their survival is largely attributable to the relatively unrestored conditions of churches of parishes which became impoverished with population decline from the Middle Ages. The most complete paintings are at Plumpton, Clayton, Coombes and Hardham. Idsworth's are also remarkable.

Dovecots

Another type of building in considerable numbers on the downs is the dovecot, where pigeons were raised for the table during winter when fresh meat was scarce. At Charlton, East Sussex, a circular flint dovecot survives, and at neighbouring West Dean there is a handsome square one with sandstone quoins. There is a double-chambered one at Alciston (Plate 60). The Hangleton (West Sussex) dovecot has been beautifully restored, whereas that at West Meon awaits attention. More modern ones in good condition exist at Droxford, Hambledon and Owslebury.

Field systems

The greatest heritage loss has been the hundreds of acres of prehistoric and Romano-British field systems which have been largely obliterated in the course of breaking up downland for tillage. Not a single site has been spared: boundary banks and ditches have been filled in, sites of countless earthworks razed to the ground as if a few extra acres of cereals were the only aim in life. Totally ignored in the austerity of the immediate post-war years were the doughty defenders of the ancient downland turf as an amenity and as an ecological and archaeological treasure. Dr Cecil Curwen, the doyen of Sussex archaeology, Professor Sir Arthur Tansley, the foremost ecologist of his day, and O.G.S. Crawford, the pioneer of aerial photography and editor of *Antiquity*, had warned that the destruction of the mantle of turf covering the higher parts of the Downs would be 'equivalent to the destruction of a priceless and unique manuscript' (Brandon, 1998). These timely words went unheeded. The scheduling of ancient field systems was totally inadequate in the 1950s and 1960s, and the work of the then Nature Conservancy also came in for criticism. The inability of the Government or any other organization to provide a measure of overall co-ordination helps to explain why, in the immediate post-war years, bulldozers shattered indiscriminately the vestiges of the past. Farmers also had little precise knowledge as to where archaeological remains were sited, and had little understanding of their cultural value.

There seems no doubt that important heritage sites suffered unnecessarily in the widespread destruction. At present notable sites which have been destructively ploughed for thirty years or more are being reprieved when put into the ESA scheme. Thus the father of the present occupier of Balmer Down broke up a good example of a Romano-British field system at Buckland Bank under the stimulus of arable subsidies and grants; his son has taken advantage of ESA payments and put what remains down to grass. Similarly Plumpton College, which destroyed much of the Bronze Age village on Plumpton Plain in the 1970s (see Chapter 3, Fig, 3.1), is now salvaging the mess in the name of 'conservation'. Yet there is little stability in sight, for the severe damage done to such sites is preventing their listing. Nevertheless, some well-known sites such as parts of Buckland Bank and Itford Hill are scheduled monuments. Others have a measure of protection in the Countryside Stewardship Schemes described in Chapter 7, but these are not necessarily long-lasting arrangements, for the history of government intervention on the Downs since the last War has been one of short-lived swings and roundabouts. The County Councils' Archaeological Sites and Monuments Records for the Downs are sprinkled with such information as 'Celtic field system (remains of)'; 'Medieval or later', 'stock enclosure (site of)', 'tumulus (site of)'. Although severely damaged in most cases such sites, can be given the belated protection they deserve and thus better enter into the archaeological record for posterity.

Building materials

Chalk was usually too soft to be suitable for building but '**clunch**' (a harder stratum at the base of the northern escarpment in West Sussex and Hampshire) has been used for several church interiors, as at Burpham in the Arun valley, and for the exterior walls of farmhouses, cottages and barns in the Meon valley and towards Duncton, Cocking (Plate 28), Elstead and Harting.

Much more generally used, and accounting for much of the charm of downland village, is **flint**, the characteristic stone building material of the Downs for the walls of churches, farmhouses, cottages, barns, stockyards, dovecots and around orchards and paddocks. Flint is quite unlike any other building material and not easily portable. Much skill is needed in its use and it is an extremely costly form of construction (Plate 32 a, b, c, d). A falling-off in building standards is often visible in Victorian restoration of the exteriors of churches, where large white flints were embedded in excessive areas of mortar. Widespread is poor workmanship with flints badly pointed, mortar being left on the face of the flints. replacing superb examples of the more lovable flintwork using little lime mortar and finishing it with galleting, the spare flakes introduced into the mortar to provide some support to the non-porous flint, and for a decorative effect, though that at Henfield is an exceptional example of traditional workmanship at its best. Splendid examples of flint-work are to be found in Lewes High Street (Nos. 139-141) and on the façade of St Michael's Church. On the open downs the best flint-work is on the landed estates of the Western Downs, for example at Goodwood and West Dean houses. The former is the finest shrine to the flint-knapper's art in Sussex. East Dean and Singleton are charming flint villages which owe their character to the Goodwood Estate. In Hampshire Selborne is an outstandingly beautiful example of a flintstone village. Brian Dawson's modest little booklet is a celebration of flint work in West Sussex and the author hoped that it would provide the inspiration for better building in the future, using local materials which encourage the use of traditional craft skills. It has helped to draw attention to our heritage and will help visitors understand the role of flint and thereby add to their enjoyment of the Downs. He adds that 'we must cherish our existing stock of flint buildings by properly maintaining them and we must seize (subject to other planning considerations!) what few opportunities arise for new flint structures'. Now there is talk of a 'new localism' which is really local, communities are expressing their love of traditional flint-work as part of the individuality of their place, and we may see some good work being produced. All too often pre-cast blocks of flints are used (Dawson, 1998).

Mills

Water-mills were a familiar part of the downland scene from Roman times. The largest of the nineteenth-century mills were the Bishopstone Tide Mills where barges brought grain up the River Ouse. As the tide rose, three large millponds were filled. As the tide receded water was released through sluice gates to drive the mill's 16 grindstones. More than one hundred people were employed at the mills, many living nearby on a site destroyed during the Second World War but now opened to the public. Ten sites of water-mills are listed in the East Sussex Downs, including three at Plumpton and two in Lewes. In the West Sussex Downs and the adjacent parts included in the proposed National Park there are forty-eight sites (Plate 61) and in East Hampshire nine. Until comparatively recently the Downs would have been dotted with numerous **windmills**, at least one and usually more for each parish or manor, of which Halnaker Mill, standing prominently on the high downs near Chichester is the only one still standing in that district (Plate 62). They disappeared rapidly with the coming of steam power. Polegate Tower Mill has been restored and is in working order. Restored but not operative are the 'Jack and Jill' Mills at Clayton, and windmills at High Salvington, Halnaker, Rottingdean, West Blatchington and Oldlands, Keymer. A number have been converted to living accommodation including Patcham, Washington Rock, Alfriston, West Chiltington, the mill in Pipe Passage, Lewes and at Chalton, Hampshire. In all, 42 notable Sussex remains were cited by Martin Brunnarius in 1979 and a further 14 have been noted in East Hampshire. R.C. Pinney (1972) urged 'all whom it may concern to do everything in their power to conserve and maintain these buildings. In a number of districts the windmill is a really beautiful, important, and distinctive feature' Further action and funds from dedicated people will be needed to restore and maintain them for our archaeological heritage. The same could be said of water-mills.

CONCLUSION

Promoting people's awareness and understanding of the historic environment of the South Downs is a matter of great importance but which is still only in its infancy. Its basis should not be solely on sites but on selected *whole landscapes* so that the subsequent occupance of various sites through time and their inter-relationships can be unravelled. Such landscape characterisation could be applied, encouraged by a National Park Authority, with particular success on the Downs with its particularly rich heritage. A good example of a project which brings together existing knowledge is 'Buriton: Beyond Living Memory', Buriton Heritage Bank, 2003. Meanwhile there is great scope for visitor information at many historic and scientific sites. For example, the numerous scrubby patches at No Man's Land near Cissbury Ring, which are scheduled sites of archaeological importance, are not in any way explained to the rambler, and the SSSI on Seaford Head is marked by a public notice which provides no explanation of the geological, historic and wildlife significance of the site. How is the public to learn?

High on the list of desiderata is also helping people to understand more about their local countryside and its needs. The growing interest in speciality foods means that Red Sussex Cattle and locally reared cross-bred sheep could again become viable parts of the food-chain. The Government's new farming strategy of moving away from subsidies on production towards management of the environment, announced in March 2005, means that the return of sustainable ley farming and its concomitants for a richer wildlife is now within the realm of probability.

REFERENCES

Brandon, P. (1998) *The South Downs*. Phillimore, Chichester. For a fuller account of the South Downs Landscape, see Chapters 3–8.

Brandon, P. and Millman, R. (eds) (1982) *Historic Landscapes*. Polytechnic of North London.

Brunnarius, M. (1979) *The Windmills of Sussex*. London.

Cunliffe, B. (1972) Saxon and medieval settlement patterns in the region of Chalton, Hants. *Medieval Archaeology* **16**, 1–12.

Dawson, B. (1998) *Flint Buildings in West Sussex*. West Sussex County Council, Chichester.

Fisher, E. A. (1970) *The Anglo-Saxon Churches of Sussex*. London.

Goring, C. (1801) Board of Agriculture Prize Essay.

MacColl, D. S. (1904) *Annual Report*. Society for the Protection of Ancient Buildings, London.

Mantell, G. (1822) *The Fossils of the South Downs*. London.

Marshall, W. (1798) *The Rural Economy of the Southern Counties*, Vol. 2. London.

Pennington, J. and Platt, P. (1999) In: Leslie, K. and Short, B. (eds) *An Historical Atlas of Sussex*. Phillimore, Chichester. pp. 48–9.

Pinney, R. C. (1972) *Windmills and their Restoration: a 1970s Perspective*. London.

Potts, G.R. (1996) *The Partridge*. London. p. 214.

Rose, F. (1995) *The Habitats and Vegetation in Sussex*. Booth Museum of Natural History, Brighton.

Tansley, Sir A. and Adamson, R. S. (1925) Studies of the vegetation of the English chalk, III: the chalk grasslands of the Hampshire-Sussex border. *Journal of Ecology* **13**, 177–233.

– (1926) Studies of the vegetation of the English chalk, IV: A preliminary survey of the chalk grassland of the Sussex Downs. *Journal of Ecology* **14**, 1–32.

Taylor, H.M. and J. (1965) *Anglo-Saxon Architecture*. Cambridge University Press, Cambridge.

Taylor, M. Archaeological Officer, West Sussex County Council. Personal communication.

Vancouver, G. (1798) *The Agriculture of Hampshire*. London.

Vera, F.W.M. (2000) *Grazing, Ecology and Forest History*. CABI, Wallingford.

Young, Revd A. (1813) *A General View of the Agriculture of the County of Sussex*. London.

Plate 60 *(above)*
A double-chambered dovecot of medieval origin at Alciston,
East Sussex; built by the monks of Battle Abbey to house the
birds that provided succulent meat for the table.
Photo: Peter Brandon.

Plate 61 *(below left)*
One of the surviving eighteenth century water-mills at Steyning,
West Sussex, now a private residence.
Photo: Peter Brandon.

Plate 62 *(below right)*
Halnaker Windmill, West Sussex; recently restored, but famed
through Hilaire Belloc's verse of 1913, when he regarded it as a
symbol of rural decline.
Photo: Peter Brandon.

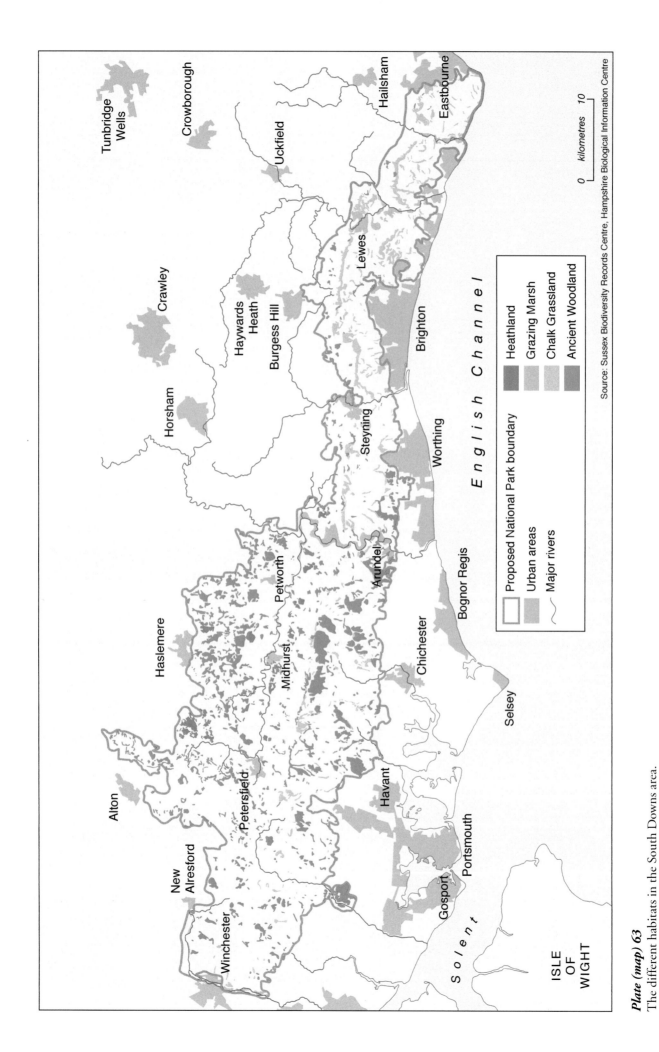

Plate (map) 63

The different habitats in the South Downs area.

Map produced by the University of Southampton Cartographic Unit from data supplied by SWT, courtesy of East Sussex, West Sussex and Hampshire County Councils (heathlands), the Environment Agency (grazing marshes and rivers), Natural England (ancient woodland), SDJC (chalk grassland and the proposed National Park boundary).

Source: Sussex Biodiversity Records Centre, Hampshire Biological Information Centre

Legend:
- Proposed National Park boundary
- Urban areas
- Major rivers
- Heathland
- Grazing Marsh
- Chalk Grassland
- Ancient Woodland

English Channel

Solent

ISLE OF WIGHT

0   kilometres   10

CHAPTER 5
Habitats and their Importance

TONY WHITBREAD

The semi-natural habitats that we see in the South Downs area today – on the chalk ridge, the dip-slope, the greensand ridge, in the Weald and in the river valleys – had their origins in the natural forest that covered the area when the last ice age came to an end. This forest would have been an immensely varied place, not just the dense impenetrable world of trees that we once imagined. Natural disturbance through storms, erosion and flooding, as well as the effects of large grazing animals, would have created variety: dense wooded forest, open grazed areas, areas looking rather like today's parkland, diverse wetland areas and so on. Indeed this natural forest would have contained the precursors of all the habitats that we know today.

We now use the term 'semi-natural' to describe most of our current habitats. They are neither totally natural (the product of natural forces alone) nor totally artificial (created by humans – we may manage the land but we did not plant every wild flower or breed every wild animal!). We therefore do not live in a natural landscape; we live in a cultural landscape. The semi-natural habitats we see in the South Downs area are the product of the (generally beneficial) interplay between natural forces and human management.

HABITATS OF THE SOUTH DOWNS

The habitats of the South Downs (Plate (map) 63) correspond broadly with the familiar natural areas described by English Nature: the chalk ridge of the South Downs itself, the greensand ridge and the Low Weald (English Nature, 1999).

The calcareous soils of the chalk ridge support chalk grassland, chalk heath, scrub and woodlands. The greensand ridge, with its acidic sandy soils contain expanses of heathland mixed in with woodland, itself often regenerated or planted on heathlands. The Low Weald (i.e. the Western Weald), a rolling landscape of sandstone ridges and clay vales, contains a high density of ancient woodlands and scattered meadows, interconnected by 'shaws' or 'rews' (thin strips of usually ancient woodlands between fields) and hedgerows.

As noted in other chapters, several river valleys cut across these three broad natural areas. Some, such as the Cuckmere, Ouse, Adur and Arun, arise in the Weald, then cut through the ridge of the South Downs before flowing south to the sea. Two others, the Meon and the Itchen arise from the chalk. These valleys support very valuable tracts of wetlands – floodplain grassland, marshes and reedbeds.

Chalk grassland

Large-scale woodland clearance on the Downs began some 5000 to 6000 years ago. By the time the Romans came to Britain an economy based on rearing sheep was already well established. Some of the chalk grasslands we know today are truly ancient, having an extremely long history of sheep-grazing and, by the early part of the last century, about 40 to 50 per cent of the South Downs was open, sheep-grazed grassland.

This process of woodland clearance followed by grazing resulted in the considerable expansion of any open areas within the pre-existing natural forest.

On the thin, nutrient-poor, calcareous soils of the South Downs this resulted in the development of an extremely rich and varied habitat referred to as chalk or calcareous grassland.

In agricultural terms, the best use for such land was often extensive grazing, generally by sheep. In ecological terms this created an ideal set of conditions for the development of an extremely rich habitat. Such stressful, nutrient-poor conditions mean that no single aggressive species can dominate (the so-called process of competitive exclusion). As a result a great array of other species are able to thrive in the absence of competition from more aggressive ones.

Today the familiar chalk grassland of the South Downs is probably the richest of all plant communities in Britain at a small scale. In some locations it is possible to count up to 40 species of flowering plant within just one square metre. Orchid species do well under these conditions, and the Downs are renowned for supporting a range of these plants. They include relatively common species, such as twayblade (*Listera ovata*) and common spotted-orchid (*Dactylorhiza fuchsii*) (Plate 64), the more restricted fragrant (*Gymnadenia conopsea*), pyramidal (*Anacamptis pyramidalis*) and bee orchids (*Ophrys apifera*) (Plate 65) to the rare musk (*Herminium monorchis*) (Plate 66), burnt-tip (*Orchis ustulata*) (Plate 67) and early spider orchids (*Ophrys sphegodes*) (Plate 68).

Only small remnants of this traditional 'sheepwalk' have escaped agricultural improvement and retain their characteristic flora and fauna. Recent surveys suggest that the remnants of unimproved chalk grassland now occupy a mere three to five per cent of the total area of the Downs.

On the Downs there is a basic difference in the plant communities found on the south-facing dip-slope and the steeper north-facing scarp-slope.

The dip-slope

The dip-slope rises gradually from the coastal plain to the south forming a landscape of hills and dry valleys, ending abruptly at the north-facing scarp-slope. The chalk grassland flora tends to be richer where the aspect of the slopes is southerly, supporting a fine array of sun-loving species. Valuable examples of this habitat can be found on south-facing slopes at Noar Hill in Hampshire, Harting Down and Cissbury Ring in West Sussex, and at Mount Caburn, Malling Down and beside the River Cuckmere in East Sussex. Castle Hill, however, just to the east of Brighton is perhaps one of the finer chalk grasslands in England, a National Nature Reserve with extensive areas of slopes facing south, south-east and south-west. These sites can be particularly rich in orchids, including bee (*O. apifera*), burnt tip (*O. ustulata*), early spider (*O. sphegodes*), frog (*Coeloglossum viride*) and green-winged (*Orchis morio*) orchids. Other uncommon plants include chalk milkwort (*Polygala calcarea*), early gentian (*Gentianella anglica*), horseshoe vetch *(Hippocrepis comosa)* (Plate 69), yellow-wort (*Blackstonia perfoliata*), bastard toadflax (*Thesium humifusum*) and field fleawort (*Senecio integrifolius*) (Rose, 1995).

In the west the dip-slope peters out to form more rolling countryside so that in some individual sites both north and south-facing slopes are in close proximity. Old Winchester Hill National Nature Reserve in Hampshire (Plate 17) is a classic example of such a variable site. This site contains one of the larger colonies of juniper in south-east England, and supports a variety of invertebrates including the butterfly, the Duke of Burgundy fritillary (Plate 76).

The scarp-slope

The scarp-slope, being north-facing, is cooler and damper, receiving much less direct sunlight than the warmer southern slopes. It therefore has a much more oceanic microclimate than the warmer dip-slopes, and supports a different range of plants as a result. The warmth-loving species of the dip-slope are rare or absent here. Two notable orchid species, however, are frequently found along the escarpment: the frog (*C. viride*) and the musk (*H. monorchis*) orchids. Indeed the musk orchid can be particularly common here, effectively having its British headquarters in this part of the South East (Rose, 1995). Other notable plants include the round-headed rampion (*Phyteuma orbiculare*), another plant that is particularly characteristic of the chalk slopes of Sussex, giving it the local name of 'pride of Sussex' (Plate 70).

The main botanical interest on the scarp-slope is, however, the rich flora of lichens, and bryophytes (mosses and liverworts) (Rose, 1995). These are of small, often unnoticed plants, but here on the scarp-slope can be found rare species that are otherwise limited to the cool, damp parts of Britain to the north and west of the country. Close examination reveals a sward often containing a deep mat of mosses, including species such as *Rhytidiadelphus loreus* and *R. triquetrus*, *Neckera crispa* and *Ctenidium molluscum*. Particularly rare bryophytes are occasionally found on bare chalk steps, in old chalk workings or small terraces on steep slopes, including the liverworts *Frullania tamersici* and *Scapania aspera* and the moss *Racomitrium lanuginosum* (usually found on rocks in the uplands). Butser Hill National Nature Reserve is designated because of its diverse and interesting bryophyte flora.

Good examples of chalk grassland can be found along much of the scarp-slope. These include Sussex Wildlife Trust nature reserves at Malling Down and Ditchling Beacon, Hampshire Wildlife Trust reserves at St Catherine's Hill and sites at Butser Hill, Old

**A diversity of orchids is characteristic of high quality chalk grassland.
A selection from the many common or rare species occuring in the South Downs appears below.**

Plate 64 (right)
Common spotted orchid (*Dactylorhiza fuchsii*)
seen here at Malling Down, West Sussex.
Photo: Sussex Wildlife Trust (SWT).

Plate 65 (below left)
Bee orchid (*Ophrys apifera*), characteristic
of dry chalk grassland.
Photo: Tony Whitbread.

Plate 66 (below centre left)
Musk orchid (*Herminium monorchis*);
an uncommon species found in only a
few locations on the Downs.
Photo: David King, courtesy of SWT.

Plate 67 (above centre right)
Burnt-tip orchid (*Orchis ustulata*); a rare species
confined to a few locations in the Downs.
Photo: SWT.

Plate 68 (above right)
Early spider orchid (*Ophrys sphegoides*),
found on a few high-quality chalk grasslands,
such as Castle Hill near Brighton.
Photo: Tony Whitbread.

Plate 69 (below left)
Horseshoe vetch (*Hippocrepis
comosa*), a characteristic downland
plant and food-plant of the Adonis
blue butterfly.
Photo: Mike Read.

Plate 70 (below centre)
Round-headed rampion (*Phyteuma
orbiculare*), frequently found in the South
Downs but rare elsewhere, hence its
popular name 'Pride of Sussex'.
Photo: Tony Whitbread.

Plate 71 (below right)
Yellow-rattle (*Rhinanthus minor*), so called
because of the sound made when the ripe
seed-heads are shaken; a semi-parasitic
plant characteristic of neutral, traditionally
grazed grassland.
Photo: SWT.

Plate 72
Ling (*Calluna vulgaris*) with birch scrub and Scots pine, characteristic of heathland.
Photo: Mark Monk-Terry, courtesy of SWT.

Plate 73 *(centre left)*
A beech wood (*Fagus sylvatica*) in winter, at Selborne Hanger, Hampshire; its dense canopy in summer shades out most ground floras.
Photo: Mike Read.

Plate 75 *(centre right)*
Ancient yew trees (*Taxus baccata*) at Kingley Vale NNR, West Sussex.
Photo: Richard Williamson.

Plate 74
Kingley Vale National Nature Reserve (NNR) and its internationally important yew forest, near Chichester, West Sussex, viewed from the air in 1964.
Photo: Richard Williamson.

Winchester Hill, Heyshot Down, Didling Down, Westonbury Hill and Kithurst Hill.

Chalk heath

Chalk heath is an incongruous mixture of plants that require acid soils, such as ling (*Calluna vulgaris*) (Plate 72) and bell heather (*Erica cinerea*), growing virtually cheek by jowl alongside lime-tolerant plants, such as dropwort (*Filipendula vulgaris*) and salad burnet (*Sanguisorba officinalis*). It occurs at sites where thin layers of wind-blown silt (called loess), deposited during the Ice Age, were frost-churned into the underlying chalk bedrock. It is also found where thin patches of clay-with-flints overlie the chalk.

Chalk heath is a nationally rare habitat, which is probably better represented in the South Downs than in any other area of comparable size in southern England. At the turn of the century it was evidently quite widely distributed on the South Downs, but only as scattered patches, almost invariably on summits and gently sloping hillsides, never on steep slopes or valley floors. Only about 20 ha of chalk heath survive on the South Downs today, mainly at Lullington Heath, Belle Tout, Butser Hill, Old Winchester Hill and Levin Down. Ploughing, fertilizing or liming have destroyed many former sites; others have been seriously damaged by scrub invasion.

Chalk heath that has been ploughed up is not re-creatable. The silt or clay-with-flints becomes thoroughly mixed with the chalk, forming a uniformly alkaline soil that the acid-loving species cannot re-colonize. Where scrub invasion occurs, and the soil structure remains intact, restoration of chalk heath can be carried out, but not without some difficulty, as English Nature discovered at Lullington Heath. Heavy grazing-pressure is needed to maintain chalk heath and prevent the heather becoming leggy or invaded by gorse. In the past some chalk heath may have been maintained by periodic burning.

Woodland and scrub

Woodlands are of broadly different types in the different Natural Areas within the South Downs.

Woodlands of the chalk ridge

The chalky soils of the Downs support a woodland mixture with varying amounts of ash, maple, hazel, wych elm, yew and whitebeam. Beech has been very widely planted on these soils, resulting in its dominance over much of the area. There are also extensive areas that have been planted with non-native conifer species, particularly in the west of the region. It is likely that relatively little of this wood is of ancient origin, much of the area being shown as sheepwalk on old maps. Nevertheless there are some fine woods along the chalk ridge of the Downs.

The nature of woodland varies with slope, topography and soil depth (Rodwell, 1991).

The lower parts of the scarp-slope have deeper soils and support tall well-grown beech trees mixed with ash and oak. The under-story often contains maple, hazel, wych elm, whitebeam and possibly holly. The ground flora is usually dominated by a thick covering of dog's mercury (*Mercurialis perennis*) often mixed with bluebell (*Hyacinthoides non-scripta*). Damper slopes may also have expanses of wood anemone (*Anemone nemorosa*) or ramsons (*Allium ursinum*). There are also some special locations on these lower slopes where the rare large-leaved lime tree is found. It used to be thought that these woods on the steep scarp-slope were all relatively recent in origin, possibly resulting from periods in history when grazing relaxed and trees were able to spread over downland. Whilst this may be true for much of the Downs, the presence of woods with large-leaved lime, and ancient woodland plants like bluebell and wood anemone, indicates that there are places with true ancient woodland (i.e. thought to be at least 400 years old) on the steep scarp-slope. It is in these woods that interesting plants such as green hellebore (*Helleborus viridis*), white helleborine (*Cephalanthera damasonium*), Solomon's seal (*Polygonatum multiflorum*) and herb-paris (*Paris quadrifolia*) can be found. These last two species are rare in Sussex, being limited to the area around Rook Clift, a private wood on the Hampshire border. This rich mixture is however more frequent further into Hampshire, for example at Selborne Hanger (Plate 73) and High Wood Hanger.

The soils on the middle and higher slopes of the Downs become more unstable and the nature of the woodland changes. Beech may remain dominant with abundant ash and field maple, but yew starts to become more common. The ground flora can be patchier, the dog's mercury (*M. perennis*) mixing with species such as wood sage (*Teucrium scorodonia*). Where slopes become still steeper, the beech starts to become more infrequent and, in the steepest locations, the wood becomes predominantly a yew wood. Perhaps the best yew wood in Europe is found on the Downs at Kingley Vale, north and west of Chichester (Plate 74). Here a dense yew forest covers large areas of the steep slopes, though the oldest trees are actually found lower in the valley (Plate 75). There might be debate about the age of these trees, but we do know that they are many centuries old.

A different type of woodland is found on the gentler dip-slope of the Downs. Here some of the superficial clay-with-flint deposits may remain, resulting in a more clayey soil that is less calcareous. Oak-ash-hazel woodland is often found here; oak on the deeper clay-with-flints and ash on the thinner chalkier areas. There are also varying amounts of maple, chestnut and sometimes hornbeam. Some of these have a classic coppice with standards structure (oak timber trees over shrubs cut on a rotation of between 10 and 20 years). A classic example of this woodland type is found at West Dean Woods, a Sussex Wildlife Trust nature reserve on the West Dean Estate. This is actively coppiced, and this activity has helped support a very rich ground flora. The wood is renowned for its wild daffodil (*Narcissus pseudonarcissus*) displays in spring, along with impressive displays of bluebell, wood anemone, primroses (*Primula vulgaris*), violets (*Viola* spp), wild strawberry (*Fragaria vesca*) and many others. The ground flora can be even more species-rich where the clay is influenced by the underlying chalk. Clappets Copse, a Hampshire Wildlife Trust reserve, is an example of this. It supports probably the largest narrow-leaved helleborine (*Cephalanthera longifolium*) population in Britain, along with good populations of fly (*Ophrys insectifera*) and bird's-nest (*Neottia nidus-avis*) orchids.

In the west of West Sussex and the east of Hampshire we find ridges of greensand in close proximity to the chalk ridges. This can be seen, for example, around Selborne where the 'Hampshire Hangers' of beech, wych elm, ash and oak cover many of the north and east-facing slopes (Plate 73). These calcareous woods support a rich ground flora including white helleborine, bird's-nest orchid, toothwort (*Lathraea squamaria*), violet helleborine (*Epipactis purpurata*), stinking hellebore (*Helleborus foetidissima*) and columbine (*Aquilegia vulgaris*). The bottom of this escarpment is often deeply incised and damp with rich growths of harts-tongue fern (*Phyllitis scolopendrium*), lady fern (*Athyrium filix-femina*), and Italian lords and ladies (*Arum italicum*). Several of these sites, Selborne Common Site of Special Scientific Interest for example, are outstanding for their moss and liverwort flora and for their mollusc fauna.

Woodlands of the sandstone

Moving from the chalk Downs to the greensand rides and Folkestone sands one sees a very different type of woodland.

Many of the woods on the Folkestone sands in West Sussex and parts of east Hampshire are the result of planting on old areas of heathland. Scots pine is often the dominant tree over a ground flora dominated by bracken (*Pteridium aquilinum*) with patches of ling (*Calluna vulgaris*) in more open areas. Such woodlands are not always of great ecological value in their own right, any associated heathland tending to hold a greater diversity of characteristic plants and animals. Oak–birch wood is the main type in areas that have not been replanted, with a ground flora dominated by bracken, wavy-hair grass (*Deschampsia flexuosa*) and heather, with bilberry

(*Vaccinium myrtillus*) in more humid areas. These woods tend to be more important for ferns, liverworts, mosses and lichens. Rake Common on the West Sussex/Hampshire border, Passfield Common and Holly Hills in Hampshire and the Local Nature Reserve at Burton Pond, near Petworth, provide good examples of these acidic heathy woods.

Much of the scarp-slope of the greensand ridge in Hampshire is very steep due to hard beds of malmstone. This is a weakly calcareous sandstone and gives rise to a different flora to that on the greensand further east. Woods with a mixture of ash, oak, hazel and maple are found, for example, at Long Copse and Milking Hanger. These often have a rich ground flora with wood anemone, moschatel (*Adoxa moschatellina*), ramsons, bluebell, shield ferns, herb-paris and Solomon's seal. Wick Hill Hanger has a similar flora but is notable for its population of small-leaved lime (*Tilia cordata*) (see Brewis *et al.*, 1996).

Woodlands of the Western Weald

The Western Weald area has a high percentage of ancient woodland. Woods here tend to be a mixed broadleaved type typical of heavy clay soils, but the bands of sandstone running through the area add variety. Oak and beech are often the key trees with some ash over hazel, holly, hornbeam and chestnut. The ground flora can be a rich mixture with abundant bluebell and wood anemone, with scattered wood melick (*Melica uniflora*), wood sorrel (*Oxalis acetosella*), daffodil (*Narcissus pseudonarcissus*), goldilocks buttercup (*Ranunculus auricomus*), sanicle (*Sanicula europaea*), butcher's broom (*Ruscus aculeatus*) and many others. Bands of Wadhurst Clay that run closer to the chalk of the South Downs tend to be slightly lime-enriched resulting in a slightly different flora. Oak and ash often form the tree layer over a hazel and maple coppice under-storey. The ground flora here can include species such as thin-spiked wood sedge (*Carex strigosa*) and spurge laurel (*Daphne laureola*).

Woodlands, however, exist in a variety of 'management types' (see Chapter 8), many having a clear coppice-with-standards structure, others are managed for timber and a few are old wooded commons. This latter type has been managed as wood pastures in the past, but most have now been left largely unmanaged for such a long time that they are developing their own 'near-natural' structure. Of these wooded commons the Sussex Wildlife Trust (SWT) reserve at Ebernoe Common stands out as an internationally important pasture woodland (Plate 92), and has been designated a Special Area of Conservation (SAC), under the EU Habitats Directive, on this basis. A second area, The Mens Nature Reserve also an SAC, is perhaps the best example of a near-natural woodland in lowland England. This area is truly exceptional in having not only a high concentration of ancient woodland but also having two key sites with the highest level of nature conservation designation.

The woodlands throughout the South Downs are very valuable for a variety of birds, invertebrates and mammals.

The high density of woodland in the Western Weald supports a range of birds, such as lesser spotted woodpecker and marsh tit (Plate 84), that require a high density of woodland at a landscape scale. The great interconnectivity of woodland here also makes it one of the best areas in Britain for nightingale. One can also catch occasional glimpses of woodcock in some of the larger blocks of woodland, and buzzard (Plate 85), having been quite rare in Sussex until recently, is now spreading across this part of the county.

Deer (Plate 80), especially Roe Deer, are frequent throughout the South Downs, their browsing of young trees causing great problems for woodland managers. There are now even occasional reports of wild boar in the area, although they are generally thought to be more associated with East Sussex and Kent. The dormouse (Plate 81) also has a stronghold here, particularly in the Western Weald. This species requires quite large blocks of woodland (usually over 20 ha in extent) in order to be able to form viable populations.

The area is rich in insects and other invertebrates. Woodland butterflies such as Wood White and Pearl-bordered fritillary are in decline across southern Britain due to lack of woodland management, but they still occur in this area near the Surrey border. These species require occasional opening up of woodland to provide sunny glades. White Admiral (Plate 77), however, seems to be getting a little more common as it is happy in less well-managed woods. Speckled Wood, Comma, Silver-washed Fritillary and other more common woodland species are all well represented throughout the area.

Hedgerows and shaws

The chalky soils of the Downs generally support a very open landscape that contains relatively few hedges. Those that are present can be quite species-rich, containing chalk-loving species such as dogwood, spindle and wayfaring-tree. Clematis is often abundant, sometimes being so aggressive that it restricts the growth of the shrub species.

Hedges are, however, far more common both where the chalk of the Downs is overlain by a clay cap and in the Western Weald. Surveys here show that there is a high density of hedgerows that are likely to be ancient in origin. Presence of certain species indicating antiquity is generally higher in this area than in many other parts of Sussex. These include tree, shrub and ground-flora plants species (such as small-leaved lime, wild service tree, midland

hawthorn and bluebell) that are indicative of ancient woodland.

It seems likely that most of the hedgerows are more than 500 years old and many are possibly Saxon (Hoskins, 1967; Pollard *et al.* 1974). Indeed, judging by the current species-content, it is likely that many of them are relicts of rews from earlier 'assarting' (thin strips of woodland remaining from the time when small clearances, or assarts, were cut from the ancient wood).

Hedgerows are important for many of our common farmland birds, such as warblers, whitethroat and black cap. They are important for a variety of insects and, again, it is the butterflies that stand out. The brown hairstreak butterfly (Plate 79) is well represented in this part of the western Weald, making the area nationally important for this species. The butterfly inhabits blackthorn, which is abundant in hedgerows in this area.

Heathland

The greensand beds that form the acid, sandy soils on which heathland develops, extend across the South Downs area from Woolmer Forest in Hampshire narrowing to a thin belt further east to Washington in West Sussex.

The formation of these heaths is complex and still not fully understood. As the last Ice Age came to an end, heathland plants gradually colonized from the south. Grazing pressure, initially from wild herds of animals, then from domestic stock, produced the low shrub growth and, in the wetter areas, bog-type communities, which together make up the heathland. Eventually, the agricultural activities of man became the dominant factor and created the heathland habitat that we recognize today. The heaths that formed on these less productive soils were used by local people for grazing their animals, gathering wood, gorse, bracken, turf, peat and heather.

The popular image of heathland is of attractive purple heather studded with the occasional gorse bush and birch tree (Plate 72); but in ecological terms the situation is much more complex. Heaths are generally defined as dwarf shrub communities developed on acid mineral soils with members of the heather family being the most common shrubs. In some situations they can also include areas of similar soils dominated by grasses. This type of vegetation is unique to the countries immediately around the North Sea and the Bay of Biscay (Rose, 1992).

Most of the heathland in the South Downs area can be described as **Dry-heath** (Rose, 1992) and consists of a mixture of ling, bell heather and small gorse (*Ulex minor*). Extensive areas can be seen, for example, in Iping and Stedham commons, Ambersham Common, Longmoor Inclosure and Woolmer Forest.

Humid-heath, on soils with a higher winter water-table, has less bell heather but more cross-leaved heath and heath rush (*Juncus squarrosus*). **Wet-heath** occurs where the water-table is still higher. Cross-leaved heath (*Erica tetralix*) becomes still more common with frequent communities of deer grass (*Trichophorum cespitosum*) and cotton grass (*Eriophorum angustifolium*). The bog mosses *Sphagnum compactum* and *S. tenellum* also occur more in this type. **Valley Mire** develops in depressions where the water-table is almost permanently at the surface. This community is now rare in the South Downs area but is marked by a complex mosaic of bog moss (sphagnum) species, including *S papillosum, S. capillifolium* and *S. recurvum* with rare patches of bog asphodel (*Narthecium ossifragum*). Pools within this complex contain other bog mosses, such as *S. cuspidatum* and *S auriculatum* occasionally with marsh St John's-wort (*Hypericum elodes*), bog pondweed (*Potamogeton polygonifolius*) and rarely cranberry (*Vaccinium oxycoccos*).

The wetter heath types are all rare in West Sussex, but where they do occur it is usually in complex patchworks. Ambersham Common has a relatively large area of valley mire, and there is a very good example of the habitat at Hurston Warren. Smaller areas occur at Iping Common, Bog Common and Hesworth Common. Wet heaths occur more frequently in Hampshire. Although many of the valley bogs in Woolmer Forest have been drained by the Ministry of Defence, there still remain good examples of wet-heath and valley mires at Longmoor Inclosure and, particularly, at Cranmer Bottom Bog. Shortheath Common is particularly notable as it is an extensive floating sphagnum bog with perhaps the largest colony of cranberry in the southern half of Britain.

Heathlands are of outstanding importance for insects. The more obvious species include the silver-studded blue butterfly, a range of solitary wasps, the small red damselfly and the black darter dragonfly. Recent studies of the West Sussex heaths have yielded long lists of interesting fauna. Edwards and Hodge (1993), for example, recorded 113 'heathland indicator species', including such characteristic species as the beefly (*Thyridanthrax fenestratus*), the sanddigger wasp (*Ammophila sabulosa*) and the mottled grasshopper (*Myrmeleotettix maculatus*). Locally, patches of acidic grassland within heathland may be extremely important, and the only remaining colony of field cricket in the UK occurs in this habitat in Sussex.

This is the most important habitat in the Downs area for reptiles. Adders, slow worms and common lizards are quite common with the rare presence of both the sand lizard (Plate 82) and the smooth snake, the UK's rarest reptiles. Woolmer Forest, the largest area of lowland heath in England outside the New Forest, supports all 12 of Britains native amphibian

and reptile species. Heathland is also particularly attractive to a range of characteristic birds, such as the Dartford warbler, stonechat, nightjar and woodlark (Plates 86 to 89).

Heathlands have decreased rapidly in extent over the last century all over north-west Europe. In West Sussex research, sponsored by the West Sussex Heathland Forum (Rose, 1992), has shown that the 7500 ha of heathland that existed (excluding that which occurred within St. Leonards Forest) in 1813 had declined to 679 ha in 1981. This represents more than a 90 per cent reduction.

Wetlands and rivers

Wetlands and the rivers associated with them are a major wildlife resource in the South Downs area. They lie in the broad valleys and flood plains of Hampshire and Sussex, and contain a rich landscape of wet meadow, fenland, reedbed, marsh and ditch. Collectively they are often referred to as grazing marshes. In summer cattle graze the wet pastures. In winter the valley bottoms might flood, enriching the soil with nutrients carried down by the river. This wet, marshy grassland is also of major importance to birds that either visit the area, as they pass through on migration, or stay to breed. These are probably some of the most important wetlands in England after the Norfolk Broads and the Somerset Levels, and, as suggested in Chapter 9, they have huge potential.

These wetlands contain very special communities of plants and invertebrates that are not found elsewhere. Among the outstanding plants are flowering rush (*Butomus umbellatus*), arrowhead (*Sagittaria sagittifolia*) and water dropworts (*Oenanthe* spp). The ditches are particularly important for invertebrates, such as freshwater molluscs, dragonflies and water beetles. Wetlands also contain a range of other special habitats: fens (peaty areas with reeds, rushes and sedges), small shallow lakes, bogs and reedbeds. It is where this combination of features occurs that the greatest variety of species can be found.

A particularly fine example of grazing marsh of national importance is found at Amberley Wildbrooks on the River Arun (Plates 19 and 20 and see Chapters 4, 7 and 9). This is an extensive area of alluvial grazing marsh dissected by drainage ditches. Species of note here include the southern marsh-orchid (*Dactylorhiza praetermissa*), true fox sedge (*Carex vulpina*), marsh cinquefoil (*Potentilla palustris*) and cut grass (*Leersia oryzoides*), the last in one of its few locations in Britain. Good examples can also be found elsewhere on the Arun and on the rivers Test, Itchen, Adur, Ouse and Cuckmere.

The rivers and streams in the area are often of extremely high nature-conservation value. Hampshire boasts some of the finest chalk rivers in

Plate 76 (above left)
The Duke of Burgundy fritillary (*Hamearis lucina*),
characteristic of scrubby grassland and sunny woodland clearings.
Photo: Andy Vidler, courtesy of SWT.

Plate 77 (above centre left)
The white admiral butterfly (*Ladoga camilla*), a locally common
woodland species.
Photo: Mark Monk-Terry, courtesy of SWT.

Plate 78 (above centre right)
The Adonis blue butterfly (*Lysandra bellargus*) characteristic of
the South Downs, pictured on its feed-plant, horseshoe vetch
(*Hippocrepis comosa*).
Photo: Simon Culpin, courtesy of SDJC.

Plate 79 (above right)
A female brown hairstreak butterfly (*Thecla betulae*), a species
characteristic of woodland and hedges; it spends much of its life
high in the tree canopy or deep in hedgerows.
Photo: SWT.

Plate 80 (centre left)
A young roe deer (*Capriolus capriolus*); a welcome sight, but its
browsing of regenerating woodland causes problems for foresters.
Photo: Jamie Cordery.

Plate 81 (centre right)
A dormouse (*Muscardinus avellanarius*); isolated colonies are
found in the South Downs area.
Photo: Hugh Clark, courtesy of SWT.

Plate 82 (below left)
A female sand lizard (*Lacerta agilis*), a very rare species that
favours dry-heath where it inhabits stands of ling in sandy areas.
Photo: SWT.

Plate 83 (below right)
A barbastelle bat (*Barbastella barbastellus*), one of the rare species
roosting in places such as Ebernoe Common, but flying a great
distance at night for food.
Photo: Frank Greenaway, courtesy of SWT.

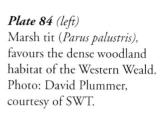

Plate 84 (*left*)
Marsh tit (*Parus palustris*), favours the dense woodland habitat of the Western Weald. Photo: David Plummer, courtesy of SWT.

Plate 85 (*right*)
Buzzards (*Buteo buteo*) are now spreading through the South Downs area. Photo: Darin Smith, courtesy of SWT.

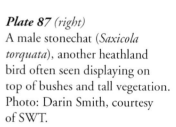

Plate 86 (*left*)
Dartford warbler (*Sylvia undata*), a resident bird, populations of which are expanding in suitable heathland habitats in the South Downs area. Photo: Andy Vidler, courtesy of SWT.

Plate 87 (*right*)
A male stonechat (*Saxicola torquata*), another heathland bird often seen displaying on top of bushes and tall vegetation. Photo: Darin Smith, courtesy of SWT.

Plate 88 (*left*)
Nightjar (*Caprimulgus europaeus*); a mainly heathland or woodland bird, characteristically active at night, it can stay motionless on the ground if approached. Photo: Mike Read.

Plate 89 (*right*)
Woodlark (*Lullula arborea*) with young; a scarce bird which tends to nest on the ground, sometimes close to woodland rides. Photo: Mike Read.

Plate 90 (*right*)
Lapwings (*Vanellus vanellus*) congregate on the flooded marshes of the Adur and Arun river valleys in winter. Photo: Darin Smith, courtesy of SWT.

Plate 91 (*left*)
Bewick's swans (*Cygnus columbarius*) migrate to Britain in winter and can be seen particularly in the flooded river valleys. Photo: Mike Read.

England, including the rivers Itchen and Meon (Plate 18). These support a healthy population of otter, now starting to spread to other nearby areas, and the native crayfish. These rivers are also very rich in invertebrate life (making the Itchen one of the best rivers in England for angling). The chalk rivers of Hampshire are renowned for the quality and clarity of their water and typically contain species such as water-crowfoot (*Ranunculus penicillatus* ssp. *Pseudofluitans*), water-dropwort (*Oenanthe fluviatilis*), water-cress (*Rorippa nasturtium-aquaticum*) and the aquatic moss (*Fontinalis antipyretica*).

The river valleys that cut through the Downs, with their grazing marshes and wetlands, are highly important for birds. The Adur and the Arun, for example, can support large numbers of lapwing, teal, golden plover, pintail and small numbers of Bewick's swan when they flood in winter (Plates 90, 91, and 95). One of the great sights and sounds of the South Downs area must be flocks of over 1000 lapwings against a setting sun over a flooded river valley!

Meadows and neutral grassland

Neutral grassland is the typical grassland of traditionally grazed hay-meadows on neutral brown-earth soils in lowland Britain. They are found on poor soils with a neutral pH within the range of 5 – 6.5. In the Western Weald this habitat is characterized by the crested dog's-tail (*Cynosurus cristatus*) and common knapweed (*Centaurea nigra*) grassland, but these grasslands can include a huge array of species that are rarely seen in more agriculturally improved pastures. These include green winged orchid (*Orchis morio*), yellow rattle (*Rhinanthus minor*) (Plate 71), pepper saxifrage (*Silaum silaus*), Dyer's greenweed (*Genista tinctoria*) and the adderstongue fern (*Ophioglossum vulgatum*) (Plate 94).

Neutral grassland is a nationally scarce habitat. It has been estimated that only 4000 ha of species-rich neutral grasslands remain in the whole of Britain. This is probably a reduction of around 95 per cent in the last 60 years. The species-rich neutral grasslands that remain are often in small, scattered fragments. These grasslands are mostly farmed; others can be found on village greens, green lanes, churchyards, sports fields and recreation grounds. Some were used primarily as meadows for cutting hay, others were mostly grazed as pastures. The vast majority of this once extensive habitat has been agriculturally improved by the application of fertilizers and herbicides, and through drainage. The result has been an increase in species-poor pasture.

It is not possible to re-create species-rich unimproved grassland in the short to medium term. The most urgent need is therefore to secure the protection of the remaining long-established areas. The potential for the conservation of the existing

stock of herb-rich meadows is strongly linked to low input – low output pastoral systems which are not favoured by current agricultural policy, although the changes described in Chapter 7 are a step in the right direction.

Re-creation of herb-rich grassland is now very difficult and expensive. The creation of new native grassland alongside existing sites could nevertheless have two important functions (Plate 96). It would enable the encouragement of a more rich and cost-effective pastoral system within which meadows could be managed, and such new grasslands could have an ecological value in their own right if carefully managed. There is however a problem of seed source; an extensive programme of re-creation might require the importation of non-native stock, so interfering with the genetic integrity of the existing meadow resource. This problem could be reduced by the harvesting of seed from local meadows for reintroduction into adjacent areas. This approach is already being progressed in the High Weald Area of Outstanding Natural Beauty.

HABITAT MATRICES – THE WHOLE IS GREATER THAN THE SUM OF THE PARTS

Whilst it is very important to conserve and maintain individual important wildlife sites, it is perhaps more important to maintain an overall landscape within which semi-natural habitats can survive. It is therefore vital not only to consider individual habitats but also to consider how they merge and interconnect, at a large scale, so that species and communities can move or adapt to changing conditions. A nature-conservation policy based on the conservation of small sites alone is doomed to failure – species disappear from such sites like books falling off an overcrowded bookshelf.

It is also often the case that the zone between two habitats – the ecotone – is the richest area, which is why hedgerows, woodland edges, woodland rides, the zone around the edge of lakes and wetlands, for example, are so important.

An example of the importance of habitat interconnectivity is provided by recent work done on bats in and around Ebernoe Common (Greenaway *et al.*, 1993). This Common (Plate 92) is among the most important sites in Europe for bats, supporting some 13 species in a relatively small area. Two of these, the Bechstein's and the barbastelle (Plate 83), are extremely rare. The barbastelle uses Ebernoe as a breeding and roosting site but disperses over a much larger area as it forages for food. In doing so, however, it relies heavily on the interconnectivity of habitats in the area, flying along tall hedges, woodland edges, wooded streams and wooded shaws. These features may not be of conservation value in their own right, but it is the continuity of this matrix that is important. If this was to be disrupted, the future of one of Europe's rarer mammals would be in jeopardy in this area.

Another example is with the woodland butterflies, such as the wood white and the pearl-bordered fritillary, both only found in a small number of isolated sites in the north Wealden part of the South Downs area. These have poor powers of dispersal so, if populations are too far apart, they are unable to interact. This makes individual populations prone to loss from an individual site and prone to local extinction. Individuals that do try to disperse do not find favourable sites, are unable to interact with other populations of the same species, so die off.

These are just well-researched examples of a wider principle: that there is a need for an area to function, ecologically, at a landscape scale. Individual sites kept in favourable condition would be insufficient to conserve these and many other species.

MANAGEMENT FOR NATURE CONSERVATION

Site Designations

Laws and policies governing nature conservation go back a very long way in Britain. The establishment of the Conservators for Epping Forest, Essex, in the late nineteenth century might be seen as a start. It could equally be argued, however, that the creation of Royal Forests many centuries earlier, or the physical conservation of ancient woodlands perhaps before the Romans arrived, were also to some extent measures of conservation.

The National Parks and Access to the Countryside Act of 1949 took a major step forward in allowing the identification of Sites of Special Scientific Interest (SSSIs), but it was not until the Wildlife and Countryside Act, 1981, that these areas received formal protection. This legal protection of SSSIs required owners and occupiers to notify the then Nature Consevancy Council of any potentially damaging operations, and opened negotiations for management agreements with payments for profit forgone to prevent any damage.

The Countryside and Rights of Way Act, 2000, included a section that further improved the situation for SSSIs. This provided better arrangements for funding, stop-orders to prevent damage and increased powers of compulsory purchase as last resort. The emphasis of this Act was more towards delivering management agreements and funding for conservation of SSSIs rather than preventing damage through compensatory payments.

We now also have layers of international designations to protect our most important sites. Under European legislation, the Habitats Directive (1994) allows the designation of Special Areas of Conservation (SACs), the Birds Directive (1979) allows the designation of Special Protection Areas (SPAs) for birds, and the Ramsar Convention allows the designation of wetlands of international importance. All of these have legal and policy-making repercussions to both national and local government.

There are also increasing levels of policy-protection ranging from a local to a national level. This is not legal protection, but policies do encourage conservation of important areas. Sites of Nature Conservation Importance (SNCIs), for example, are county-level sites, identified (not designated) and protected by policies in Structure and Local Plans. Strategic planning has gone through something of a change in the last few years away from Local and Structure Plans and towards Local Development Frameworks and Regional Plans. Efforts are now being made to ensure that policy-protection provided by the previous system is continued and enhanced by these new arrangements.

There is similar protection for ancient woodland. As noted in Chapter 8, this provides a certain level of protection but also enables the targeting of grants and advice to the benefit of nature conservation.

Conservation in the wider landscape

Legal protection for nature conservation in Britain is now, arguably, about as good as it is likely to get, yet the natural world is still in retreat. Maintenance of the most important sites in favourable condition, vital though it is, is not enough to conserve nature. The natural world must function at a landscape scale, not just at the scale of an individual site. For example, it is difficult to conserve habitats that require grazing if there are no grazing animals and no grazing infrastructure in the area. In this respect it is other measures, in parallel with the site-designation approach, that are likely to have a key impact. These are the measures that work on a large scale, creating the conditions within which individual sites might be conserved.

Agri-environment schemes, such as the Environmentally Sensitive Areas scheme on the grasslands of the South Downs or Countryside Stewardship in the heaths and wetlands, are examples of the methods that can achieve this. Chapter 7 describes how these pay farmers to farm in an environmentally beneficial way. On the South Downs this may mean encouraging more sheep-grazing. If there is more sheep-grazing in the area generally then there is more possibility of getting valuable sites grazed. A similar effect may be created if Southdown or Hampshire Down lamb can attract a higher price and so make grazing sheep a more viable option for farmers.

Whilst not abandoning the need for strong protection for special sites, attention is now turning

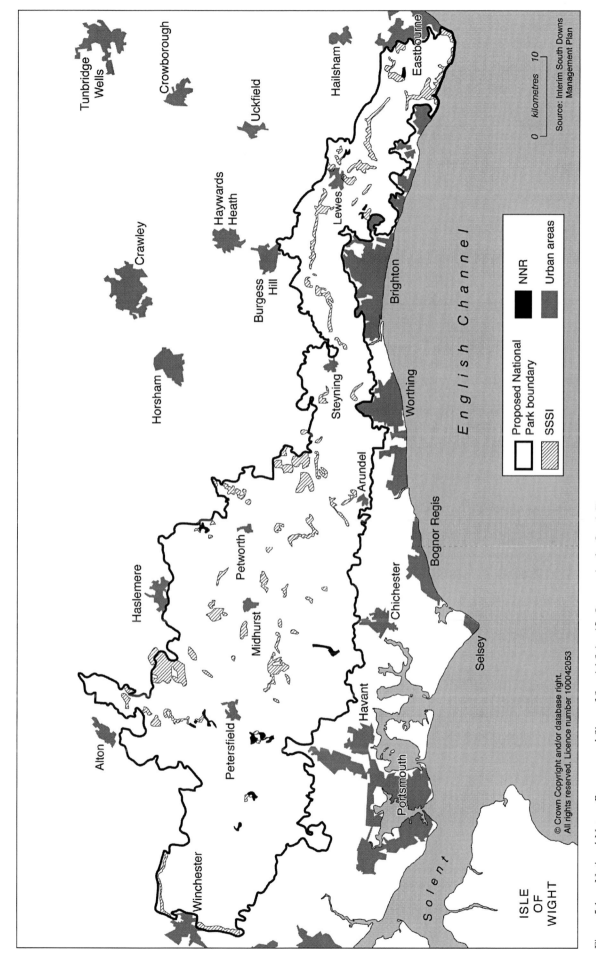

Figure 5.1 National Nature Reserves and Sites of Special Scientific Interest in the South Downs area.

Source: Interim South Downs Management Plan

more towards these landscape-scale systems. This is a very 'partnership forming' approach. Whilst site designations are sometimes perceived as something of an imposition to landowners, systems that encourage particular managerial approaches with funding and advice may be more welcomed. These may be seen as less restrictive and may come across more as a list of options to be discussed and negotiated.

Nature reserve ownership and management

Nature conservation is doomed if it is left just to nature conservationists! Ownership and management of nature reserves have vital roles to play in nature conservation but they can (should) only occupy relatively small landholdings within an area. For example, nature reserves occupy less than 0.5 per cent of the whole of Sussex; in the South Downs it is probably less (Fig, 5.1). The only answer for nature conservation is if all people are able to manage the areas for which they are responsible in ways that are beneficial to wildlife.

Nevertheless nature reserves do play a very positive role, conserving particularly sensitive habitats and sites that no longer form part of the farming (e.g. meadows and heaths) or forestry (e.g. old-growth forests) systems. They can also have a role in trialing managerial systems that might then be spread out over wider areas (e.g. naturalistic grazing-regimes). In the future nature reserves may form important nodes within a wider matrix of beneficially-managed landscape – perhaps filling a niche that private landowners might find difficult to fill.

Several organizations have nature reserves in the South Downs. The Hampshire and Isle of Wight Wildlife Trust has nature reserves at Noar Hill and St Catherine's Hill; Sussex Wildlife Trust (SWT) has sites at Malling Down, Ditchling Beacon and Levin Down, on the chalk, with heathland sites at Stedham and the large wetland at Amberley Wildbrooks referred to above. Woodland SWT reserves include a traditionally-managed coppice at West Dean Woods, an 'old-growth' woodland at The Mens near Petworth and a pasture woodland at Ebernoe Common. The RSPB has one of the major visitor attractions along the Downs with its Pulborough Brooks nature reserve, and the South Downs Society has a reserve at Harting. The National Trust owns large parts of the South Downs, including around Ditchling Beacon, New Timber Hill, Harting Down and Selborne Common.

Conflicts between conservation and recreation

Leisure, recreation and access present particular challenges to nature conservation. Quiet, informal recreation is often a key way that people gain benefit from such a high-quality environment. It could be argued that there is little point in conserving an area if people are unable to enjoy it. Nevertheless, the very act of enjoying an area places pressure upon it.

People are generally welcomed on nature reserves. If people did not wish to visit the area, there would be little demand to conserve its special qualities, and therefore few resources would be made available for management. It is also true that people rarely do deliberate damage; it is more usually the result of a lack of understanding. Therefore more, sensitive access will help drive the general policy to conserve the countryside. Also better education through better access should aim to overcome problems due to lack of knowledge.

It may also be true that the effects of access are not as clear as might first be thought. Recent work on woodlarks (Plate 89) has shown that there are indeed fewer nests near to public rights of way, but nests close to paths have a larger number of healthier chicks. (The reason for this is bird population-density: woodlarks further from paths have more competition from others in the same area). Overall there is little difference in breeding success between woodlarks near to or away from footpaths. There are also many examples of wildlife simply learning to live with a larger number of people in the neighbourhood. On the other hand, some species (e.g. stone-curlew) are very easily disturbed, and the popularity of the area to people may be one reason for the loss of stone-curlew from the Downs.

The South Downs are among the most visited landscapes in Britain, and some problems are therefore inevitable. Butser Hill National Nature Reserve in East Hampshire, for example, receives about 100,000 visitors per year. Visitor-pressure is likely to remain a key issue into the future, but conservation managers are becoming more adept in managing it to overcome problems. Carefully-sited footpaths, the transfer of car parks to less sensitive areas, the use of screening, prevention of erosion, locating 'honey-pot' sites in robust areas, and so on, all help to reduce recreation-pressure.

Climate change

Many factors are going to affect habitats in the South Downs in the future, but it is climate change that is going to be 'super-imposed' across any other factor. Climate change is with us, and, because of previous emissions of greenhouse gases, we are already committed to a certain level of change. Effects on wildlife seem almost certain. Some effects are fairly easy to predict – sea-level rise should occur in a relatively predictable way – whereas others, such as increases in storminess, will be more unpredictable.

The general pattern for the South East (and hence the South Downs area) is of drier, hotter summers with mild, wetter and stormier winters. Wildlife could be affected in a number of ways. In the short term at least, it may be that some of the warmth-loving plants and animals may do well. Previously rare species such as the wasp spider are now cropping up along the south coast near the South Downs, and some southern butterfly species (Adonis blue (Plate 78), or clouded yellow) may be expected to increase. We are also noticing that some birds that usually migrate in winter are staying in Britain in larger numbers (e.g. blackcap), whilst swallows seem to be appearing earlier in the year.

Yet there could be major threats to the ecology of the South Downs. Species that require damp humid conditions are likely to be affected by the hotter summers, and the shrinkage of the spring season could affect the spring flowers in our ancient woods.

AIMS FOR NATURE CONSERVATION

There are many good reasons for conserving nature, whether globally, or just at the level of the South Downs. Ultimately, a healthy, functioning environment is a basic need for our very survival, and it is wildlife that forms the basic building-block of this global life-support system. Linked to this is the maxim that wildlife is a key indicator of the health of our environment. Reduction in wildlife is a sign that ecological systems are not functioning as well as they could, and this will have an effect on human well-being. The natural world delivers ecosystems from which we benefit, services that range from oxygen in the air to an equitable global climate, or to more local effects like the amelioration of flooding, aquifer recharge and the control of erosion.

Often, however, it is with the small-scale and local that we tend to identify when we are concerned about nature conservation. This attitude relates more to our own sense of well-being and affinity for an area, the reasons we move to a place, our quiet enjoyment and the inspiration we get from a place.

Justification of nature conservation is very easy at a global scale – it is simply essential. Yet at the scale of the South Downs, we are more likely to justify nature conservation in terms of the special nature of the place. In practice these two ends of the spectrum join up; they are complementary rather than alternatives.

The broad vision for the future must therefore be to pass on to future generations a South Downs that is at least as good as, if not better than, the South Downs we inherited. If we take a period of, say, 50 years and compare what we have now with what we had previously, our record would not be good. We now need to turn a corner and start expanding our natural resources rather than preside over their continual reduction.

The UK Biodiversity Action Plan (BAP) gives details of the nature of biodiversity targets we should

be working towards and the actions that will be needed to achieve them. This is one of several BAPs at local, national and international level and is the result of the UK, together with about 150 other countries, signing the Convention on Biological Diversity in 1992.

Biodiversity (or biological diversity) is the current term that encompasses the variety of life. This is far more than just the number of species. It includes genetic variety within species, diversity of species, the habitats that they form and the ecological processes that operate from local to global levels. Targets for biodiversity therefore include objectives for habitats, their extent and quality, as well as for species survival, populations and viability.

Specific targets for biodiversity in the South Downs include proposals for the expansion of chalk grassland, wetland, woodlands, heathland and grassland. They also include proposals for particular rare species, such as the field cricket, although most species will be conserved through appropriate habitat-management. Other work to achieve targets for biodiversity includes proposals for landscape-scale projects incorporating a diversity of habitats along with the transition zones in between.

Furthermore, conservationists no longer consider that nature conservation should be just one issue that is 'balanced' against a range of others. The achievement of biodiversity-targets is an integral part of the sustainable management of our natural world – if we fail to deliver these aims then our own long-term sustainability is in question. It is perfectly possible to deliver mutual gain across economic, social and environmental objectives. Balancing one against the others is not a long-term solution. For example, sensitive woodland-management, as described in Chapter 8, can improve woodlands for biodiversity, enhance the landscape, deliver timber for fuel, building and wood-products, and provide employment. These 'win-win' solutions will form part of the answer not only for nature conservation, but also for our own long-term survivability.

THE FUTURE FOR THE SOUTH DOWNS
A PERSONAL VIEW

My own view for the future of the South Downs is essentially optimistic! I hope that in the future we will have broken the link between economic growth and environmental decay. Win-win solutions across social, economic and environmental objectives will be the norm rather than the exception. As a result the Downs will be sustainably managed in an environmentally sympathetic way. Chalk grassland, woodlands, heathland, wetlands and meadows will be ecologically rich and will have expanded considerably, and they will be linked and merged in such diverse ways that boundaries between them will be difficult to draw. Farming, forestry, commercial and business sectors will value the local far above the global, emphasizing a local economy in partnership with local social and environmental responsibility. These should be the main aims for National Park management, so far as habitats are concerned.

The 'driver' in this direction is likely to be escalating costs of energy and transport. As demand for oil outstrips supply (maybe in as little as 10 to 20 years), cheap transport will come to an end. There will be modern alternatives, but these will not be direct replacements for oil. Transport will be more difficult, more expensive and hence local economies will be favoured. If planned intelligently this could deliver a local economy that supplies all our needs and which is environmentally sustainable. Handled well, this could be excellent news for the South Downs. Handled badly, however, by attempting to reproduce the failures of the past, it will leave a greatly impoverished area.

REFERENCES

Edwards, M. and Hodge, P. (1993) *An entomological survey of the remaining heathlands of West Sussex 1991-92.* West Sussex County Council, Chichester.

English Nature (1999) *Natural Areas in London and the South East Region.* English Nature, Peterborough.

Greenaway, F., Hill, D. and Fitzsimons, P. (2001) *Bats of Ebernoe Common.* A survey commissioned by the Sussex Wildlife Trust, Henfield.

Hoskins, W.G. (1967) *Fieldwork in Local History.* Faber, London.

Pollard, E., Hooper, M.D. and Moore, N.W. (1974) *Hedges.* New Naturalist Series 58. Collins, London.

Rodwell, J. S. (ed) (1991) *British Plant Communities*, vol. 1. *Woodlands and scrub.* Cambridge University Press, Cambridge.

Rose, F. (1995) *The Habitats and Vegetation of Sussex.* Booth Museum of Natural History, Brighton.

Rose, F. (1992) *Report on the remaining heathlands of West Sussex 1991–92.* West Sussex Heathland Forum, Chichester.

Further reading

Brewis, A., Bowman, P. and Rose, F. (1996). *The Flora of Hampshire.* Harley Books, Colchester.

Sussex Wildlife Trust (1996) *A Vision for the Wildlife of Sussex.* SWT, Henfield.

KINGLY VALE.

Plate 92
Ebernoe Common, West Sussex; woodland pasture, which is an internationally important habitat for bats.
Photo: SWT.

Plate 93 *(below right)*
Cross-leaved heath (*Erica tetralix*), characteristic of humid and wet-heaths.
Photo: Mike Read.

Plate 95 *(below left)*
The River Arun flooding; the annual cycle of flooding in winter and marshy conditions in summer create wetlands of national importance to wildlife.
Photo: Julian Gray, courtesy of SDJC.

Plate 94 *(above)*
Adderstongue fern (*Ophioglossum vulgatum*), typical of damp, neutral grassland.
Photo: Mike Read.

Plate 96 *(left)*
Restored sheepwalk at Harting Down, West Sussex, looking north, with buttercup, crosswort, bird's foot trefoil and plantain flourishing.
Photo: Patrick Leonard.

Plate 97 *(top)*
East Meon village, Hampshire; visibly linked to the landscape and purposefully sited.
Photo: SDJC.

Plate 98 *(centre left)*
Newly-built affordable housing at Rodmell, East Sussex.
Photo: Martin Small, courtesy of SDJC.

Plate 99 *(centre)*
The new Westmeston village hall, East Sussex. Well-equipped centres such as this provide important facilities for the inhabitants of country villages, and a focal point for the local community.
Photo: Martin Small, courtesy of SDJC.

Plate 100 *(centre right)*
Downland pubs are very popular, thereby encouraging local employment; with increasing mobility people now enjoy the traditional Sunday lunch away from home or by picnicking outside, as here at East Dean, East Sussex, August 1983.
Photo Phil Belden.

Plate 101 *(above left)*
With the continuing interest in riding horses on the Downs, the demand for a farrier's services is strong.
Photo: Martin Small, courtesy of SDJC.

Plate 102 *(above centre left)*
Thatching for cottages in the South Downs is still in demand, although the thatching reeds often originate from outside the area.
Photo: Peter Greenhalf, courtesy of Natural England/SDJC.

Plate 103 *(above centre right)*
Firle village stores, East Sussex; vital to the local community, but such shops are continually under threat of closure due to lack of custom or competition from superstores in larger towns.
Photo: Peter Greenhalf, courtesy of Natural England/SDJC.

Plate 104 *(above right)*
The launch of 'bus walks', to encourage urban dwellers to explore the Downs in a controlled way, Stanmer Park, Brighton, July 1997.
Photo: Phil Belden, courtesy of SDJC.

Commentary on Part 1

Setting the context for the book as a whole, the five chapters in Part 1 suggest that an absolutely critical stage has been reached in the story of the Downs from antiquity to the foreseeable future. The effect of millions of years of rock formation and ecological development and some thousands of years of human settlement has created a landscape of chalk downs and sandy weald that is treasured by residents and visitors alike. Chapter I reveals that, with changing tastes, this has not always been so, but it is by now a landscape lovingly depicted by writers and artists and widely recorded in environmental and archaeological studies. Nevertheless, the pressures of modern life are threatening it with serious damage.

Undoubtedly this landscape is a national heritage in terms of the resources described in all these chapters. As shown in Chapters 2, 3 , 4 and 5, its character is infinitely varied. It has remarkably distinct localities: open chalk down and scarp, woodland and sheltered fields (especially in the Western Weald), river valleys, coastal cliffs and estuaries, small towns and villages still with a natural setting and traditional buildings, quiet lanes, and the huge variety of historic features. These combine to make a recognizable whole, a region of southern England that is valued for its outstanding beauty, a living, working and recreational countryside, worthy of conservation for its own sake.

The South Downs need an assured, sustainable future, but unfortunately there are many issues that detract from its qualities. The main ones arising from these chapters are the loss of valuable landscape, cultural heritage and habitats: downland, heathlands, wetlands, neutral grassland; and the damage done to landscape and its tranquility by insensitive road construction, by past mineral working, and by unsuitable building design. It is a landscape at risk from threats that society is well aware of and is acting to mitigate, but its conservation urgently needs strengthened policy and financial measures.

Looking ahead, one can elicit from these chapters a series of inter-related themes, aesthetic, cultural and environmental that could give the Downs a sustainable future. These are:

- A need to re-create as far as possible the lost characteristics that contributed so much to the attraction of the area, in particular the soft, springy carpet of chalk downland, and the variety of its wildlife;

- Measures to stop the further loss of geological and archaeological sites;

- Positive action to create and extend habitats at a landscape scale;

- Underlying each of these priorities, there is a need for 'joined-up' policy-making and implementation by public authorities in conjunction with local interests and communities. Examples include:

- Environmental projects such as the linking of habitats to achieve greater biodiversity through the creation of 'corridors' of ecologically rich countryside, in which nature reserves act as nodal points. This is a process that also brings benefits to local economies through employment, improved services and through income generated from wildlife-based recreation and tourism;

- Equally, strengthened campaigns in schools and visitor centres to interpret historic heritage, bringing benefit to the local economy through tourism and recreation, and encouraging more widespread preservation of geological, archaeological and historic features and their settings, in which voluntary effort can play an important part.

These are but instances of the many ways in which policy and community action could complement each other to resolve the issues mentioned above. Chapter 14 will develop themes of this kind further, along with those emerging from Parts 2 and 3 of the book. Collectively, they will indicate the leadership and resources required from a National Park Authority for the South Downs, or an alternative organization based on an area-wide South Downs Conservation Board.

From HARTING HILL. W. Kemp.

PART 2

Issues

Introduction to Part 2

Part 1 of this book traces the history of the landscape we see and love today in the South Downs, its beauty, geological structure, archaeological heritage, and the human influences that have shaped it up to the present day. There is long-standing concern about what is happening to it: the loss of traditional downland, other valuable landscape types, historic sites and the damage caused to habitats.

Part 2 now examines some important issues more closely. In Chapter 6, Trevor Cherrett recounts briefly the development of the local economy and its current problems, and pinpoints the kind of research and action required of all authorities and agencies in the area to sustain mixed communities of all ages, incomes and occupations, in a way that respects their landscape setting. In Chapter 7, Patrick Leonard describes in notable detail the changing role of agriculture in the twentieth century and its severe consequences for the landscape and local economy. He analyses the policies responsible for this, and takes a realistic view, supported by a case study, of how agricultural support and farmers themselves might work towards a re-balancing of land use. Forests and woodlands are also major land uses in the area, and in Chapter 8 Donald Macdonald vividly demonstrates, again from a case study, the role of the woodland owner in conserving landscape and habitats and providing an input to the local economy. Water is an issue of increasing importance, and Jason Lavender tackles, in Chapter 9, the controversial problem of how to improve quantity and quality by a programme of river restoration. Although he has necessarily to approach the subject in a largely conceptual way, for reasons clearly explained in the chapter, his message is a very important one, both for professionals and the general public. In Chapter 10, Paul Millmore examines the rapidly growing popularity of the South Downs as an area for quiet (and not so quiet) recreation within easy reach of London and the South East's urban areas, and the resulting pressures on the environment. Using a wealth of recreational data, supplemented by two case studies, he comments upon the problems and opportunities of providing access for young, old or disabled, to enjoy the area's history, its sense of space, its views, path networks, coast and wildlife. He lists the challenges facing a National Park Authority to achieve this. The final issue dealt with in this part of the book is the impact of built development on the landscape. Martin Small gives in Chapter 11 an historical perspective of the role of planning in its efforts to protect the Downs from damaging development. In the context of unrelenting pressure for development, he looks into likely future trends and the need for the highest standards of planning by a future National Park Authority in its efforts to obtain sustainable development.

East Dean   JEvans

CHAPTER 6
The South Downs Economy and Society

TREVOR CHERRETT

Earlier chapters describe the South Downs as one of England's most distinctive, even iconic, landscapes. The area is often represented as the emblem of Englishness, or even Britishness, 'what we fought the war for' (Plate 5). Yet while its topography has been formed over millions of years of natural processes, much of what we now see when we look at the South Downs has of course been created by human activity and settlement. This chapter briefly traces this human activity and how it relates to the landscape, both in the past and today. It then explores how the new rural economy and society of the twenty-first century can be sustained in ways which respect the special quality and distinctiveness of this precious countryside.

Early settlement on the South Downs

The South Downs have been occupied by human beings since the hunter-gatherers of the Stone Age period, some half a million years ago. In many ways the Downs themselves became the 'location of choice' for early man, who preferred the drier terrain of the chalk over the wetter clays of the Weald and the river valleys. This location of choice extended right through the Bronze and Iron Ages.

The Romans continued the pattern of settlement (Rudling, 1999), the majority of sites being associated with farming, growing cereals and keeping sheep on the Downs and cattle on lower lands. But they also introduced new patterns of administration and communications which were to make a long-lasting impact on life in the South Downs. These include the creation of the Roman Province of Britannia,

with client kingdoms and regional tribal units. Much of Sussex, especially the area south of the Weald, and part of south-eastern Hampshire, formed the *civitas* of the Regni, with its capital at Chichester, the only town in the territory. Most famously of all, the Romans built roads, primarily for military purposes but also for trade: for example, to serve the burgeoning iron-ore industry of the Weald, and the development of regional routes linking the Downs to London and Winchester, with a main east–west route along the Greensand Way immediately north of the Downs. Sea and river transport were also becoming more important. Already we are beginning to see the shape of a modern map of the South Downs within its region.

The Saxons continued to develop a network of large estates, settlements and markets, supported by fortifications, the church, and a tax system based on Rapes and Hundreds; while the Normans consolidated the estates with new baronies, towns and castles, overseeing a pastoral economy in the Downs. Links to London as the Royal Capital became increasingly important.

And so by the Middle Ages the foundations of the economy and society of the South Downs were in place: prosperous cereal and sheep farming on the coast, downs and northern scarp-face; large estates with feudal powers over many parishes, supported by the Church; market towns, often situated in the gaps within the Downs; and important north–south routes through those gaps to the coastal ports and London. The template had been laid down for the South Downs to form part of the dominant coastal fringe in the economic and political development of the South East, characterized by the large estate, the strip parish, and the Church (Adams, 1999; Gardiner, 1999; Bleach & Gardiner, 1999).

This growth and development of the South Downs economy was not all one-way, however. As shown in Chapter 4, the Black Death of 1348–49, together with coastal erosion, agricultural misfortunes, the creation of new parks, as well as the Enclosures of the seventeenth and eighteenth centuries, led to population-loss and the abandonment of over 100 settlements in Sussex alone, many of them in the Downs. This is a salutary reminder that the relative decline of rural population characteristic of the nineteenth century had already begun in medieval times.

The Victorian South Downs

Nevertheless, the agricultural economy of the South Downs continued to prosper through a mixture of cereal-growing and sheep-rearing. By 1840 Southdown sheep had achieved international repute, and provided cheap meat and wool for the growing industrial towns. This land-based economy was serviced by agricultural labourers housed in the small towns and villages associated with the chalk. Many of these were the 'closed' villages of large estates, characterized by strong communities of occupation controlled by the twin institutions of manor and church. Traditions of deference and paternalism were characteristic, with the community dominated socially, economically and culturally by large landowners:

Populations were kept low to keep the poor rates down, in-migration was discouraged except for the necessary seasonal harvesting migrations, the larger tenanted farms were commercialised, the minimum amount of housing was provided by the estate, and a conservative landowner might control jobs and housing and exert a hegemonic control of the parish vestry and church (Short, 1999a).

It is perhaps unsurprising that the rural population was not always characterized by harmony and well-being. Civil War, religious strife, the plague, and enclosure had served to limit the growth of downland agricultural communities in the sixteenth and seventeenth centuries, while the operation of the Poor Law caused great suffering and bitterness in the eighteenth century. By the early nineteenth century, agricultural depression, the Corn Laws, demobilization, and mechanization led to widespread rioting and arson in the 1830s. Imprisonment, transportation and executions followed. Although there were some improvements in pay, and trade unionism increased generally, such changes were not reflected very strongly in the working conditions and

society of the South Downs. Emigration increased: as many as 1800 individuals being 'encouraged to leave' Lord Egremont's lands and other parishes in western Sussex in the 1830s (Short, 1999b).

Thus although by the nineteenth century the national and regional populations were growing faster than at any other time before or since, the growth was concentrated in urban areas. 'The period 1801–1851 was a period of spectacular urban growth at the coast, more selected and muted growth inland, and *low growth or losses of population in many downland parishes* [my italics]. Rural under-employment and the pull of the towns was now beginning to be felt, accelerating in the last decade of the period when the railways came to exert their influence more widely' (Short, 1999b).

If the South Downs did not share in this Victorian growth of population and industry, however, as pointed out in Chapter 1, they did provide a powerful allure for recreation and retreat, a 'rural arcadia' which emerged as a reaction to the ugliness, dirt and squalor of the industrial revolution. Thus 'the London middle classes annexed much of the countryside of the South East within reasonable reach of London termini as a playground, sanatorium, health resort, field laboratory and open-air studio all thrown into one' (Brandon & Short, 1990). The South Downs were a particular focus for this escape and retreat, reflecting Raymond Williams's notion of 'an almost inverse relationship between the decline of farmscape as a working environment and its cultural importance as a source of rural ideology for urban needs' (Brandon & Short, 1990).

Indeed many South Down villages still portray the visual integrity and charm which springs from their purposeful siting – sheltered, close to sources of water, accessible to downland and meadow – and the use of local materials. They appear to fit into the landscape, to be a part of it. There is a wholeness to the scene (see Plate 97).

By the end of the nineteenth century the outstanding characteristics of the economy, society and culture of the South Downs had therefore emerged: a relatively prosperous agricultural regime dominated largely by landowners and tenant farmers but with a dwindling agricultural workforce living in static or declining villages; massive population growth to the north in London and its suburbs, and the new coastal towns to the south in the Downs and Western Weald; slower-growing market towns inland with important service, administrative and communication functions. Above all, the South Downs had a new role as a park, playground and retreat for the burgeoning urban populations nearby.

The South Downs in the 20th Century

These trends continued into the twentieth century. Its first half was characterized by agricultural

Table 6a Parishes in the South Downs lacking key village services
(percentage % compared with county and national averages).

Village service	Sussex Downs AONB	East Sussex	West Sussex	Hampshire	East Hampshire AONB	England
Permanent Shop	46	15	29	28.6	42.5	39
Post Office	52	26	37	36	50	40
Pub	22	7	10			26
Pre-school	62	32	34			60
Primary School	63	35	38			51
GP (resident or visiting)	71	46	48	67.2	52.5	84
Pharmacy/Prescription	76	51	54	100	100	64
Village Hall/ community centre	25	9	19	7	15	29
Sports Field	38	23	30			51
Bus Service (6 days per week)	46	78	62	56.5	22.5	63
Community Transport	63	75	62			73
Police	89	74	76			89

Sources: Rural Development Commission, *Village Services Survey*, 1991, and *Disadvantage in Rural Hampshire*, 1998.

depression and continued population decline (shared with other areas and prompting the establishment of the national Development Commission in 1909); and by economic difficulties for many estates, especially after the First World War; but also by increased recreation and retreat at all levels, from bicycling and walking groups to the country houses of the Bloomsbury set.

After the Second World War, as shown in Chapter 7, state intervention on an unprecedented scale saw the creation of a subsidized agricultural regime which brought prosperity back to farmers through greater mechanization and more productive methods. National standards in health, education and utilities raised considerably the living standards of rural communities, especially the more 'countrified' settlements of old. Furthermore a statutory planning system was introduced which on the one hand exempted most farming operations from control, but on the other protected the countryside from urban intrusion and sprawl (see Chapter 1). But alongside this progress there was a rapid and continued decline of the agricultural workforce.

From the late 1950s onwards, urban prosperity and the motor car opened up the countryside in general, and the South Downs in particular, to people wishing to live in these newly serviced villages, whether to commute to work, or to retire in a beautiful country setting. Similarly, access to the South Downs for recreation was opened up on a huge scale. Meanwhile the land-based workforce was declining even more rapidly, so that by 1991 there were, for example, only 142 residents employed in agriculture in the Sussex Downs AONB, less than 13 per cent of the total workforce, a 25 per cent reduction since 1981. From the 1960s onwards a substantial population exchange was in full swing, as local farm-workers' cottages were bought by more affluent incomers.

By the second half of the twentieth century, most people living in the South Downs were no longer directly connected with the land. A study, undertaken in 1994 by the former Sussex Rural Community Council (now Action in rural Sussex) (1993) for the Sussex Downs Conservation Board, showed that between 1981 and 1991 most growth in employment was in banking and finance (up 54%), construction (20%) and public administration (15%). Also relatively more people, especially women, were coming to the labour market.

This study highlighted other changes too, as indeed did a study done for Community Action Hampshire, in 1998 (see Table 6a) (Milbourne *et al.*, 1998). In the Sussex Downs AONB, the proportion of parishes lacking basic village services such as shops, post-offices, schools and health care was generally higher than in the two counties (but often closer to the national average). For example, around 50 per cent of them lacked a shop or post office, and one quarter had no village hall. This poor provision partly reflects the smaller size of downland parish, but also high car-ownership and communal transport enabling people to travel to larger villages and towns for service needs. Broadly similar figures for the East Hampshire AONB, though varying in some respects due, no doubt, to time and geographical differences, were revealed by the Hampshire study. In the Downs, only 14 per cent of households were without a car in 1991, down from 20 per cent in 1981. Meanwhile two-car ownership rose from 26 to 34 per cent. Again, there were broadly similar figures for East Hampshire.

At the same time age structure was changing rapidly. Figures for the Sussex AONB indicate there were proportional increases in the working-age bracket 16–64 that were lower than in the rest of the county (a 4.7% increase between 1981 and 1991 compared with around 11%), but a 52 per cent increase in the over 85s in the AONB. Clearly, this

Table 6b Car ownership by households, 1981–1991 and 1998 (per cent)

	Sussex Downs AONB 1981	East Sussex 1981	West Sussex 1981	Hampshire
No Car	20.3	35.7	29.7	
One Car	48.3	46.8	49.5	
Two Cars	25.7	14.7	17.5	
Three + Cars	5.7	2.7	3.2	

	Sussex Downs AONB 1991	East Sussex 1991	West Sussex 1991	Hampshire 1998
No Car	14.5	28.3	23.7	13.2
One Car	42.5	45.2	45.9	41.2
Two + cars	42.9	26.4	30.5	

Source: *Rural Community Needs*, Sussex Rural Community Council, November 1993, and *Disadvantage in Rural Hampshire*, 1998.

places potentially higher burdens on local health and transport services. On the other hand, migration was much lower into the AONB than to other rural areas, as Table 6c illustrates.

Lack of affordable housing had also become a serious problem. Surveys carried out in 16 parishes in the early 1990s showed substantial levels of housing need, with limited opportunities to meet them due to a shortage of suitable sites, tight planning restrictions, the sale of council houses, and in some cases local opposition (Sussex Rural Community Council, Centre for Rural Development, various dates).

The 1994 report concluded that the Sussex Downs were experiencing many of the problems faced by English rural communities in general, but often in a more acute way. Key trends were a rapid decline in land-based employment, a low level of village services and a severe shortage of affordable housing. In Hampshire the same conclusions applied; indeed, of the 10 most deprived parishes in Hampshire four were within the East Hampshire AONB, lacking at least five essential services.

The South Downs communities today

It is clear that the rural economy and society of the South Downs has changed almost beyond recognition during the last 100 years. It has gone from a predominantly land-based economy served by workers from small towns and villages, to a mix of local land-based employment, service trades, commuters to well-paid jobs in urban areas, and the retired. The contrast between this new potpourri of

incomes, classes and occupations and the former communities of common occupation is striking. Yet the physical settlements in which they live are familiar. The villages remain visibly linked to the landscape in siting and form, but their functional relationships are more opaque and complex (Plate 97).

Such changes are typical of rural England, although the rate of decline in agricultural employment has been faster in the South Downs because of a higher initial base-level. Overall they reflect the profound changes which have been going on in the rural economy, especially in south-east England where there is a huge market for tourism and services of all kinds. A recent research study undertaken by Oxford Brookes University (Piper *et al.*, 2005) for the two South Downs AONB authorities throws much interesting light on this new rural economy. Key findings are shown below:

- A 5.3% growth in population between 1991 and 2001, similar to the south-east region, lower than rural England (6%); with higher rates in Hampshire (7%) and lower in East Sussex (3.6%);
- Household income levels are 7% above the south-east average and 26% above the English average;
- Over half of the South Downs wards are ranked in the worst 20% nationally for access to services; 15% households do not own a car;
- The employment structure is similar to the rest of the rural South East, but different from existing National Parks, viz: only 4.7% in agriculture (9% in National Parks); over 20%

Table 6c Migration to rural Sussex, 1991

East Sussex (whole)	East Sussex (Rural)	East Sussex (Sussex Downs AONB)
23,455 (100%)	4930 (21%)	312 (1.3%)

West Sussex (whole)	West Sussex (Rural)	West Sussex (Sussex Downs AONB)
25,073 (100%)	10,223 (40.8%)	1,464 (5.8%)

Source: *Rural Community Needs*, Sussex Rural Community Council, November 1993.

in financial and business services (11.9% in National Parks); less than 5% in hotels and catering (11.7% in National Parks);

- There are high levels of self-employment (24%), and low unemployment at 2.7% (3.3 % in East Sussex);
- Rapid job growth of 41% during 1991–2002, compared with 28% in the South East; mainly in distribution and business sectors; fastest in West Sussex, slowest in Hampshire; and more businesses per head of population than for rural England;
- More long-distance commuting – 24% of residents travel 20km or more to work (SE 19 %; rural SE 21%), with public-transport use (7.9% of residents) higher than rural England (5.7%) and National Parks (2.7%) but lower than the rural South East (8.4%);
- Average house prices £248,000 in 2002, 32% above rural South East and 70% above rural England; but second homes only 1.4% of housing stock, well below National Park average (10.5%).

This new research indicates that the economy of the South Downs has moved on again. It is not just a retreat for commuters and the retired. Rather, it is becoming more typical of the 'rural-urban' south-east economy, where recent research (Land Use Consultants, 2003) highlights the growth of financial services and distribution activities, and the spawning of new 'home-grown' enterprises linked to tourism, ICT, services, and even manufacturing, in a prestige environment. The South Downs are tentatively reasserting some of their 'dominant' characteristics in the rural power relations of the region over and above the traditional land-based role. This contrasts with the declining economies of much of the south coast, the subject of regeneration policies in the draft South East Plan (South East England Regional Assembly, 2005). The South Downs are certainly making a dynamic contribution to the South East's economic growth and change.

Along with this economic dynamism, however, go problems of housing affordability and declining village services. High car-ownership has focused the impact of this decline on those marginalized by lack of access to personal transport, heightening the social and economic distance between the affluent and the less well-off. This is characteristic of rural deprivation in the South East, a juxtaposition of extreme differences of wealth and income in many parishes rather than a geographical concentration of disadvantage, as recent research undertaken for the South East Plan by the Bartlett School of Planning illustrates (Gallent et al., 2004). This study analysed spatially a wide range of social, economic, and environmental characteristics in the region and found major clusters of the top three socio-economic

indicators alongside significant groupings of benefit claimants, access deprivation, and certain social groups effectively locked out of the housing market. These clusters of social extremes are spread across the region with large swathes in the generally more affluent western parts.

The rural communities of the South Downs have suffered vicissitudes in the past and life in the villages has, at times, been hard. But now most people are comfortably off, many extremely so, and, despite the occasional lapse of design sense, the villages have been lovingly repaired and restored. The scene is visually very attractive, the communities look prosperous and tranquil, but the changes of the twentieth century have brought new problems too. Surveys after survey over the last 20 years or so (Sussex Rural Community Council, Centre for Rural Development, various dates) have pointed to the substantial numbers of residents in the Downs who are in housing need and have little prospect of meeting that need within the open property market. The towns and villages have become too expensive for local people, and the lack of affordable housing and local employment has forced many of them to leave. This is out-migration on a scale of which we can only guess at, since their places have been taken only too quickly by more affluent incomers, drawn in by the prospect of attractive homes in 'picture-book' surroundings, whether to commute, to retire, or to set up business locally (increasingly at home).

This forced out-migration has not only been harsh on the individuals and families who wanted to live and work where they grew up, but it has also led to a narrowing of the social composition of villages with fewer young people, fewer people on lower incomes and, arguably, less 'local culture'. In other words, each has become a less-balanced community, which is now heavily dominated by the more affluent and mobile.

The Duke of Richmond, President of Action in rural Sussex, and Chairman of the Sussex Rural Housing Partnership, has a long-standing commitment to housing local people. As the family owner of the Goodwood Estate, which includes parts of five villages, he also has a wealth of experience of the changing society and economy of a part of the South Downs. In his view:

> To maintain the quality of life of the people who live in the South Downs, these places must retain a social balance as well as being living and working communities. This means, among other things, rented homes for the less well-off in every village . . . If conservation of the countryside is to be given greater priority, it has to be paid for. With agricultural subsidies and farming profits reducing, landowners and farmers will need to be given both special conservation subsidies and more opportunities to develop other forms of economic activity . . . To achieve all this will require much more flexible

planning policies related more specifically to the needs of each particular area. (Duke of Richmond, pers. comm.)

Demographic change has led in a strange way to a reversal of the polarity between the rich and poor in rural communities. Formerly there were a few rich and powerful, such as the estate-owners and some of the larger farmers and traders, but many poor and powerless, in particular the agricultural workers and other land-based employees. Now the latter are in a minority, and often 'invisible' in the local community – 'hard to reach' and no longer at the heart of the life of the community. Whilst migrant workers and travellers may be more visible on the land, they are even more regarded as 'outsiders'. Social exclusion is just as significant an issue for many rural communities as it is for urban ones, even if its scale and nature is very different. Although we can rightly claim to have eliminated most of the grinding poverty associated with the 'rogues, vagabonds, and sturdy beggars' of previous centuries, the gap between rich and poor remains, such that a comparison can be made between the forced emigrations of the early nineteenth century and the pricing of local people out of the rural housing market today.

The steady diminution of local services has also contributed to the diminution of rural life. Partly because of the greater proportion of smaller parishes (with populations of less than 500) in the Downs, the percentage of parishes without shops, post-offices, pubs, schools, health-facilities, and community-facilities has been much higher than in the surrounding rural counties (Table 6a). Only church or chapel and transport facilities declined less rapidly.

Today the picture can be presented in terms of the percentages of rural households within given distances to key services, compared with regional and national figures – see Table 6d below. Once again, access to rural services is lower than in the surrounding region and country, although comparisons with earlier years (2000–2003) show

that there has been no decrease in the South Downs, and thus the situation is holding more steadily than elsewhere generally (Countryside Agency, 2002–2004).

Conversely car-ownership has been rising steadily so that the number of households not owning a car has declined, as mentioned above, to 15 per cent in the South Downs in 2004, compared with 20 per cent in 1981 (for the Sussex Downs). Although these high levels of access to the private vehicle have provided individual freedom of mobility for rural residents, freedom has come at a price: the further demise of local shops and services in competition with the supermarket, and increased danger and noise from traffic through villages and along narrow country lanes.

The organization, Action in rural Sussex, has been trying to tackle these problems for decades in the whole area. Are they any worse in the South Downs? Teresa Gittins manages a wide range of social and economic programmes which have an impact on the South Downs, and her view (pers. comm) is that:

> The economic and social issues identified in local parish plans are broadly the same throughout Sussex but are much more starkly defined within the South Downs. Issues such as local jobs, traffic, car parking and affordable homes are often harder to address because of the priority given to conserving environmental and landscape quality. The challenge for the communities in the South Downs is to manage change and retain community vitality within the necessary controls that emanate from AONB status.

Planning for the future: coping with rural change

Gittins's view confirms the fears of many that because the South Downs enjoys AONB status, planning controls are tighter, and if a National Park is approved, it may to be difficult to get permission for new housing schemes or employment sites. In fact, AONBs and National Parks have the same

Table 6d Percentage of rural households at set distances from individual key services, 2003

Key Service (distances to service in kilometres)	South Downs AONBs %	South East %	England %	South Downs worse than elsewhere? %
Banks & Building Societies (4)	76.0	79.6	76.0	Yes (SE)
Cashpoints (4)	89.0	91.9	90.0	Yes
Post Offices (2)	87.5	90.2	91.0	Yes
Supermarkets (4)	78.0	78.4	78.0	No
Petrol Stations (4)	94.0	94.6	93.0	No
Primary Schools (2)	88.0	92.4	91.0	Yes
Secondary Schools (4)	76.0	76.2	76.0	No
GP Surgeries (4)	84.0	89.2	86.0	Yes
Job Centres (8)	71.0		71.0	No
Libraries (4)	74.5		80.0	Yes

Source: Centre for Rural Development, Action in rural Sussex, 2003

status in terms of planning policy, but in either case there is a fear that existing settlement forms, and the activities associated with them, are 'preserved in aspic'. The village can no longer change and adapt organically in response to a changing society. It is effectively type-cast in its role as an attractive environment for affluent residents and visitors to enjoy, a role that may appeal to many, but risks the fate of rural communities becoming living museums rather than 'vital villages' (see Plates 98 to 103).

This issue lies at the heart of perceptions concerning the future role of the countryside in general and rural communities in particular. Such a debate has been difficult to pursue with any coherence because of very different understandings of the term 'rural', which in turn are linked to different economic, social and cultural imperatives. For example, there is the 'rural-traditionalist' view that the countryside represents a very different and distinctive way of life, misunderstood by 'townies' who make policies on the basis of broad principles but without regard to rural traditions. The fox-hunting debate was often conducted on those terms, which has served to over-simplify the town–country divide and obscure many of the wider arguments. Equally, in the conservationists' view it is necessary to preserve the countryside 'for its own sake' and resist the spread of concrete and tarmac. On the other hand, urban dwellers may often see the countryside as mainly a place for recreation and retreat, whether for retiring, commuting, or visiting. But for some people living in the countryside, however, 'rural' means poor access to housing, jobs and services.

In truth, rurality means all these things. How can we make sense of these conflicting perceptions and priorities in the context of the special landscape of the South Downs and the region in which it is located?

A starting-point might be to recognize the geographic, economic and social position of the South Downs within the rural South East. What stands out is its juxtaposition to large urban populations on the coast, inland and, above all, with the metropolis of London in the background. One has only to think for a moment on what the South Downs might be like if London was not where it is, in order to understand the importance of the area's linkages with a wider, heavily urbanized and dynamically prosperous region. First, the value of the South Downs as a relief and retreat from town and city is at a premium (although one must not forget that there are many other rural parts of the region which also serve this purpose, for example, the North Downs, the High Weald, parts of the coast). Second, the economy and society of the South Downs are closely connected to the surrounding sub-regional economies by providing homes for some of its commuting (and retiring) workforce, and by establishing new businesses,

including tourism, new field-sports opportunities (e.g. game management), high-tech services, and home-based enterprises as it diversifies (Land Use Consultants, 2003). Crucially the South Downs, like the rest of the rural South East, has to be seen as part of the wider regional economy, and the linkages and inter-communications which go with that.

Given this geographical and economic context, what future can be envisaged for the economy and society of the South Downs? The Countryside Agency's draft Rural Vision for the South East (2005) attempted to define what we mean by sustainable rural economies, communities, environments and natural resources: a countryside that is environmentally healthy, economically more successful, and socially stronger. This stated vision is helpful, positive and integrated, but necessarily very generalized. What would it mean in terms of practical policies and decisions? In the preparation of the draft South East Plan, the South East England Regional Assembly (SEERA) Rural Advisory Group identified four strategic options for rural policy and their consequences, summarized below.

Option 1 'Carry On As Usual'; describes new development concentrated in larger villages and market towns with a fuller range of services; smaller villages limited to minor infilling and 'exceptions' housing schemes. Diversification of the rural economy subject to tight planning controls. Continued reliance on private cars, with limited investment in public transport. Strong protection in AONBs, together with a general presumption against development in the countryside. Departures from policy made as necessary in response to particular local circumstances, and changes in national polices. (This approach is typical of Regional and Local Development Plans.)

Advantages of this option include familiarity for existing institutions and decision-makers, but also some flexibility; a proven track record for protecting the countryside from 'megalopolis', although some might argue that the planning system has been less than wholly successful in preventing unwarranted development in the South Downs.

Disadvantages include a weak understanding of the changing rural economy, its needs and potential; a weak understanding of the role of rural settlements and dispersed travel patterns, and over-reliance on 'lines on maps', rather than assessing appropriateness; fails properly to tackle rural disadvantage, social exclusion and the need for affordable housing.

Option 2 'Follow the Market': exhibits a greater degree of confidence in the role of the market economy in making spatial decisions, leading to more exclusive housing developments in the countryside, both in villages and outside. Proliferation of rural diversification, limited only by the most essential regulations. New factories and offices in rural campus-sites close to main roads. Almost total reliance on road transport. Continued protection of designated landscapes where locally supported by influential residents. Many would argue that this approach has been adopted by the Government in its current aim to make the planning system more responsive to market demand (see The Government's Response (ARHC, 2006) to Kate Barker's Review of Housing Supply, HM Treasury & ODPM, 2004).

Advantages include freer housing markets enabling more people to live in the countryside; wider economic opportunities for business in the countryside; and a more varied and dynamic countryside.

Disadvantages include greater social divisions within villages; more traffic creating danger, pollution and congestion; loss of countryside character.

Option 3 'Protect and Preserve': sets out a distinct policy seeking to protect the countryside, not least because of economic pressures. Only limited development in rural settlements to meet 'local needs'. Tight controls on economic developments, limited opportunities for diversification. Constraints on road transport. Very strong protective policies in AONBs, with general presumptions against any development in the countryside. Very few departures from policy. (This approach is typical of National Park and AONB plans.)

Advantages include strong protection of settlement forms; reduced traffic congestion, pollution and danger; strong protection of the countryside and landscapes (assuming resources are available to pay for this).

Disadvantages include very limited housing for local people; decline of population, employment and services in villages; limited opportunities for the economy to diversify.

Option 4 'Link and Sustain': recognizes the links between the rural and urban parts of the region and seeks to integrate the two whilst enhancing rural functions and character. It incorporates:

- Mixed housing development for rural communities, but strong design requirements;
- Recognition of the complex functions of rural settlements and a rejection of standard 'one size fits all' development polices;
- Encouragement for sustainable economic diversification;
- Careful assessment of new economic development, such as sustainable tourism and recreation;

- Promotion of effective commercial and community-based rural transport schemes, strongly linked to regional networks;
- Conservation of the countryside based on assessments of the impact of proposed developments.

Advantages of this approach are that it allows rural communities to grow and change according to needs; supports a changing rural economy; integrates rural areas with urban, especially through more effective transport; allows landscape to reflect changes in the economy and society, sustaining and enhancing its character.

Disadvantages are concerned with how effectively it could be implemented, relying heavily on local communities; better interpretations of sustainability by sophisticated technical assessments.

At first sight, Options 1 and 3 might seem more appropriate for the South Downs as a prospective National Park. However, although conservation of the landscape would be the policy priority for this – and indeed of the existing AONB – the changing needs of its rural economy and communities deserve greater recognition and understanding, not least because they have a direct impact on the landscape. This is as true for the South Downs as it is for the rest of the rural South East. In my view there is a need to think more deeply about the relationship between the new rural economy and communities of the South Downs and the landscape, and the meaning of a sustainable rural economy, community and environment. Option 4 attempts to do this by exploring the links between them, and reaching a better understanding of sustainability. The rest of this chapter explores what this might mean in terms of practical policies and actions in a potential National Park.

Policy implications

If the 'Link and Sustain' approach described in Option 4 is preferred, a number of policy challenges arise in the quest for sustainable economies and communities.

- Taking the **economy** first; what will be the likely future impact of EU policy and international trade on agriculture in the South Downs, and on landscapes, habitats, and bio-diversity? What land-based industries will be able, profitably, to sustain their activities? How can local products and markets be stimulated and sustained? What development will there be in the local economies of tourism, services, home-based working, etc? What will be needed for their links to the wider regional economy, for improved support by way of training, business advice, broadband, etc? It is essential that there should be more research such as the South Downs Rural Economy Study by Oxford Brookes University (Piper *et al.*, 2005) to help point the way to a more sustainable local economy.

- Linked to this issue is the question of the *future of the landscape*. To what extent should land-based industries be steered in certain directions, for example to create more wilderness areas, more woodlands, or other special habitats? How can the needs and priorities of local people and visitors be assessed and reconciled? Essential here is the need for these questions to be considered by local communities and the wider public as well as policy-makers and land-managers. One way of addressing them could be through Parish Plans and Local Community Strategies (see below).

- Turning now to the *future of rural communities*, the challenges are equally tough. Organizations such as Rural Community Councils (RCCs) have a great deal of experience in tackling these problems, but a 'step change' is needed in delivering solutions. What is the future for affordable housing, perhaps the most urgent provision of all? Action for affordable housing needs better and quicker methods of implementation as the recent report of the Government's Affordable Rural Housing Commission (ARHO, 2006) made clear. The 'exceptions' policy works by releasing sites which would not normally be approved for housing, and which are therefore much cheaper and can effectively subsidize the total costs of new housing-association schemes. But it relies on landowners coming forward with appropriate sites, is slow and time-consuming to operate, and can be easily thwarted by local resistance, by planning constraints, or by lack of funding. Delivery through agreements with developers has proved fraught with difficulties too, and is perhaps more likely to work in larger villages and towns (Centre for Rural Development, 2004). The Government's revised Planning Policy Statement 3 of 2005 advocates a more proactive approach by allocating sites for affordable housing in or close to villages. Is there a risk that this will raise the 'hope value' for such sites beyond the limits of affordability? In any case the exceptions policy is probably more appropriate for areas such as AONBs or National Parks, where normal housing allocations are likely to be very limited, and where tight village boundaries are drawn. Currently, some villages have embarked on such schemes and

even more are likely to follow suit in the years to come. The involvement of the local community is essential for success and help is available from RCCs and others to work in close partnership with housing officials, planners, and housing associations (Centre for Rural Development, 2004), in particular through the independent rural-housing enablers (Plates 98 and 99).

- *Transport* is another activity which needs a step-change in provision. How can one move beyond the level of inflexible and infrequent bus services, even where complemented by excellent, but limited, community transport-schemes? As with housing, the latter are difficult and time-consuming to establish; finding volunteer drivers has become a problem, and running costs are difficult to cover. A more flexible, demand-led, sustainable community transport system is needed which links regional networks and is attractive to a wider public – commuters, shoppers, entertainment trips as well as those without access to personal vehicles. Can systems such as the Cango buses in Hampshire and the kind of experiments being undertaken with modest fee-paying 'community taxis' meet these requirements? In the South Downs such systems might also be linked to the much greater potential of the tourist market. Current experiments include Tourism Without Traffic (Sussex Downs AONB, ongoing), which aims to develop new opportunities for sustainable tourism in ways to reduce the impact of recreational traffic, whilst supporting the local economy (Plate 104).

- *Community facilities* are crucial to village life, and it was shown above that South Downs villages suffer from limited provision, especially of shops, post offices, primary schools and GP doctors (Plate 103). Clearly there is a real need to 'rural-proof' current policies in these areas to ensure that towns and villages in the South Downs get their fair share of the cake. Can Parish Plans and Local Community Strategies offer new ways of achieving this?

- *Social inclusion* is another important but much neglected issue. The influx of affluent incomers to attractive Downland villages tends to obscure the problems of the less well-off, who become more marginalized within individual communities. As also shown above, disadvantage is 'pepper-potted' about the rural region, polarizing affluence and poverty within individual villages (Gallent *et al.*, 2004). The low level of service access indicated in Table 6a makes life especially difficult for these small groups of less well-off rural residents. Is there need for a move away from designated areas of disadvantage to a more generic approach? Once again, Parish Plans and Local Community Strategies can play a part in tackling this issue.

The introduction of *Local Community Strategies* is indeed one way of successfully responding to these challenges. They are initiated by local government and charged with identifying priorities and actions. They can be informed by widely represented Local Strategic Partnerships, offering a new 'road map' towards a more integrated, prioritized approach to the service delivery. Equally, at the town or village level, Parish Plans, prepared by local councils offer a way for communities to survey their particular needs and prepare Action Plans to address them. Some 16 parishes in the South Downs have embarked on preparing Parish Plans, and the key action proposals arising from them are summarized below, giving a flavour of the issues concerning local communities (Action in rural Sussex, 2005). The most frequent action proposals are:

- Improve and maintain the local environment (e.g. recycling, litter reduction, hedge maintenance);
- Improve communications (e.g. website, newsletters, village welcome pack, better ICT access);
- Provide for youth activities (e.g. acquisition and development of land and buildings);
- Traffic calming and speed restrictions;
- Participation in community life (e.g. parish council membership, volunteer activities);
- Improving public transport (especially buses);
- Supporting the local economy (e.g. agricultural diversification, local businesses);
- Encouraging the enjoyment and understanding of the local environment (e.g. local maps – Plate 105);
- Improving safety (e.g. greater police presence, community wardens, Neighbourhood Watch, pavement repairs, safe cycle routes;
- Improve car-parking facilities, working with local people;
- Discuss housing development proposals with District Council;
- Carry out a Village Design Statement;
- Promote activities at village halls and community centres (Plate 99).

There is now a considerable body of advice on how such Action Plans can feed into statutory Development Plans (i.e. the new Local Development Frameworks – see Chapter 11 in this book) and local Community Strategies through bridging processes (Countryside Agency, 2004) although the complexity of these processes does not always make

it straightforward! One of the particular problems facing the South Downs is that the area contains many local authorities with each one leading its own Community Strategy, which will make a common approach more difficult within the Downs as a whole. Thus a special effort will need to be made to compare and contrast the content and processes of different schemes, and develop best practice from such monitoring.

Conclusions

In this chapter I have tried to show how the South Downs have evolved as a 'location of choice' for early settlers; how the area developed first as a successful agricultural economy, then later also as a playground and retreat for its urban areas in the region. Within that evolution the social structure itself changed radically, from communities of land-based occupation to settlements of commuters and the retired, with a minority working on the land. Now there is further change as the agricultural economy diversifies – on and off the farm – and new economic activities spring up in rural locations, such as tourism, home working, and service trades of all kinds.

The economy and society of the Downs have indeed been transformed, yet the physical settlements themselves have for the most part been lovingly preserved, reflecting the siting imperatives and materials of previous ages. The challenge facing the South Downs, and in particular a new National Park if approved, will be how to sustain and enhance the integrity and charm of that relationship between settlement and landscape in ways which are also relevant and appropriate to its new economy and society. We need to celebrate the new as well as the old, and above all avoid relying on preservation and pastiche.

There are, nevertheless, deeper social issues which a new National Park must also face. Designating an area does not by itself change its appearance or beauty, but it does reinforce the perception of its desirability and 'specialness'. Given planning policies which will inevitably be restrictive, such designation is also likely to reinforce its exclusiveness as a place to live. Put simply, this would mean that house-prices would rise even higher and more local people would be forced away. This in turn would heighten the polarity between the well-off and the less so, with the latter surviving as a minority in danger of social exclusion. It might also put more pressure for development on surrounding areas.

A major challenge for a new National Park will be for local government within it to reduce that polarity and pressure, and to find innovative ways of sustaining the towns and villages of the South Downs as mixed communities of all ages, incomes and occupations. This will require the closest possible co-operation in research and action between the many authorities, agencies and voluntary bodies working within and adjoining the area and the National Park Authority itself. Their powers and processes are to an extent complementary to each other, and both will have regular contact with local communities through Parish Councils and the voluntary sector, and with landowners. National and local governments' rural programmes and local delivery agreements will play a critical part in supporting the kind of sustainable rural development put forward in this chapter. But throughout the various official and informal plans of these bodies there should be a common strategic theme: to sustain the new economy and society of the South Downs as living and working communities, alongside and as part of the area's role as a beautiful landscape to be enjoyed, a habitat to be conserved, and a playground and retreat for the South East and beyond.

REFERENCES

Adams, C. (1999) Medieval Administration. In: Leslie, K. and Short, B. (eds) *An Historical Atlas of Sussex*. Phillimore, Chichester. pp. 40–1.

Affordable Rural Housing Commission (ARHC) (2006) *Final Report*. TSO, London.

Barker, K. (2004) *Reviews of Housing Supply: Delivering Stability – Securing our Housing Needs*. HM Treasury and Office of the Deputy Prime Minister, London.

Bleach, J. and Gardiner, M. (1999) Medieval Markets and Ports. In: Leslie, K. and Short, B. (eds) *An Historical Atlas of Sussex*. Phillimore, Chichester. pp. 42–3.

Brandon, P. and Short, B. (1990) *The South East from AD 1000*. Longman, London.

Centre for Rural Development (various dates) *Housing Needs Surveys for Chichester, Horsham, Mid-Sussex, Lewes, and Wealden Districts*. Sussex Rural Community Council & Action in rural Sussex, Lewes.

Centre for Rural Development (2004) *Meeting Affordable Housing Needs in Rural Communities. A Good Practice Guide*. CRD, Sussex Rural Community Council, Lewes.

Countryside Agency (2000–2004) *Rural Services Surveys* and *State of the Countryside Reports*. Countryside Agency, Cheltenham.

Countryside Agency (2004) *Bridging the gap between parish and market town action plans and community strategies. A Good Practice Guide*. Countryside Agency, Cheltenham.

Countryside Agency (2005) *A Vision for the Rural South East*. Countryside Agency, Cheltenham.

Gallent, N., Greatbatch, I., Oades, R. and Bianconi, M. (2004) *Spatial Dimensions of Rural Policy in South East England*. Bartlett School of Planning, University College London.

Gardiner, M. (1999) The Medieval Rural Economy and Landscape. In: Leslie, K. and Short, B. (eds) *An Historical Atlas of Sussex*. Phillimore, Chichester. pp. 38–9.

Land Use Consultants (2003) *Planning for Sustainable Rural Economic Development*. Report for the South East England Regional Assembly, Guildford.

Milbourne, P., Cursons, J. and Clark, M. (1998) *Disadvantage in Rural Hampshire*. A report to Community Action Hampshire. Community Action Hampshire, Winchester, Hampshire County Council Social Services, Winchester, and Gloucester College of Higher Education, Cheltenham.

Piper, J., Downing, L., Chadwick, A., Crawford, J. and Glasson, J. (2005) *The Rural Economy of the South Downs*. Research study for the East Hampshire Joint Advisory Committee and the Sussex Downs Conservation Board (Findings published in *South Downs Focus*, Newsletter of the (now) South Downs Joint Committee, Ford).

Rudling, D. (1999) Roman Sussex. In: Leslie, K. and Short, B. (eds) *An Historical Atlas of Sussex*. Phillimore, Chichester. pp. 24–5.

Short, B. (1990a) Landownership in Victorian Sussex. In: Leslie, K. and Short, B. (eds) *An Historical Atlas of Sussex*. Phillimore, Chichester. p. 98.

Short, B. (1999b) Population Change 1801–1851. In: Leslie, K. and Short, B. (eds) *An Historical Atlas of Sussex*. Phillimore, Chichester. pp. 88–9.

South East England Regional Assembly (2005) *A Clear Vision for the South East: Draft South East Plan*. SEERA, Guildford.

Sussex Downs AONB Partnership Scheme (ongoing) *Tourism Without Traffic*. Project co-ordinated by the South Downs Joint Committee, Ford.

Sussex Rural Community Council (1993) *Rural Community Needs in the South Downs*. SRCC, Lewes.

Acknowledgements

I would like to thank in particular Professor Brian Short for all his advice and support during the preparation of this chapter; also Dr Peter Brandon and Professor Gerald Smart for their editorial guidance; the Duke of Richmond for his contribution; and former colleagues at Action in rural Sussex for their information and help, in particular Teresa Gittins, Ruth Goldstone, Iuean Sherwood and Fanny Peltre. However, the opinions expressed, and the shortcomings incurred, are entirely my responsibility.

T.C.

CHAPTER 7

The Role of Agriculture in the South Downs Landscape

PATRICK LEONARD

This is an account of the changing role that agriculture has played in making the landscape of the South Downs, its people and historic towns and villages. Farming has formed the basis of the economy for almost 5000 years. The origins of the corn-and-sheep farming system which created the classic Downs landscape are briefly described to set the scene. Much of that farming system was evolved in the South Downs using local methods, materials and innovations, creating a unique landscape. But different systems evolved in Hampshire and the Western Weald giving a strong local character to those landscapes too.

Farming has undergone very rapid change since World War II, driven by policies developed in London and then Brussels; these policies are briefly described and their impact on the Downs landscape assessed. This chapter describes agriculture in the South Downs as a process of change, but one farm is highlighted as a case study of continuing good practice. As the role of farming has changed, so other players have taken on roles previously undertaken by farmers. Reforms of the Common Agricultural Policy (CAP) in 2003 and 2004 are starting to be implemented and imply a further period of uncertainty ahead and yet more radical changes to farming and the landscape.

Within a generation, farming on the South Downs has moved from centre stage in the local community and economy, sustaining a distinct and characteristic landscape, to a position of exploiting and destroying landscape, shedding most of its workforce, changing the social fabric of small towns and villages and threatening wildlife and our shared cultural heritage. The chapter ends with an attempt to see how the conflicts of the last 50 years might be resolved and the landscape sustained for future generations to enjoy.

The South Downs is taken to be the area covered by the Sussex Downs and East Hampshire AONBs, broadly the area being considered for designation as the South Downs National Park. Official statistics are largely unavailable for the South Downs. The Ministry of Agriculture, Fisheries and Food (MAFF) and its successors at the Department for Environment, Food and Rural Affairs (DEFRA) have become guarded about statistics describing the nature of farming and its funding. As a consequence, figures for the counties of East and West Sussex and Hampshire, and for Brighton and Hove, have been used where these throw light on change.

THE DEVELOPMENT OF SOUTH DOWNS AGRICULTURE

The South Downs were among the first areas of Britain to be settled. Evidence of that early colonization is still widespread and suggests that a distinctive pattern of downland farming was already emerging as long ago as 3000 BC. That pattern involved growing wheat, barley and oats and grazing sheep and cattle on pastures carved from the originalwildwood. The soils on the chalk itself were well drained and species-rich, yielding good grazing for most of the year, and they were relatively easy to cultivate using the primitive techniques available to early man. It was therefore on the chalk itself that the agricultural systems developed, and evidence of these small patches of tillage can still be seen in places. This was subsistence farming and it continued until the Black Death in the mid-fourteenth century.

The subsequent history of farming on the Downs is very much a history of improvements in the techniques of arable and sheep farming. Sheep farming for the developing wool trade dominated from the fifteenth century to the start of the Napoleonic wars at the end of the eighteenth century. Farming became a commercial activity. Corn prices and production increased in times of war and civil unrest. Pasturing livestock and farming crops became interdependent: in simple terms, the livestock manured the crop land and by-products of the crops fed the livestock.

This long history led to the evolution of very distinctive systems of farming that could be recognized as South Downs agriculture: sheep and corn. It led to the development of distinctive breeds of Southdown and Hampshire Down sheep (Plates 10, 11 and 51), and Sussex cattle (Plate 52), that were suited to the local conditions. The dewponds on the downs and the flint barns are all part of a farming system that adapted to local circumstance and made best use of local materials. The gradual evolution of agriculture and its continuity and stability over long periods of time meant that many of the plants and wildlife of the original wildwood had time to adapt and become part of the agricultural systems. It was this rich diversity that gave the South Downs a great deal of their special character.

At its most developed, South Downs system of corn-and-sheep agriculture was among the most productive and profitable in England (Brandon, 1998). The sheep were grazed on the permanent rich grasslands of the downs by day, and folded by night. The practice of folding was one of the improvements that became central to the arable farming. It involved enclosing the sheep at high densities on the arable land by means of hurdles made from coppiced woodlands of the Downs and the Weald (Plates 50 and 106). The hurdles could easily be moved and the sheep were rotated around the arable land. The effect of the folding was the deposition of manure, which enhanced the fertility of the land, and trampling by the sheep improved soil compaction on the lighter soils, making a better seedbed for the wheat, oats and barley that were the main crops. Nutrients were being robbed from the sheepwalks to enhance the cultivated fields below the downs. The Southdown breed of sheep was developed specifically for this system (Southdown Sheep Society, 2000).

When grass was short, especially in the hungry gap in spring, or during drought in high summer, sheep and cattle were often grazed on the water meadows of the River Ouse, the Cuckmere, the Adur and the Arun, in the Eastern Downs. To the west of the Arun there were few water meadows, and the generally more wooded countryside meant that sheep and cattle were also run on wood pasture and even shared the grazing of some of the deer parks. Gradually rotations were introduced and fallows abandoned; peas and beans were grown to enhance fertility, and sheep were also fed on stubbles, legumes and root crops.

Interestingly, the ploughs, farm implements and carts in the South Downs were traditionally drawn by oxen rather than by horses; the oxen being the ancestors of the red Sussex cattle (Plate 52) raised for beef today. The steep hills and clay soils in parts of the Downs are thought to have given an edge to oxen which gave way to horses only at the end of the nineteenth century. This influenced the means and speed of cultivation as well as lending another distinctive character to South Downs agriculture.

The agriculture of the South Downs was not uniform, but adapted to local conditions. The most extreme form of 'sheep-and-corn' was practised in the eastern Downs from Beachy Head to the Arun. Water meadows played an important part here. Sheep densities were highest in the east and woodland cover lowest. West of the Arun, woodlands were more common and large landed estates helped retain these and the medieval deer parks. Corn was as important as sheep, and the heathlands also gave a distinctive local character. Further west, fruit and even hops were grown on the better soils in Hampshire (Hampshire County Council, 1997).

Large tracts of semi-natural vegetation were retained within the farming system: permanent herb-rich pastures on the chalk, seasonally-flooded meadows in the river valleys, which were grazed in spring and shut up for hay in summer, grazed woodland in the western downs and extensive lowland heaths on the sandy soils of the Western Weald. These permanently vegetated areas were dominated by plant communities which were directly derived from the natural vegetation that predates agriculture and tillage. Their use for agriculture meant change: species that could withstand heavy grazing were favoured at the expense of taller herbs; birds, insects, lichens and fungi adapted or died out. But the downland, the heaths and water meadows were unfenced, sheep wandered and, despite the best efforts of the shepherd and his dog (Hudson, 1900), tall plant and shrub communities survived. Most of the wildlife of the wildwood found a place somewhere,. and because the habitats were permanent and changes in farming practice were slow, many species had time to adapt to the new conditions.

The Downs thus retained a rich wildlife and supported a wide range of both higher and lower plants, insects and birds, most of them characteristic of the area. The arable-farming system was highly productive and at times very profitable (Orwin, 1949), but it was also characterized by having weeds which were derived from the local flora, inefficient harvesting and fallen grain, and stubbles that lasted through the winter – all of which provided sustenance for insects and birds.

Although there have been fluctuations in the amount of arable farming in the South Downs (Brandon, 1998), the fact is that for centuries there has been a large amount of permanent semi-natural habitat on which no cultivation had taken place. During the Napoleonic Wars in the first decades of the nineteenth century, cereal prices rose and more land was taken into cultivation. Depression followed, but the repeal of the corn laws gradually improved farming conditions which were at their most prosperous between 1850 and 1879, the Golden Age of British farming.

When the Downs became accessible to urban populations through the advent of the railways in the late nineteenth century, visitors found large unfenced open areas on which to walk and enjoy this rich evocative countryside (Hudson, 1900 & 1903). The public had no right of access then, but they were tolerated by enlightened landowners who genuinely saw little conflict with their farming activities (Shoard, 1980). It was this combination of factors which led many people to place the highest public value on the South Downs for its wildlife, landscape, public access and historical and cultural significance from the late nineteenth century onwards (See Chapters 1, 4, 11 and 13). This was a system that was sustainable, it produced food and fibre, but it supported a rich and diverse wildlife as well.

The opening of markets to imports from North America and Australia towards the end of the nineteenth century led to steep falls in prices for wheat and wool, and started a deep depression in agriculture which became worse in the inter-war years of the twentieth century. Much land reverted to rough grazing and was farmed on the 'dog and stick' basis, or in some cases virtually abandoned. There were changes in land ownership in this period too, many traditional landowners sold up and new owners came in from London and from the Empire. Their interest was in part in the amenity afforded by the Downs landscapes, and many were said to be chiefly interested in the quality of the partridge shoots. Farmers also came from other parts of the country and some established new farming methods that they had brought with them.

Post-war agricultural change 1947–2000

From the outbreak of World War II there was a fundamental shift in British agricultural policy. Severe food shortages brought about by the German U-boat blockade resulted in the Government taking powers to direct farmers to plant certain crops. Whitehall issued diktats through the War Agricultural Executive Committees, which resulted in thousands of acres of 'virgin' soil being ploughed for the first time. Some of these changes were postponed on the parts of the Downs which were taken over by the War Office for military training and defence. The war saw other changes: large numbers of farm workers and estate staff enlisted and went to war, and were replaced in part by Land Army girls, and more significantly by the Fordson Tractor and a whole array of new farm machinery (Plates 12, 53, and 107).

Almost 5000 years of gentle and sympathetic change came to an abrupt end in the decade following the outbreak of the Second World War. It is impossible to over-emphasize the difference between the agriculture that we see now – much of it using methods and livestock evolved all over the world – with that which went before and breathed Sussex, Hampshire and the South Downs from its every pore. A fundamental shift occurred in the balance between the semi-natural permanent pastures, the heaths and traditional woodlands, and cultivated lands. More change has taken place in the last 50 years than in the previous 5000 (Sussex Wildlife Trust, 1995). Those that speak of the fluctuations between arable and livestock farming being part of a continuing pattern are being deeply disingenuous. It is no longer the benign and sustainable system that drew on the natural resources of the Downs, made handsome livings for its farmers, yet sustained the continuity and allowed wildlife and culture to survive.

So how did this dramatic change come about? Unlike earlier changes that were initiated by farmers and landowners and came from improved agricultural techniques, new crops or rotations, this agricultural revolution was driven by public policy and the deliberate use of public monies derived from taxation to pursue political ends.

Post-war policy sought to make Britain self-sufficient in temperate food stuffs. This was enshrined in the 1947 Agriculture Act brought in by the post-war Labour Government. It then evolved under successive Conservative and Labour Governments, all of which had the slogan 'food from our own resources' and featured highly interventionist policies. Financial incentives were made available to farmers on an unprecedented scale with grants to plough, fence and drain land. Higher levels of capital grants were available to encourage so-called 'rough pasture' and permanent pasture to be ploughed, drained and fenced. Farmers were guaranteed a market for whatever they produced through a system of deficiency payments. They were exempted from paying local rates and freed from many of the controls brought in by the Town and Country

Plate 105

A millennium project to encourage local awareness in East Hampshire consisting of a montage of typical pictures of parishes, cut to actual shape, and the whole made into a jigsaw puzzle. Building on the Countryside Agency's encouragement of parish maps, it was hoped to create a picture of the South Downs area. Photo: Nick Heasman, courtesy of SDJC.

Plate 106

Hurdle-making at Harting Coombe, West Sussex; a posed picture from an old postcard showing the tools of the trade, and the resulting product used for folding sheep. Photographer unknown, courtesy of Rendel Williams.

Plate 107

Threshing corn in the early decades of the 20th century at East Dean, East Sussex; a posed photograph showing the transition from animal-based to mechanized farming. The steam-powered traction engine drives the belts of the threshing machine (centre), where the grain flows into sacks, and the elevator lifts the straw to be stacked. Piles of chaff can be seen to the right of the picture. The sacks of corn are then taken away by horse and cart, to be stored before being sold, or milled for animal feed. Photographer unknown, courtesy of Rendel Williams.

Plate 108 (above)
The way it used to be between the two world wars; Newmarket
Hill photographed from the Rottingdean road, 1938, as part of
a downland survey commissioned by Sussex County Council.
Photo: © Edward Reeves, Lewes.

Plate 109 (above)
Prairie-like arable fields; Loose Bottom, near Falmer, East Sussex,
looking north-east, October 1983.
Photo: Phil Belden.

Plate 110 (below)
An Environmentally Sensitive Area (ESA) landscape; looking
south from Chanctonbury Ring, West Sussex, 1990.
Photo: Phil Belden.

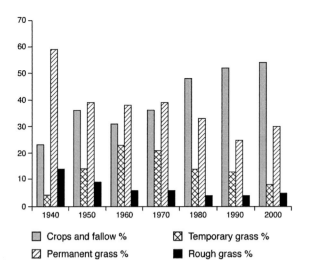

Figure 7.1   Land use changes on farms in the South Downs.

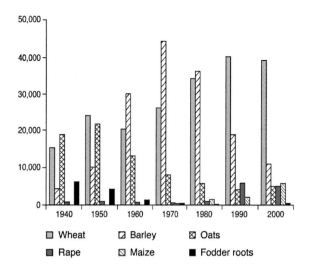

Figure 7.2   Main arable crops. (Figures for Sussex from DEFRA).

Planning Acts (Davidson & Lloyd, 1977). Similar forestry policies paid grants and offered tax incentives, which resulted in many heathland sites in the Western Weald being planted with conifers. The chalk grasslands which so characterized the high Downs, and the heathlands of the west, were both reduced at a rapid rate, and the rich wildlife which had survived 5000 years went into full retreat.

South Downs farmers responded with enthusiasm to the post-war policy changes, using newly available farm machinery and applying artificial fertilizers, and newly developed fungicides and insecticides which were the by-products of wartime research on nerve gasses (Mellanby, 1967 & 1981). They converted large parts of the permanent grassland of the Downs to intensive grass and arable production. Farms grew larger and more specialized, and traditional slack-season tasks of laying hedges, clearing ditches or repairing dewponds were discontinued. The accession of the United Kingdom to the European Union changed the agricultural grant systems but continued to support intensive agriculture (Plates 108 and 109). In parallel, there were government grants and tax incentives to establish mainly conifer woodland on lowland heaths.

The broad changes can be traced by looking at the changes in four categories of land use on farms (Fig. 7.1). The figures are derived from the June census, and the 1940 figure therefore reflects the pre-war picture, as the wartime measures had not had time to take effect. The dramatic reduction in permanent grassland and rough grazings brought about by the wartime measures and the 1947 Act is evident by comparing the 1940 and 1950 figures. These permanent areas were replaced by arable production and short-term grassland leys. Arable farming continued to increase up to 2000, but permanent grassland is also beginning to recover due to the introduction of the Environmentally Sensitive Areas Scheme (ESAs) (Plate 110).

It was not just land use that changed, but the crops that were grown also differed over the 50 years (Fig. 7.2). Cereal acreages increased, but not dramatically; the production of oats fell away after the demise of the horse, and barley went through a boom period only to be replaced in turn by wheat. Winter cereals replaced spring cereals and stubbles disappeared. Oil-seed rape and maize are relative newcomers on the Downs, the former encouraged by an advantageous CAP subsidy, the latter as a result of plant-breeding advances that have made the growing of forage maize much more secure. These changes in turn gave rise to other consequences within the arable field. The weeds, insect and fungal life that once flourished in arable fields were gradually eliminated by more vigorous and effective cultivation using higher-horsepower machinery, and by more effective spraying regimes using new generation herbicides and pesticides (Mellanby, 1981). New combine-harvesters were much more efficient and produced less wastage. There were no longer any winter stubbles, in fact cultivation became so timely that stubbles could only be seen for a matter of days after the harvest. The effects of these changes were to remove sources of food from the bottom of the food chain upon which all manner of wildlife was dependent, and to increase the incidence of serious soil erosion.

Grassland production was improved by seeding new hybrid rye grasses developed at grassland research institutes at Aberystwyth and elsewhere, and by judicious application of fertilizers and herbicides. Pastures could be made productive with two species per square metre rather than the old-fashioned 50 of the chalk sheepwalks. This allowed sheep numbers to rise whilst the grazing area remained fairly constant, or actually fell for some years (Fig. 7.3). This intensification not only led to reductions in plant species, but also of invertebrates and to consequent losses of the wildlife that depended on them for

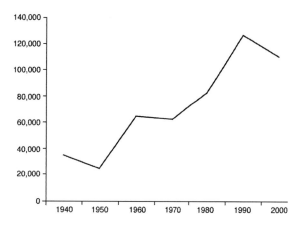

Figure 7.3 Sheep numbers increased as grassland production improved.

their sources of food. The loss of shepherds during and immediately after the war, the introduction of paddock grazing-systems from New Zealand and concerns about damage caused by rustlers and urban-based dogs, all added to changes in sheep management and greatly increased fencing. These, in turn, discouraged the access which had been traditional on the Downs up to the outbreak of the war in 1939.

THE LANDSCAPE AND ENVIRONMENTAL CONSEQUENCES OF CHANGES IN FARMING

It is really rather surprising how long it took for anyone to notice the effects of all these changes on wildlife, landscape and archaeology (Davidson & Lloyd, 1977). At first the concerns tended to be about farm chemicals, organo-chlorine based insecticides used as seed dressings and their effect on farmland birds, and some action was taken in the late 1960s and early 1970s (Mellanby, 1967 & 1981). The arguments involved complex issues that required knowledge of biochemistry and food chains and were largely led by scientists.

The effect that public grants and subsidies to agriculture were having on wildlife, landscape and archaeology only really began to come to the fore in the late 1970s (Body, 1982). It was through a public inquiry in the South Downs that the issue first came to wider notice. Almost 60 per cent of Sussex wetlands were intensively drained between the end of the war and 1980. The case for drainage was often put forward by Internal Drainage Boards: if these marshes are drained, farmers can improve their pastures or grow more cereals and make more profits; therefore the Government should offer a grant to carry out the work because on balance the nation will benefit. In essence this was the case put forward at Amberley Wildbrooks. A cost-benefit analysis was prepared showing how the benefits to the nation outweighed the costs. But, Amberley was a special

place with over 400 species of flowering plants, a significant place for over-wintering waterfowl, full of duckweeds and other aquatic specialities, let alone water beetles and snails (Plates 19 and 20). Natural historians loved this quiet corner of Sussex, and through the Sussex Wildlife Trust, the CPRE and the RSPB they made their displeasure felt so that the Minister decided it might be wise to call a public inquiry. It became apparent during the inquiry that many of the benefits claimed in favour of the drainage scheme were in fact public subsidies to agriculture, and many of the costs in terms of lost wildlife and amenity had not been properly assessed. The group which would nowadays be called conservationists won the day, a small but significant victory.

It was at this time too that widespread changes to the landscape started to be noted in research publications of the Countryside Commission and the Nature Conservancy Council. In another case involving drainage and the loss of traditional grazing, at the Halvergate Marshes in the Norfolk Broads referred to in Chapter 9, the CC set up an experiment with MAFF, to protect the marshes by offering compensation to farmers who continued to farm in the traditional way, and thus produced substantial public benefits in the form of landscape and wildlife. By the mid-1980s there was a noticeable groundswell of public opinion regarding damaging farm practices such as hedgerow removal. From these small beginnings were born the ESA schemes introduced by MAFF under the Agriculture Act 1986 and agreed and funded by the European Union.

The South Downs were in the very first batch of ESA schemes when they were launched nationally in 1986. By then the stone curlew and the cirl bunting no longer bred in the Downs; grey partridges that had been so common before the war had become rare; the skylark and the song thrush, the linnet and the corn bunting were all in sharp decline. And it was not just birds: the Adonis blue and Duke of Burgundy butterflies (Plates 78 and 76), the wartbiter cricket, the brown hare, waxcap fungi, the burnt and early spider orchids were all victims of changing farming practices.

The South Downs ESA scheme had two tiers initially, later increased to four, representing various levels of environment-friendly practices, with differing levels of subsidy. Single payments for capital works were also available. Agreements ran for five years and could then be renegotiated.

The ESA scheme (see Figure 7.4) was in some respects a resounding success because losses of key ancient habitats were reduced, the drift to arable farming was halted and reversed (ADAS, 1996), as can be seen by comparing the 1990 and 2000 land-use figures in Figure 7.1. By 2000, over 15,500 hectares of land had been entered in the scheme, representing 22 per cent of the land eligible in the

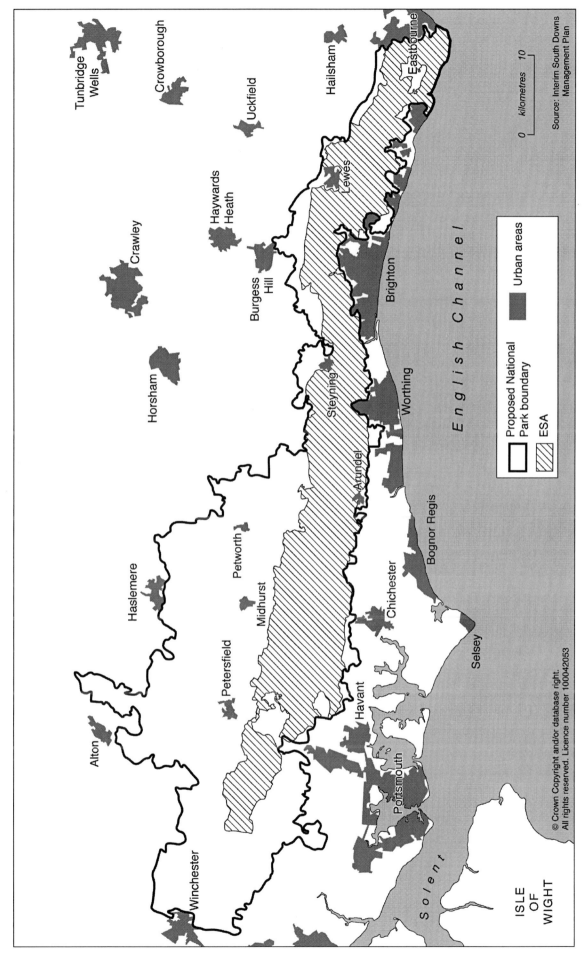

Figure 7.4 The South Downs area showing the Environmentally Sensitive Area (ESA) in relation to the proposed National Park.

South Downs. This included 5500 hectares of permanent grassland on chalk.

The ESA schemes worked by means of fairly rigid prescriptions set out by MAFF, much in the manner of recipes in old cookery books: if you followed the recipe, you received the money; never mind that neither the bread had risen nor the hare and the stone curlew returned. So by 1991 the Countryside Commission had embarked on another experiment, 'Countryside Stewardship' (CS), which had a much more flexible approach and allowed more discretion to the project officers to negotiate a deal that worked for the individual farmer and his system of farming. This too was a success and was available in the South Downs in the areas not covered by the ESA, and after five years was also taken over by MAFF.

These schemes were particularly helpful to those farmers who valued their Sussex countryside (but see Plates 111 and 112) and who had continued to under-plant their stubbles and maintain their grasslands, even when it was costing them a good deal of money. And one only had to visit the Passmores' farm on the Downs above Lancing to see the beneficial effects of mixed farming being celebrated by the skylarks singing.

APPLESHAM FARM, LANCING – A CASE STUDY

On a fine summer's day when visiting at the beginning of August 2004, with the cereal harvest in full swing, Applesham Farm looked just a little like any other modern well-farmed downland farm. But look a little closer and listen carefully to Christopher Passmore, who farms Applesham in partnership with his nephew Hugh, and you realize quickly that the skylarks singing overhead and the round-headed rampions (Plate 70) flowering profusely on the bank, are not here by chance. There is a whiff of scent from clover in the air, large beef herds graze on pastures between the fields of corn, and there are flocks of sheep out on the Downs. This is rotational, mixed farming at its best, with much the same benefits for landscape and wildlife that might have existed in the 1940s and 1950s, but with the farming brought right up to date (Passmore, 1992).

The farm covers 850 acres (approximately 344 hectares) in a great shallow coombe on the eastern flank of the chalk hills between the Rivers Adur and Arun. It has some 36 ha of alluvial brookland beside the Adur. Originally used for grazing and for hay, this is the only part of the farm that has changed dramatically since the Second World War. The fields are now pump-drained, and the water-meadows that used to support a dairy herd have given way to continuous arable production: winter wheat, oil-seed rape and winter beans. Dairying ceased in the 1950s, as it did on so many farms on the Downs, as a result of the ravages of tuberculosis and the need to invest

large sums in new dairying equipment. The pastures once used by the dairy herd on the downland portion of the farm (see Fig.7.5), now support single suckler-beef production; a change that was assisted by introduction of the Government's Deficiency Payments system after the war.

Mixed farming

The main farm comprises 760 acres (308 ha) of free-draining, flinty, loamy soils on the rolling downs of the upper chalk. Some 540 acres (218 ha) are in the main rotational farming system, a further 73 ha in permanent pasture, and the remaining 16 ha taken up by woodland, scrub, ponds, roads and buildings. The farm has three main enterprises:

- cereal production, quality winter wheat and spring barley for the seed and malting markets;
- beef production based on a 100-head herd of pedigree Limousin suckler cows which are out all year; and,
- a traditional sheep flock of 420 breeding ewes made up of a nucleus of pedigree Lleyns and a main productive flock of Lleyns crossbred with Texels. They are lambed out of doors in a pen made from straw bales.

This part of the farm can truly be described as mixed farming, and corn, beef and sheep are the three farm enterprises that have characterized farming on the Downs over the years. Very few farms now remain on the Downs that have this mixture; many have gone over to continuous cereals whilst others have become solely livestock farms. The mixture of enterprises is one of the keys to the very high standards of environmental management.

Rotational farming

The idea of rotating crops around a farm is ancient. In the early open-field systems a two-course rotation was practised where half the field would grow corn and the other half left fallow to recover its fertility. The principle of the rotation on Applesham farm is the same, but the system is much more sophisticated. It is shown in simplified outline below:

Each field spends three years in a grass ley, followed by two in winter wheat and then two in spring barley, the second of which is undersown with the ley mixture. The leys are themselves rotationally grazed. In the first year the young grass and clover mix is ideal for feeding the milking ewes and their lambs. To avoid a build-up of worm infestations, the sheep are taken off the pastures in the second year and replaced by the suckler cows; crops of hay and silage can also be taken. In the final year, before being ploughed up in the autumn, the leys may be used to graze either the sheep or cattle. The three years ingrazing deters many cereal weeds and pests, builds

Table 7a Crop rotation on Applesham Farm

Year	Crop	Use	Notes
1	Ley	Ewes & lambs	Grass clover mix, 3 grasses & 3 legumes.
2	Ley	Suckler cows	Winter feeding of barley straw in field
3	Ley	Sheep or cattle	High fertility due to clover and manure
4	Winter wheat	Seed	Over 8 tonnes per hectare
5	Winter wheat	Seed	Stubbles grazed
6	Spring Barley	Malting/seed	Over 6 tonnes per hectare
7	Spring Barley	Malting/seed	Undersown with grass clover mix
8	Ley	Ewes & lambs	Grass clover mix, 3 grasses & 3 legumes.

up fertility from the clover and the manure, and improves the soilstructure and its water-retentive properties. The four years in cereals deters animal parasites. The high-fertility and low-parasite regime means that the farm uses far lower levels of nitrogen fertilizers, other farm chemicals and veterinary products than similar arable-only or livestock-only farms, and thereby saves money. This is good sustainable farming.

Landscape and wildlife

The rotational system benefits wildlife in three distinctive ways:

- low chemical usage on the arable land and rich grazed pastures benefit many insects and soil micro-organisms which form the base of the food chain for wildlife;

- the rotation means that, as the crop in the field changes, there is always another field adjoining with the right habitat for wildlife – whereas on all arable farms the grassland species have nowhere to go, and vice versa on all grass farms;

- many species, and particularly farmland birds, seem to be reliant on having a mix of grass and cereals, both spring and winter-sown, and rely in part on the availability of stubbles for food between September and the New Year.

The rich wildlife on the farm has been confirmed by many studies. The Game Conservancy has studied grey partridge populations between the Arun and the Adur; those on Applesham remain at healthy levels whilst there have been sharp declines on the cereal and all grass farms in the area. English Nature and the RSPB have looked at the populations of skylarks and corn buntings, and the picture is the same. Studies of insects, spiders and brown hares all tell the same story: mixed rotational farming involving spring and winter cereals, grass leys, undersown crops and both sheep and cattle are good news for wildlife. But the story does not end here.

A fine 28-hectare bank of traditional chalk grassland, over 1.5 kilometres long, forms the southern boundary of Applesham farm. The bank is species-rich permanent chalk grassland supporting over 100 species of plants. It is split, none the less, into four sections which each form part of an adjoining field in the rotational farming system. When the adjoining field is in cereals, the bank is rested and plants can flower and set seed. When the adjoining field is down to a ley, the bank is grazed as part of the field. The way in which the farming is organized thus allows this very rich wildlife resource to be managed as part of the farming system. The chalk grassland area on Applesham Farm was among the first areas entered in the ESA scheme when it got under way in 1987. It was in Tier 1 of the scheme which paid £60 per hectare.

There are also about 45 ha of permanent pasture, less species-rich, but improving rapidly, part of which has been permanently reverted from arable farming, and is entered in Tier 3B of the ESA scheme. It fits into the farming system as pasture for the dry ewes once the lambs have gone. The 73 ha of permanent grass represent 20 per cent of the whole area of the farm.

Conclusions

The farming system developed by the Passmores over the past century is complex and undoubtedly requires high managerial skills and understanding of the complexities of arable and livestock farming. But it is a robust system, and in the same way that the six species sown in the grass leys each come into their own as the years bring drought or downpour, so the mix of enterprises provides some safeguard against changing farming markets, as reflected by the sign in the butcher's shop in Steyning offering Applesham lamb for sale. The farm supports a rich native wildlife as part of the farming system. There are still two full-time agricultural workers and a farm student on Applesham Farm. It is perhaps better placed to withstand the coming storms of CAP reform and a new round of World Trade negotiations which propose the removal of agricultural subsidies. To cap it all, Chrstopher Passmore was appointed an OBE in the 2006 New Years Honours for services to agriculture and nature conservation.

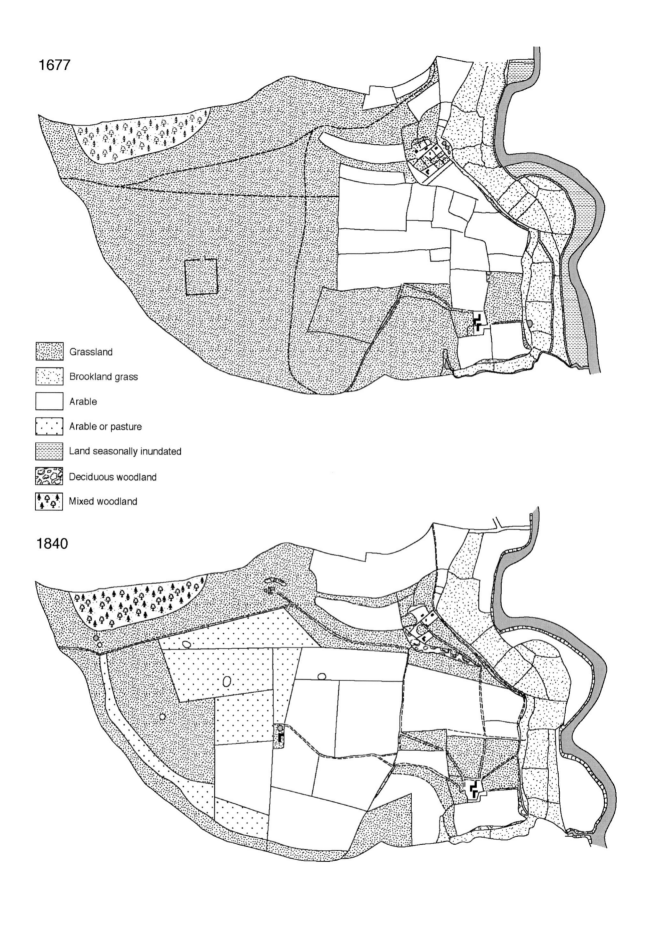

1677

Grassland

Brookland grass

Arable

Arable or pasture

Land seasonally inundated

Deciduous woodland

Mixed woodland

1840

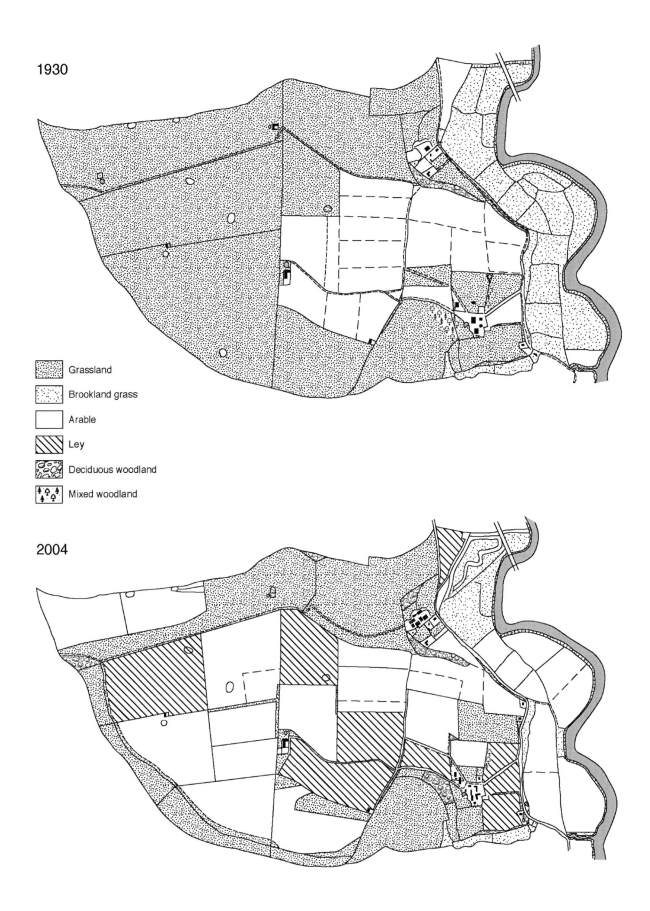

1930

Grassland

Brookland grass

Arable

Ley

Deciduous woodland

Mixed woodland

2004

Figure 7.5 Applesham Farm through the ages.

ASSESSMENT OF GOVERNMENT INTERVENTION IN SOUTH DOWNS AGRICULTURE: 1947–2000

So what have the public policies of the post-war years achieved? The Sussex Downs Conservation Board, in partnership with DEFRA, English Nature, the Countryside Agency and others, commissioned a study to evaluate the effectiveness of mechanisms to achieve landscape and habitat enhancement of the South Downs. The study was carried out by a team from the University of Reading (Ansell *et al.*, 2002). The report is revealing despite being dogged by difficulties in obtaining detailed statistics from DEFRA.

Public sector costs

By the year 2000, government was spending something over £21.5 million per annum in subsidies for crops and livestock in the South Downs. Another £3 million per annum was being spent to counter the effects of the production-subsidies through the agri-environment schemes (mainly ESA and CS). The resulting agriculture gives rise to external costs through damage to air, water, soil and biodiversity, and damage to human health by pesticides, fertilizers, micro-organisms and disease agents. All this was estimated to cost a further £20.235 million per annum for the South Downs. In addition, Sussex and Hampshire consumers were paying more for their food than they would have to if the CAP did not exist.

Effects of agricultural policy on rural society

Farming has always been seen as the backbone of the rural community. Before the war farmers and landowners put a great deal of time and effort into their local communities. Every cricket club, women's institute, parish council and many district and county councils, were run by farmers and their wives, or at least had substantial representation in those institutions. Most of the people who lived in the rural villages of the South Downs would have had some connection to the farming industry through employment or family. All that has changed, and employment in farming has shrunk dramatically (Harvey, 1997).

Full-time farm-workers have largely disappeared from the land, except on the large estates (Fig. 7.6). Many tasks that might previously have involved local people are now undertaken by agricultural contractors. The sprayer-driver may well be from Kent or Lincolnshire, the sheep shearer from Bahia Blanca (Northern Patagonia) or Timaru (New Zealand). This reduction in the workforce has had important consequences for the landscape. A whole

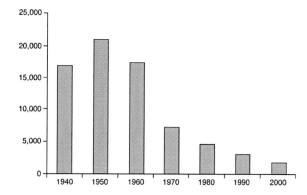

Figure 7.6   Farm workers.

host of detailed tasks that farm workers (and farmers) undertook in slack times – hedging and ditching, repairs to stiles and dewponds, pollarding, management of small woods and many others – have ceased. Many of these jobs were highly skilled, and the way in which they were done had been developed over the centuries in the South Downs. Those skills have now gone. The same agricultural policy that funded a capital-intensive agriculture directly caused farmers to shed their labour.

The depth of the changes in rural society can perhaps be illustrated best by comparing a harvest festival in the 1930s with the same kind of festival today. Then, it would have taken place after the corn had been gathered in, and the vast majority of those attending would have had some direct link to farming. The harvest festival in the twenty-first century takes place long after harvest, and often features vegetables from the third world and an audience of financial advisers, tourist operators and public servants; more local amateur dramatics than local celebration. And this alienation between many rural dwellers and the farming community is a two-way process. You would be unable to go into a local supermarket to buy a cut of beef from a Sussex beast, or South Downs lamb, which had been raised by a farmer whose name you recognized. Your only hope would be to try one of the very few local butchers who have survived in a small market town. It can be done, as the case study of Applesham farm demonstrates, but this now seems to be the exception rather than the rule.

Farming and the rural economy

The economic success of the South Downs, from the Middle Ages to the middle of the nineteenth century, was built on sheep and then on corn. Chichester, Lewes, Petersfield, Midhurst and many of the other small towns and villages, still reflect the wealth created by farming over the centuries. Farming directly would have accounted for over half the economic activity of the area well into the nineteenth century. Related trades comprising corn and wool merchants, suppliers of farm machinery, farriers, coopers, drovers and auctioneers, to select but a few, would have accounted for much of the remainder. The coming of the railways in the mid-nineteenth century began to change the economic balance, with tourism and other service industries starting to assume a greater importance in the rural economy.

No detailed figures for employment in the South Downs are yet available, although the Sussex Downs AONB has recently commissioned work on this. Figures for a wider area of Sussex and Hampshire, suggest that the dominant employment is now in the public services, which include the health and legal services as well as local government. They are very closely followed by tourism, catering and distribution. These two employment sectors account for over half of all employment. Banking and financial and other business services account for a further 20 per cent, agriculture for less than three. Agriculture accounts for 0.6 per cent of gross national product in the South-East Region; no figures are available for the South Downs, but one might postulate that the figure might be slightly higher.

Farm size

This contraction of the agricultural industry is evident in the figures on the size of farms. The Reading report indicates that in recent years there has been a sharp decrease in the number of medium-sized farms of 50 to 100 ha, and a significant increase in the number of holdings less than five hectares in size, particularly in the areas of the chalk scarp, and the Weald. Many of these 'smaller farms' are actually hobby farms or pony paddocks. Farms over 200 ha doubled in number between 1950 and 1970, but more recent indications suggest that they have reduced in number again whilst growing bigger in size. There are probably between 250 and 350 viable farms left in the South Downs.

Landscapes and habitats

After all this effort, and spending upwards of £25 million on agri-environment schemes, what remains of the sheepwalk and the wildwood? Not much, other than memories and a rich literary heritage. The main types of habitat and landscape of high amenity value that remain are shown in Table 7b.

The figures show that chalk grassland now occupies less than three per cent of the area. It has been estimated that about 900 ha of chalk grassland were lost between 1966 and 1980. A more recent study by the National Environment Research Council (NERC) in 2000 suggests that a further 20 per cent of the calcareous grasslands in south-east England were lost between 1990 and 1998. Data for West Sussex shows a decrease in unimproved grassland from 5.4 per cent of the county in 1971 to 0.7 per

Table 7b Valued landscapes and habitats in the South Downs

Landscape type	Area (ha)	%
Species-rich chalk grassland	3300	<3
Lowland heath	1100	<1
River floodplain meadows	30	<1
Woodland	33,000	24

cent in 1991 (Hill, 2004). Ironically the condition of a good deal of this remaining grassland is poor due to under-grazing and neglect. It tends to be the awkward and steep corners that cannot be ploughed or economically grazed. And despite record numbers of sheep, finding the right sort of animal to graze these areas has become so difficult that Hampshire County Council and the SDCB have had to set up a 'grazing animals project' to assist in the task. Once again the contrast with Applesham farm could not be stronger.

Heathland has also been severely degraded through planting with conifers, conversion to arable land or through lack of management and withdrawal of grazing. Action by the West Sussex Heathland Forum has stemmed the decline, but past losses have not been reversed. No heathland now forms part of an economically viable farming-system.

About 60 per cent of the flood-plain grasslands were drained between 1960 and 1980, so only small areas remain, but they are of national importance to nature conservation. Amberley Wildbrooks is now better protected through the actions of the Sussex Wildlife Trust and the RSPB and still provides a delight for conservationists and visitors, and there are hopeful signs that soon the Cuckmere valley may also be improved through the actions of the Environment Agency. Semi-natural woodlands are probably the best protected of all types of landscape, and it appears that the area of woodland in the South Downs is actually increasing. But many woodlands are unmanaged or under-managed, and increases in area are not necessarily beneficial, if, for example, pine seedlings are invading a heath. Wild boar have escaped from farms and are restocking the ancient Saxon woods, and a few cattle may now be seen playing their part in re-creating some shadow of the wildwood at Ebernoe Common in West Sussex.

AN ASSESSMENT

Agricultural and conservation policies developed in the UK between 1947 and 1963, promised:

- self-sufficiency in temperate foodstuffs;
- a self-sustaining and healthy rural economy;
- a beautiful landscape rich in wildlife;
- access to the countryside for quiet enjoyment and understanding.

From 1963 to 1997, new agricultural policies were developed by the EEC, later the EU, in Brussels. We must also remember the fine words of the politicians who founded the European Union in the 1960s and who designed the CAP to:

- provide good-quality cheap food,
- support the small farmer, the backbone of Europe,
- support communities and rural society, and
- bring stability to the countryside.

These worthy objectives were applied as much to the South Downs, once the finest farming area in Britain, as they were to other parts of Europe.

An honest assessment of what has happened in the South Downs in the last 50 years can only conclude that on balance the policies of successive governments have failed. Farming has been industrialized, but it could no more feed the population of Britain during a war, were oil-supplies to be cut off, than it could have done in 1939. People have been driven from the land, the rural economy has collapsed, the landscape has declined in interest and value – it has a more global feel, more Midwest America than South Downs – wildlife is in retreat, consumers pay more for their food, the public is more at risk from pollutants and disease, the countryside is less accessible and farm practices are less sustainable.

In the summer of 1940 the landscape of the South Downs had three distinct and roughly equal-sized components:

- ***Woods, heaths and commons*** on which the dominant vegetation and wildlife had derived from the wildwood and would have been recognized by the average Roman or Saxon. Most were used to produce fuel, fencing and fodder and formed a part of the broad farming system.
- ***Chalk downlands and rough grazings***, much modified by centuries of sheep-grazing, and a core part of the farming system. They supported a wide range of specialized plants and animals which were largely derived from the original wildwood.

On these two areas wildlife was abundant, the remains of man's earlier activities were plentiful, and people enjoyed largely unencumbered access which did not conflict with the forms of farming and forestry then practised.

- ***Cultivated lands***, which were used for cereals, roots and short-term leys, the second core part of the farming system. These were species-poor, and yet they supported much wildlife. Arable weeds like the poppy and the corncockle abounded, birds fed on stubbles, insects were encouraged by manuring. The sort of environmentally-responsible farming you can see at Applesham Farm today.

This is the South Downs landscape, the landscape that the Country Land and Business Association (CLBA) so eloquently and rightly described as 'museum farming' in 2004; even down to the detail of the farm-workers having smocks, although by 1940 many had gone to war and the land-girls kept theirs in a drawer.

In the summer of 2004 the landscape of the South Downs still has three distinct components, but they are no longer of equal size:

- ***Ancient woods***, and particularly the heaths and commons, have shrunk in size; the dominant vegetation and the wildlife derived from the wildwood are still there, but they are no longer used to produce fuel, fencing and fodder, and form no part of modern farming systems. A Roman or Saxon visitor would be surprised, probably shocked, to find that at weekends the woods and commons were full of urban peasants undertaking management tasks for their own enjoyment.
- ***Chalk downlands*** and ***rough grazings*** now form a tiny fraction of the Downs. They are mostly confined to steep unploughable north-facing slopes. Many now belong to conservation bodies such as the National Trust or the Wildlife Trusts, or are owned by the East Sussex, West Sussex and Hampshire County Councils, Brighton & Hove Authority and Eastbourne Borough Council. Their management is supported by the ESA, CS and other steward-ship schemes, but many no longer form a part of the modern farming-system. They still support a wide range of specialized plants and animals derived from the original wildlife of the South Downs and are a reservoir for these species.

On these two areas, which together comprise less than a third of the land, wildlife survives, and people still enjoy largely unencumbered access.

- ***Cultivated lands*** now dominate the South Downs. They are used to grow cereals; maize and oilseed rape have replaced oats and root-crops. Short-term grass leys are often of single species and intensively managed. Any wildlife that appears, tends to be blasted by high-horsepower machinery, artificial fertilizers, herbicides, fungicides, insecticides and growth regulators. The use of chemicals is tempered on farms using integrated crop-management, on organic farms and those in the ESA and CS schemes, but this is largely a wildlife-unfriendly world to which visitors are not welcome.

That is the South Downs farming landscape today.

In summary, since 1940, public benefit has been sacrificed to private gain by injudicious use of taxpayers' money. Ironically, not many farmers have benefited, nor rural communities. If anyone has strongly benefited from these post-war policies it is probably the manufacturers of farm machinery and the suppliers of farm chemicals, and a very few large-scale farmers.

THE FUTURE

This rather bleak assessment of current policies and their outcomes might suggest that there is no future for the treasured landscapes of the South Downs, but that is far from true, as the case study of the Passmores at Applesham and the rest of this book demonstrates. The issue rather is what role the agricultural industry might play in delivering the public benefits that Governments promise, the South Downs Joint Committee is statutorily required to deliver, that conservationists demand and the public expects.

The public benefit agenda

There seems to be a degree of consensus that the expenditure of public monies to deliver public benefits from agriculture is now an acceptable use of taxpayers' money (DEFRA, 2004a). The Government's Rural Strategy published in the summer of 2004 accepts this (DEFRA, 2004b). Only the deregulation lobby led by a few hardliners in the CLBA and NFU seem to have serious reservations. So what might a sensible set of goals be for the South Downs of the future?

Goals

The Rural Strategy published by the Government in 2004 emphasizes sustainable development and gives priority to the rural economy, social justice for rural people and the environment. It builds on extensive reviews conducted by the Cabinet Office (1999) and Lord Haskins (2003), but it is very difficult to detect a clear set of goals. This is somewhat unexpected given the clarity of public-policy objectives and actions in 1947. Yet this is the age of 'mission statements' and 'corporate agendas', it seems as if targets have gone out of fashion again. So we must turn to the voluntary bodies to get a feel for this. In 1993 the Sussex Wildlife Trust rather cheekily published a *Vision for the South Downs* (Sussex Wildlife Trust, 1993) in which it began to put together an

agenda for action. In 1995 it published the more ambitious *Vision for the Wildlife of Sussex* (Sussex Wildlife Trust, 1995) which had targets and dates. It identified which public and voluntary bodies might take responsibility for delivering these, and by implication, who might take responsibility if it didn't happen. Implicit in the analysis and proposals is that some landscapes and habitats had become so eroded that extensive restoration and re-creation to link the remnants would be required if these were to be sustained.

The South Downs Conservation Board and the East Hampshire AONB Joint Advisory Council (2004) tried to pull this together in their *South Downs Interim Management Plan* (*SDIMP*)published in the summer of 2004. The broad aims of this plan are to protect, conserve and enhance the natural beauty of the South Downs, encourage people's quiet enjoyment of the Downs and promote sustainable economic and social development. It conforms to the policies set out in the Rural Strategy and is consistent with the Sussex Wildlife Trust Vision, without a commitment to deliver it.

Specific environmental goals were presented in the Sussex Downs Conservation Board's paper on its Landscape Enhancement Initiative (LEI) published in 2001 summarized in Table 7c. Some of these are carried forward into the Interim Management Plan. One can now see a more explicit 'restoration and re-creation agenda'. The precise figures will no doubt be argued about, but in a sense they are not important (Plates 96, 113 and 114). The key questions are:

- Will the new policies currently being put in place by DEFRA be robust enough to deliver? Will chalk grassland, heathland and other landscapes be restored and re-created in large enough blocks, so that they are sustainable and can be managed economically?

- How will the areas fit with modern farming on the Downs, and how far will farmers be able to deliver the agenda?

- What role should the AONBs or a future South Downs National Park Authority play in delivering these?

The changing agricultural policy agenda

Pressure on the European Union at the World Trade talks finally led to the first stage in the reform of the Common Agricultural Policy, which is now being implemented. The link between subsidies and the production of specific agricultural products was broken in January 2005. A **Single Farm Payment (SFP)** now replaces production-subsidies by stages over the next eight years. It will be an area-based flat-rate payment in the South Downs, adjusted initially to reflect historic subsidy receipts. Payment will be made subject to cross-compliance; that is,

Table 7c Targets for enhancement of the South Downs under the Landscape Enhancement Initiative

	Chalk grassland	Heathland	Floodplain grassland	Ancient woodland
Sustainable Management	All sites (4000 ha) ST	All sites (640 ha) ST	Priority sites ST	50% of total woodland resource MT
Restoration	Increase in area by 10% (400 ha) ST	At least 50% extensively grazed MT	At least 1000 ha of lowland wet grassland MT	Non-native species removed from 10% of former ancient sites MT
	Revert 750 ha arable land ST	500 ha from forestry or other land MT	1000 ha of grazing marsh from cultivated land MT	Increase woodland area by 5% through colonization and planting MT

Note: Targets are all for the medium term (marked MT – 10 years) except for those in the short term (ST – 5 years).

farmers will be required to meet certain environmental regulations. These include meeting legal requirements and following codes of good farming practice. How 'compliance' is to be audited has not been explained. Farmers will receive between £200 and £250 per qualifying hectare; that is £1.7 – £2 billion annually in England. They will not be required to grow anything in particular, indeed it appears that they will not be required to grow anything at all. Ministers and senior officials at DEFRA have claimed that the payments are for the public good that farmers supply. Many undoubtedly do so, but even the most short-sighted minister would be hard put to point to the public benefit in a field of wheat growing on chalk rubble and flints on the Downs, or a field of lettuces on the better soils. The real unstated objective of the policy seems to be 'to minimise the financial impact on our farmers and food industry whilst doing a deal with the USA and the Cairns Group at the next round of the World Trade talks in some unlikely Latin American seaside resort like Punta del Este or Cancun'.

What these changes mean for the South Downs is not yet clear. The livestock-sector seems likely to decline, particularly with regard to beef and dairying. Grazing, which is such an important component in maintaining landscape, wildlife and archaeology, will come under further pressure. On the positive side, the grazing projects, the South Downs lamb project initiated by the Conservation Board and growing consumer interest through farmer's markets and specialist shops, all point towards a strengthening of the specialist livestock market. But these reforms and projects will do nothing to deliver the indicative goals set out in the *SDIMP* on their own.

Entry Level Scheme

A new environmental scheme was introduced in 2005 based on the recommendations of the Curry Commission (DEFRA, 2002) which looked into the crises in the countryside that followed the BSE and

Foot and Mouth outbreaks. This Entry Level Scheme(ELS) has the rather grand objectives of addressing problems of:

- environmental pollution;
- loss of biodiversity;
- damage to the historic environment; and
- loss of landscape character.

Farmers present a simple environmental farm record and then choose from a wide range of options linked to management of field boundaries, trees and woodlands, buffer strips, arable and forage crops, increased crop diversity, erosion control and grassland. Each option is linked to a number of qualifying points and a points target is calculated depending on the type of land and its total area. Payment of £30 per hectare for the whole qualifying holding is made to farmers reaching the points target through successful implementation of selected options. Scheme applications are to be made electronically and no monitoring proposals have been made public. There is an Organic Entry Level Scheme (OELS) that is similar to the ELS but tailored to organic farming systems, and payments are at the higher rate of £60 per hectare.

The ELS has the great merit of being simple and applicable to all farmers, but this is very much a case of the jam spread thinly, an approach where one size fits all. It will rightly reward farmers like the Passmores who take a very conscientious approach to environmental management. It may encourage some to dig more farm ponds, leave wider field margins and install a few more beetle banks. It may well engage a few more farmers' interest in the environment, and its benefits will probably be greatest in the arable fields of eastern England, where little of the natural world survives and, ironically, where BSE and Foot and Mouth had least impact. At a forecast national expenditure of £150 million annually it will not deliver any of the indicative goals set out in the *SDIMP*. There are no options in the scheme for restoring or re-creating habitats, and farmers can in any event reach their points-targets without doing any of those difficult things.

Higher Level Scheme

The ESA and CS schemes were combined in a new Higher Level Scheme (HLS) from January 2005. The main objectives of the scheme are wildlife conservation, protection of the historic environment, maintenance of landscape quality and character, promotion of public access and understanding, and natural resource protection. Two secondary objectives are flood management and genetic conservation.

The HLS has a four-tier structure, with priority given to the maintenance-tier, that is, the ongoing specialized management of land and assets of high-environmental-value , as this represents the best value for money. There will in addition be a restoration-tier aimed at the restoration of degraded habitats, and a tier to create or re-create new habitats, features or access, and a support-tier that bridges any gaps between the HLS and the ELS.

Cross-compliance under the SFP provisions is compulsory, so the HLS will only pay for management that goes beyond the compulsory provisions. Entry to the scheme is based on a farm audit, and farmers can choose from a range of managerial options for different types of land, such as arable, grass, heathlands, or coastal areas, or for different objectives such as access, or more generic managerial options. This provides the basis for an agreed farm-level, environmental management plan. Payments will be based on calculations of income forgone as under the existing ESA scheme. Agreements are for a five-year period, and outcome-monitoring will be an important part of the scheme. Details of implementation-arrangements and payment-levels are under discussion and will not be made public until the launch of the scheme.

The HLS scheme will be targeted at National Parks and Sites of Special Scientific Interest (SSSIs) and, by implication, other areas will have a lower priority. The Scheme could help deliver the targets in the *SDIMP* if it is locally targeted, and if farmers can be persuaded to change their farming systems so that they can incorporate key landscapes and habitats into their farm-plans. There is some scepticism, however, as to whether the rules of the scheme will be flexible enough to allow this to happen, and whether funding will be sufficient to move beyond the status quo in the South Downs.

Assessment of the impact of the proposed agricultural policy changes on the South Downs

DEFRA was created by an unequal merger between the Ministry of Agriculture Fisheries and Food MAFF) and part of the Department of the Environment. Its Ministers require the South Downs AONB authorities to prepare a management plan as they do for all other National Parks and AONBs. It sets the national framework for Biodiversity Action Plans, and it sponsors Natural England. It thus has an interest in all the public-sector participants who define the landscape, access and wildlife goals for the South Downs, but it chooses to run the agri-environment schemes that might deliver them, directly, by itself.

It is a requirement of government that public funding delivers the goals of policy in an effective and economically efficient manner. Yet one normally needs to ask whether the mechanisms in place are the best ones to deliver the outcomes, and then to monitor the results to ensure that this is the case. In the past, some benefits have been shown to occur, if the monitoring and assessing functions are slightly removed from those who deliver the policy and who have a vested interest in the results. It is necessary to point out that these things did not happen under MAFF and do not appear to be happening with regard to DEFRA.

So will the new policies deliver the desired objectives in the South Downs area? Probably not! This is mainly due to:

- the continuing imbalance between Single Farm Payment and funding for agri-environment schemes;
- agreements not being permanent;
- the schemes being open to all on demand rather than being targeted to local landscape-needs;
- agreements that are prescriptive rather than outcome-based;
- no independent monitoring arrangements; and
- schemes that are designed to fit national rather than local environmental circumstances.

Funding

The Reading University team collected invaluable information on the barriers to success in the South Downs ESA project (Ansell *et al.*, 2002). The survey confirmed that landowners regarded the rates of payment as too low, and that mainly poor-quality land had been entered into the scheme, particularly where the maintenance and restoration of chalk grassland were concerned. The scheme had not reflected changes in the agricultural sector as a whole and, in particular, changes to the livestock industry after the BSE and Foot and Mouth outbreaks. At the time of writing it is not clear whether the new HLS will address these concerns.

Alternative approaches

So far as one can tell, there has been no serious consideration of alternative means of delivering the desired outcomes. No one in Brussels, London or Guildford has sat down and asked the question: 'If I want to deliver an environmental agenda in the South Downs and have between £3 million and £30 million a year to spend, what would be the best way of doing it?'

A number of alternative mechanisms were suggested by the SDCB as part of the LEI proposals in 2001. They included:

- *An Environmental Land Bank Scheme* to assist NGOs such as the National Trust, RSPB, SWT or others to purchase land, on condition that it is managed to meet agreed environmental and social objectives. This option is initially costly, because of the high price of land in the South East, but it ensures permanence and is focused on realizing the desired outcome.

- *A Farm Income and Retirement Scheme*, in which a farmer is offered an additional pension on condition that his land is sold to an approved NGO or other body for permanent conversion to semi-natural habitats.

- *A Farm Capital Conversion Scheme* in which landowners could tender to return permanently part of their land to traditional habitats, with funding calculated on the cost of achieving specified objectives.

- *An Amenity Farm Scheme* to encourage hobby farmers to use the land for environmental purposes.

- *Incentives for tenant farmers* on publicly-owned land to achieve permanent reversion.

- The extension of *conditional exemption from Inheritance Taxation* for management of areas of outstanding scenic, scientific or cultural interest.

These were reviewed by the Reading University team (Ansell *et al*) in 2002, but they would all require positive action by DEFRA. None has been pursued. The existing and proposed measures all aim to do one of two things:

1. To persuade farmers to farm differently, that is, to put some land down permanently to a valued habitat and to adjust their farming-systems so that they have the right stock to graze the land; or,

2. To persuade voluntary bodies which are already managing such land as valued habitat to extend their holdings. They too face a problem of finding suitable grazing animals.

Elsewhere in Europe, and particularly in Holland and Denmark, publicly-funded schemes have been launched to restore and re-create large wetlands and heathlands, now managed extensively with semi-wild grazing herds. They have the advantages of being closer to the original management of the Downs in

concept, and are likely to be cheap to run in the long term. They can deliver much better access-benefits than the alternatives, but they would be very difficult to set up in today's complex land-owning pattern. Such schemes require detailed study and proposals for their development, but could provide alternative means of ensuring that payments from public funds are more directly linked to delivery of the public benefits.

Priorities and targeting

The *South Downs Interim Management Plan* highlights the importance of setting priorities for landscape restoration and then targeting resources to these areas. The Sussex Downs Conservation Board (2004) and the East Hampshire AONB have worked together to do a great deal of research on the conditions likely for success in restorative re-creation schemes, such as on soil conditions and farm-type. The Reading report indicates that many farmers are either unwilling or unable to participate in an extended ESA scheme. It therefore seems very unlikely that the revamped HLS scheme will deliver the *SDIMP* targets, or at least, not the right results in the right places.

Partnerships and agreements

Experience in other national parks shows the critical need to build and develop partnerships with farmers and other landowners, as well as with other agencies responsible for the planning and delivery of projects and programmes affecting landscape management (Council for National Parks, 1991). The formulation of such partnerships is made difficult by the HLS scheme, which is designed nationally and administered regionally, and where the rules result in all applications that technically qualify being considered on an equal footing. The Reading team reported that the ESA scheme had not produced an effective working partnership between DEFRA and the SDCB. Delegating the running of all agri-environment schemes to a future South Downs National Park Authority would produce a more locally relevant if not a better result.

Monitoring

The South Downs ESA scheme was systematically monitored from its inception in 1987. Although criticized at the time because the work was done by an internal MAFF team, it did produce a useful report after five years (ADAS, 1996). Although there had been much success in signing up farmers to the scheme, it indicated that there was little evidence of high-quality outcomes for the options of restoration and re-creation. In essence the farmers had returned the fields to grass, but there were not many species characteristic of the chalk in them. To be fair, farmers were not asked to produce a species-rich grassland, just to follow a prescription, which most did. In 1995 this monitoring of the outcome was discontinued by MAFF without explanation. The Reading team was asked to take a view on outcomes, but had difficulty in fulfilling this part of their brief due to lack of data. The anecdotal evidence is that there are some successful restoration and re-creation projects going ahead, but they are very few in number, may take 50 to 100 years to come to fruition and are almost exclusively undertaken by public bodies (Eastbourne Borough Council) or voluntary bodies (National Trust and Sussex Wildlife Trust). This is a fairly shocking condemnation of the use of public funds. The importance of monitoring inputs, primarily of funding, and outcomes, cannot be overemphasized and should be a fundamental part of any strategy.

A South Downs National Park

The designation of a South Downs National Park would provide a stronger and more permanent body responsible for the Downs (Countryside Agency, 2002). The Authority will have a position which will allow it to argue strongly for priority for public funding to deliver its plan, either directly or through the various schemes and policies of DEFRA and other public-sector agencies. It would have a duty to ensure that public benefits are achieved in an economic and efficient manner.

CONCLUSION

The South Downs were once covered by the wildwood, known in ancient times. It will never return; nor can the Downs be brought back to their condition at the start of the Napoleonic wars when half were sheepwalks. The sheep-and-corn landscape of the summer of 1940 cannot be re-created either, and we should not seek to do so. But something a good deal more valuable than the current situation could be created by a much clearer statement of public policies and more judicious use of public funds. It will require a new kind of partnership between farmers, voluntary bodies, public authorities and the Government.

A new settlement should aim to achieve a rebalancing of land use. For the ancient woods, the chalk grassland, water meadows and heaths that remain, the HLS scheme and cross-compliance will do much to sustain them. How far management of these areas will be undertaken by farmers is questionable. The mixed and livestock farms that remain should play a central role, but there are few left and they are in decline. Present trends suggest that public and voluntary bodies, in particular, will continue to play a major role using voluntary labour and funding, as well as the public schemes to assist

them. Part of the landscapes that were lost between 1940 and the present should be restored to link the abandoned islands of heath and down in the arable system, to create larger habitats that will be easier to manage and would extend public access. How much should be done will depend on resources; how it should be done will require innovative new thinking, by farmers and by voluntary bodies, for schemes currently in the pipeline do not look as if they will deliver. Some of the alternatives outlined above should be tried.

How far commercial farmers will be able to change their systems or want to deliver this agenda is unclear. When they are willing to do so, they should be given priority and every encouragement; when they are unwilling, they should not be allowed to stand in the way of others. On the commercial farm, in the cultivated field, agriculture needs to be more accountable for the damage it does to others. There is no moral or ethical basis for exempting the farmer from the polluter-pays principle. Cross-compliance for the SFP may help alleviate some of the problems of pollution and soil erosion. The ELS may also help tone down some of the practices that are most destructive to landscape and wildlife.

The new farmed landscape of baby lettuces and bio-fuels, rape and radishes, forage maize and other industrial crops (Plates 115 to 117) might be more acceptable if the great bustard had a home and some suitable food, the skylark sang and there were orchids, waxcaps and wartbiters in fields across the Downs. Not everywhere, just somewhere.

Farmers made the landscape of the South Downs. They created great wealth, achieved continuity and incorporated much of the best of the natural world that they had inherited. Some argue that it is farmers who are now unmaking the Downs but, as this chapter has tried to show, it is politicians who must carry most of the blame for that. There is still much to value in the Downs – this book is testimony to that – but the most precious bits of the Downs are often not in the farmer's field as they once were, and that is what is wrong. Much of the farming in the commercial farmer's field is unsustainable.

REFERENCES

Agricultural Development & Advisory Service (1996) *Environmental Monitoring in the South Downs ESA, 1987-1995.* ADAS, London.

Ansell, D.J., Jones, P.J., Mortimer, S.R. and Park, J.R. (2002) *Evaluating the effectiveness of mechanisms to achieve landscape and habitat enhancement in the South Downs.* University of Reading.

Body, R. (1982) *Agriculture: The Triumph and the Shame.* Temple Smith, London.

Brandon, P. (1998) *The South Downs.* Phillimore, Chichester.

Cabinet Office (1999) *Rural Economies.* HMSO, London.

Council for National Parks (1991) *South Downs National Park – Opportunities for Enhancement*. Council for National Parks, London.

Countryside Agency (2002) *A South Downs National Park – Local Authority Consultation*. Countryside Agency, Cheltenham.

Countryside Commission (1996) *The Landscape of the South Downs*. Sussex Downs Conservation Board, Midhurst.

Davidson, J. and Lloyd, R. (1977) *Conservation and Agriculture*. Wiley, Chichester.

Department for Environment, Food and Rural Affairs (2002) *Strategy for Sustainable Farming and Food*. DEFRA, London. (**The 'Curry Commission'**)

Department for Environment, Food and Rural Affairs (2004a) *Rural White Paper – Review*. DEFRA, London.

Department for Environment, Food and Rural Affairs (2004b) *Rural Strategy 2004*. DEFRA, London.

Department of the Environment (2000) *Rural White Paper*. HMSO, London.

Hampshire County Council (1997) *Hampshire Farming Study*. HCC, Winchester.

Harvey, G. (1997) *The Killing of the Countryside*. Cape, London.

Haskins, Lord (2003) *Rural Delivery Review*. DEFRA, London.

Hill, I. (2004) *Agriculture and Land Management in the South Downs*. South Downs Campaign submission to the South Downs National Park Inquiry. SDC, Brighton.

Hudson, W.H. (1900) *Nature in Downland*. Longman, London.

Hudson, W.H. (1903) *Hampshire Days*. Longman, London.

Mellanby, K. (1967) *Pesticides and Pollution*. The New Naturalist series 50. Collins, London.

Mellanby, K. (1981) *Farming and Wildlife*. The New Naturalist series 67. Collins, London.

Orwin, C.S. (1949) *A History of English Farming*. Nelson, London.

Passmore, C.W. (1992) Farming in an Environmentally Sensitive Area. *Journal of the Royal Agricultural Society of England*, Volume **153**.

Shoard, M. (1980) *The Theft of the Countryside*. Temple Smith, London.

Southdown Sheep Society (2000) *Millennium Yearbook*. SSS, Cardington, Bedford.

Sussex Downs Conservation Board (2004) *Interim South Downs Management Plan*. SDCB, Ford.

Sussex Wildlife Trust (1993) *A Vision for the South Downs*. SWT, Henfield.

Sussex Wildlife Trust (1996) *A Vision for the Wildlife of Sussex*. SWT, Henfield.

CHARLTON   D. PRINCE.

Plate 111 *(above left)*
Part of Offham Down, East Sussex, 1997; ploughed by the farmer, who could earn more from government subsidy for crops than from payments to protect the site.
Photo: Julian Gray, courtesy of SDJC.

Plate 112 *(above right)*
'Unploughing'; local people, enraged by the ploughing up at Offham Down try to put back the sward, 1997.
Photo: Julian Gray, courtesy of SDJC.

Plate 113 *(left)*
A close-up of restored sheepwalk at Harting Down, West Sussex – also see Plate 96 – with crosswort, bird's-foot trefoil and common spotted orchid in the sward, and bramble already starting to invade.
Photo: Patrick Leonard.

Plate 114 *(below)*
Sheepwalk beside ploughed downland, which is now severely eroded, near Eastbourne.
Photo: Patrick Leonard

Modern trends in farming: products of the highly profitable deregulated systems favoured by the CLBA

Plate 115 *(above left)*
The changing arable landscape today: potatoes and power lines.
Photo: Patrick Leonard.

Plate 116 *(above centre)*
'Lettuscapes'; intensively planted salad crops brought on early by the use of horticultural fleece.
Photo: Patrick Leonard.

Plate 117 *(above right)*
'Plasticization' of the landscape; vegetable crops protected from the elements in order to gain quicker maturity in spring.
Photo: Patrick Leonard.

Plate 118 *(above)*
Ancient semi-natural woodland at Paddock Wood, Cowdray Estate, West Sussex, 2005.
Photo: Donald Macdonald.

Plate 119 *(far left)*
Seventeen year-old sweet chestnut (*Castanea sativa*) poles being coppiced at Pathfield, near Lodsworth, on the Cowdray Estate, October 2006.
Photo: Donald Macdonald.

Plate 120 *(left)*
More modest woodland products from hazel (*Corylus avellana*) coppicing at Blagdon Farm, near Clanfield, Hampshire: in the foreground, bean poles (left) and a wattle hurdle (right). In the background the coppiced stools can be seen, which will re-grow; in the meantime a rich ground flora will burst forth on the cleared site.
Photo: Nick Heasman, courtesy of SDJC.

CHAPTER 8

Forestry in the South Downs

DONALD W. MACDONALD

Woodland accounts for approximately twenty-five per cent of the area of the proposed National Park (Forestry Commission, 2000). The wealden section of the area, in particular, is among the most wooded parts of England and Wales, with a high proportion of Ancient Woodland. This chapter is concerned with the management of forestry and with its implications for the area as a whole, taking the experience of Cowdray, a large, well-wooded estate near Midhurst in West Sussex, as a case study (Figure 8.1).

THE GROWTH AND DECLINE OF WOODLAND: AN HISTORICAL BACKGROUND

To set the scene, it is at first worth looking briefly at historical trends in the extent and use of woodland. It is well to remember that open forest was widespread over most of the country after the Ice Age. The frozen wastes had not come south of the Thames, and the Downs had retained some cover of tundra-like dwarf scrub, but the four thousand years after the retreat of the ice saw gradual re-colonization of the newly exposed land, forming one huge and diversified wildwood. This would have covered most of Britain with the exception of the shoreline and mountain tops.

Thus, six thousand years ago, all the land in the proposed National Park would have been forest of some kind. It would have varied a great deal, with small-leaved lime probably being the dominant tree amongst some oak and beech on the chalk of the Downs, principally oak on the clays of the Weald, with birch predominant on the lighter, sandier soils and beech on the steep slopes.

As shown in earlier chapters, Bronze Age man began clearing these woods. The tribes, at first nomadic, then sedentary, cleared for fuel and for pasture, and to provide building materials. By the time the Romans arrived, most of the Downs themselves were already bare, with much of the better ground coming under the plough. Only the more dense woods of the Weald were left, though these were managed to some extent, for example by coppicing. Coppicing, in particular, was to become quite extensive in due course, perhaps more than half of the country's woods being of this type in the Middle Ages.

Even the wealden woods, forbidding as their thickest parts were, did eventually begin to yield to the woodman's axe, as the ever-increasing population made great demands on them for fuel, building and industrial needs, while land-hungry peasants gained pasture and the opportunity to farm. This trend accelerated with the growth of the iron industry in the late fifteenth century, where the presence of large amounts of timber became as important as the ore itself. One ton of iron needed two tons of charcoal, which, in turn, had been made from twelve tons of firewood.

Not all was lost, though. Indeed, in Sussex, the present amount of woodland, particularly in the Weald, is due to its active conservation, even in those days, by coppicing and for the iron industry.

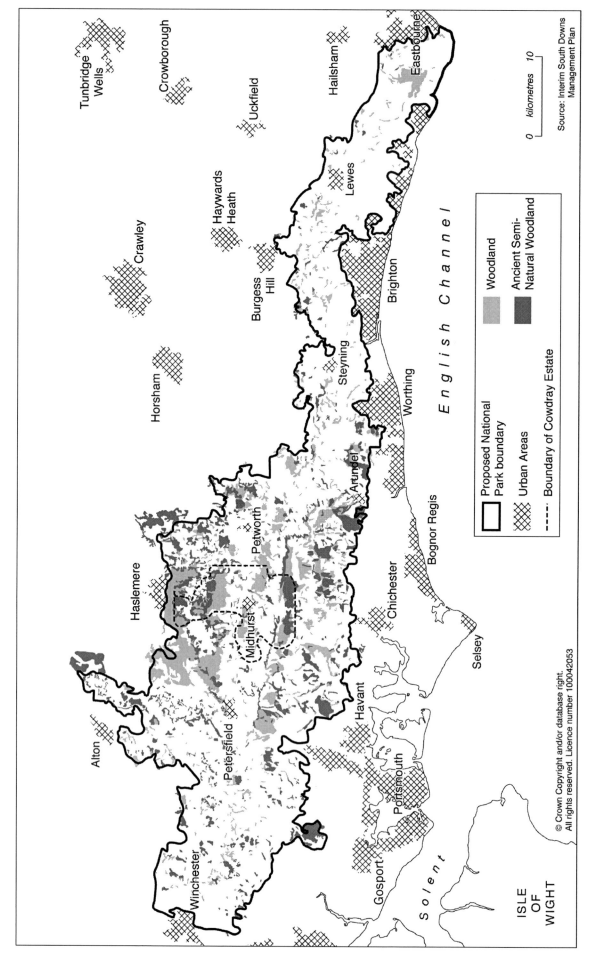

Figure 8.1   Woodland in the South Downs area

Conservation became even more important in the next two centuries, with the growth of maritime power and trade. Indeed the Royal Navy was one of the first major institutions to voice concern about the run-down of this vital source of raw materials in an era when ships were made almost entirely of wood, particularly oak.

In contrast it was also the Navy's success in creating good conditions for maritime trade, together with the expansion of the British Empire, that made it easier to gain access to timber from other parts of the globe. It seemed pointless to grow timber in this country when there were vast quantities to be plucked 'straight off the shelf' in Canada, Africa and India. Why bother to plant trees here and wait a hundred years to get a crop, when you could find timber in British Columbia at densities ten times greater than you could ever hope for at home?

Later, with the increasing use of iron to replace wood in the building of ships, and coal replacing charcoal as a fuel, one of the final utilitarian justifications for managing and retaining British woodlands was removed; by 1905 only 4.7 per cent of the UK was wooded (Forestry Commission, 2005a), and almost all timber requirements were met by imports. Except for the royal hunting forests there was little interest in woodland conservation, other than where it was seen in terms of landscape embellishments to grand country estates or as a source of cover for game. Outside the earth's desert regions Britain had become one of the least wooded countries in the world.

World War I (1914–18) saw an end to the complacent idea that the nation could survive without timber-producing woodlands. With maritime trade severely curtailed, the country had to turn to its own woods, or what was left of them, to survive industrially during those years – this at a time when the major source of energy was coal, the mining of which required the use of huge quantities of timber as pit-props.

After the Great War, a government report by the Acland Committee (Ministry of Reconstruction, 1918) recommended that, in order to prevent a repeat of the devastation of woodland that had occurred, a Forestry Commission should be formed, charged with creating a strategic reserve of timber in the event of another war. This was to be done by creating new state-owned forests such as the Queen Elizabeth Forest in Hampshire, as well as by encouraging private investment. Little did people know that only another twenty years would pass before Britain's woodlands again would be under similar pressure.

WOODLAND IN THE SOUTH DOWNS

A measure of the success of these schemes can be seen locally from the fact that, as noted at the

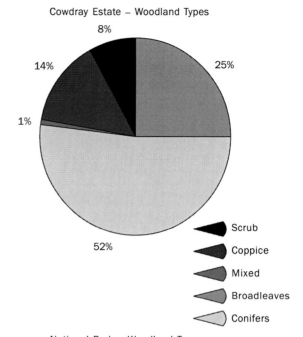

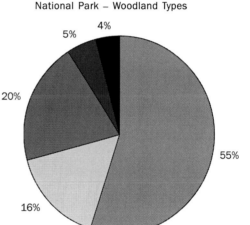

Figure 8.2   A comparison of woodland types on the Cowdray Estate with those in the proposed South Downs National Park area.

beginning of this chapter, around 25 per cent of the land (about 30,000 hectares) in the proposed National Park is wooded, a figure which is twice the UK coverage and three times that of England as a whole (Forestry Commission, 2005a). More than half this area consists of blocks in excess of 500 hectares, with the greatest concentration at the western end of the Sussex Downs where it is possible to walk for miles without ever breaking cover (Fig. 8.2). In terms of timber-growing – and especially timber-harvesting – this scale is of great importance, and it is in these larger blocks that forest management has continued to be applied. In the more scattered areas, many woodlands have suffered from neglect in recent years, either being totally abandoned to nature or simply being used as cover for game – mostly for pheasants – yet the overall contribution of the private sector to woodland regeneration has, nevertheless, been significant, with less than 16 per cent of today's woods in the South Downs being state-run (Forestry Commission, 2000).

The classification of 'Ancient' is one of the more important designations pertaining to woodland at present. This description is defined as woodland that has been in continuous existence since 1600. That date was chosen because at around that time universal map coverage of the country had begun; the extent of the woodland before then being mostly a matter of speculation. Ancient woodland may well have been felled and replanted or regenerated several times over the past 400 years, but in so doing it should not have lost valuable sylvan characteristics that are important for biodiversity (Plate 118). Forty-one per cent of the woodlands within the proposed National Park are classified as Ancient. This is a very high proportion in national terms, and it is split fairly evenly between woodlands that are further defined as either 'Plantations' or 'Semi-natural', some of the best examples of which include the yews at Kingley Vale (Plate 75) and also at Butser Hill National Nature Reserves, and the beech and ash 'hangers' in East Hampshire. Plantations could involve the use of exotic tree species, whilst 'semi-natural' must mainly consist of native ones. It has for some time been government policy to have a proportion of these planted woods returned to a more natural state in the hope that this will bring about an improvement in biodiversity.

The role of the woodland-owner

While the nation's timber-deficiencies were being reported in 1918, a similar exercise was being undertaken on a much smaller scale at the Cowdray Estate, which is situated in the most densely-wooded part of the proposed National Park. The Estate had been bought by the Pearson family in 1908, and was subject to a study (Cowdray Estate,1922), which described the forests plundered by war-time felling as 'waste-woods' which were, at the end of 1921, reckoned to cover 71 per cent of the then total of 1900 hectares of estate woodlands. The report envisaged not only a return to productivity in those areas but also to an expansion of the forest on the estate with the planting up of some of the more marginal farmland.

Although the Estate has changed shape over the intervening years, by buying some parcels of land and selling others, it still amounts to around 7800 hectares overall, about one-third of which is wooded. Almost half of this is ancient woodland, a proportion not dissimilar to that in the South Downs as a whole, the main difference being in the ratio of planted to semi-natural woodland; some 90 per cent of Cowdray's is planted, mostly with coniferous species.

The Estate's woodland business, employing 15 people full time in 2006, with the equivalent of at least another 10 full-time jobs engaged indirectly,

needs to operate within the context of national forest policy. This, originally established in the early 1920s as a result of the Acland Committee's report (Ministry of Reconstruction, 1918) mentioned earlier, was primarily about providing the nation with a strategic reserve of timber in the event of war. Understandably, it has changed over time to accommodate ever-widening objectives. Forestry Commission grants, which had aimed to encourage woodland expansion particularly with timber production in mind, have in recent years gradually refocused on woodland maintenance where public benefit in terms of access, landscape and biodiversity is foremost. Thus, policy now recognizes the value of forestry as an economic, social and environmental resource. It is, nevertheless, principally as an economic resource that the larger private woodland-owners, if they wish to run viable woodland enterprises, usually need to evaluate their woodlands. All the same, part of the art of good forest management is to ensure that, overall, despite an emphasis on timber production, the woodland environment is of value. Laudable as the environmental aims of landscape enhancement, recreation and wildlife conservation may be, they remain rather ephemeral, however, when compared with the commercial world of providing for the needs of the timber market. This market currently amounts to slightly less than one tonne of timber or timber-products per person per annum in the UK. Despite the national increase to a large stock of home-grown wood, 85 per cent of our needs for timber is still imported at an annual cost of £8 billion (see Royal Forestry Society website).

At Cowdray, since the early 1920s, as a result of the Cowdray Woods report mentioned previously, the emphasis has centred on the production of timber. This has always been on a sustainable basis – a concept only recently taken up at national and international levels, but recognized many years before by landowning families fully conscious of the need to pass on to future generations something of as great a value as that inherited from previous ones. Thus, whilst over half a million tonnes of timber were felled at Cowdray during the twentieth century, the area of woodland has actually increased.

Originally, this timber was intended only for use on the Estate itself, and even then timber grown more than five miles from the estate sawmill was thought uneconomic to use. In those first few years, the estate's timber did indeed find a guaranteed use within the Estate itself, but, in line with most other private estates at that time, the closure of the estate sawmill in the 1960s opened up new challenges. The demise of estate sawmills was further aggravated by extensive closures of small local privately-owned mills in the 1980s and 1990s, so that now much of the produce from the Estate's woods has to travel great distances for processing at mills that have

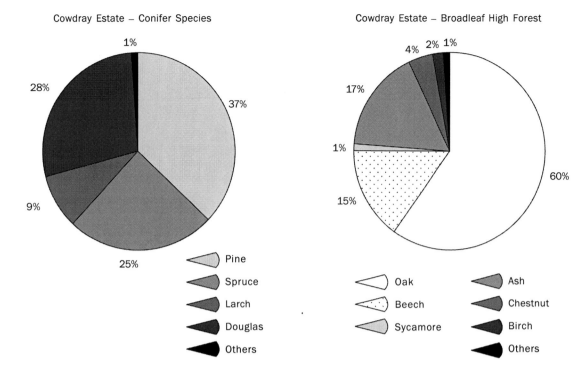

Figure 8.3   Woodland types and species on the Cowdray Estate, 2005.

managed to survive rationalization through the scale of their operations. In the UK, in 1994, 483 sawmills processed 3.68 million cubic metres of timber; six years later, by 2000, there were only 285 sawmills left, but they processed over 4.12 million cubic metres (see Royal Forestry Society website).

For many years the business of private woodlands was somewhat distorted by a favourable tax regime that recognized the long-term nature of the timber-growing process. On many private estates this regime was much used to produce well-maintained, high-quality forests. The system fell out of favour in a welter of bad publicity following exploitation of the loopholes by wealthy individuals, some of whose money was used in ill-favoured planting schemes in environmentally-sensitive areas in uplands, especially in the north of Scotland. Following this, and with the introduction to international timber-trading of former Soviet countries, particularly on the Baltic, putting downward pressure on prices for home-grown timber, many estates, particularly the smaller ones, have run down their woods departments or withdrawn from the market altogether.

Cowdray, as the largest block of privately-owned woodland in the region, had to face the challenges of these altered market conditions. Its managers have chosen to place an emphasis on quantity and quality, the latter being best achieved by high-input early maintenance and by thinning, so that when crops are finally ready to be harvested, they will consist of high proportions of the best available material. Thinning is carried out to provide more growing space for the remaining better-quality trees and helps to

increase the amount of usable timber throughout the life of a stand, as well as to provide intermediate income. Thus a crop of spruce, for instance, may be reduced from a stocking density of 3000 trees to the hectare at planting to a stock of only 400 by the time it is ready for felling at age fifty-five. It is likely that by that time it will have been thinned at least five times, and to consist, at maturity, of mainly **sawlogs:** round lengths of timber, commonly measuring a minimum of eight feet long (2.44 metres) and with a minimum diameter of eight inches (20.32 centimetres) taken from the main stem of a tree and straight enough to be processed economically by a sawmill.

WOODLAND TYPE AND SPECIES CHOICE

The majority of woodlands (80%) in the area of the proposed National Park have been planted. At Cowdray this proportion is even higher (95%) (Figure 8.3). Woodlands can be categorized in a number of ways. One of the most valuable concerns their structure. **High forest** is the term applied to woods that are not likely to be cleared as a crop until they have reached maturity, and consist mainly of trees of the same age. Most coniferous species, even in their natural state, are grown in this fashion. It is also the best way of growing broadleaved trees, where the main object is the production of long clean stems of timber. High forest is mostly regenerated by planting, though natural regeneration by self-seeding is a possibility. Another woodland type, **Coppice**, is created by using the shoots arising from the cut-stumps of a previous crop that has been harvested prior to its reaching maturity. The most common form of pure coppice-woodland has been of sweet chestnut, planted extensively throughout the nineteenth century, particularly in south-east England (Plate 119). Hazel provides another example, especially in Hampshire (Plate 120). A compromise between high forest and coppice is called *Coppice with standards*, when the under-storey wood would be harvested several times over the rotation. In the year 2000, high forest accounted for 85 per cent of woodland within the proposed Park boundary, coppice and coppice-with-standards 10 per cent, and scrub five per cent. The high forest can be further subdivided into 74 per cent broadleaf, and 26 per cent conifer (Smith & Gilbert, 2003).

As seems obvious, species choice is not an option when dealing with coppice or semi-natural woods. With planted high forest, however, the decision as to what to plant on a particular site is the most important one that foresters are ever likely to make, given that they will be saddled with their choice for decades to come. The first consideration, of course, has to be: what are the objectives of management? Is the purpose simply to grow timber, and if so, to be measured only in respect of volume? Is it to provide cover for game? (Remember that there are probably more gamekeepers employed in woodlands in the Downs area than woodsmen.) Is it to provide wildlife-refuges? At Cowdray, the main object has always been to grow timber, but different criteria apply to different sites. Timber-growing may seem the best choice on good terrain with easy access, but what of places like the north face of the Downs, where the prospects of ever being able to harvest timber economically are low? What also of parkland areas, where landscape design is of great importance?

The Cowdray woodlands, in common with most managed woods in Britain, are worked on a *clear fell* basis where a crop of trees is planted and maintained in an even-aged state before being felled as a whole at maturity, ready to start the growing cycle once more. Although this form of management has been chosen for its simplicity, it also has many environmental benefits. This may seem odd, given what seems like a scene of devastation in the immediate aftermath of a clear fell. By continually providing the woodland environment with a variety of age-classes, however, biodiversity can be increased, and insects, birds and plants that have different requirements are catered for.

Clearfelling, using limited coupe-sizes and spread evenly throughout the forest, provides a rolling programme of sites appropriate for species that are suited to one particular niche. Thus, in the few years following clearfelling, most sites provide suitable homes for nightjars, woodlarks and tree pipits, to name but a few species of bird, habitats that would

be in limited supply in a system that involved continuous woodland cover. Similarly, there is usually a recovery of wildflower populations in the aftermath of a clear fell, often from seeds that have lain dormant for years under close-canopy forest cover. Clearfelling also allows opportunities to change the structure of woodlands and open up vistas that would otherwise remain obscured. Many woodlands, particularly on the Downs, were established over short periods of time and benefit from restructuring.

Having decided on what strategy to follow, the decision as to what species to plant to fulfil these objectives on a particular site is rarely straight forward. Fortunately, we are blessed in the South with a wide range of tree species to choose from, unlike most forest areas of Britain where harsh conditions severely limit choice. In order to spread the risks for future marketability it is essential to make use of a broad range of species, though rarely in an intimate way: conifers, in particular, do much better and are easier to manage when growing in blocks of the same species. This variety, along with a mix of ages of crops within a forest brings benefits as far as ecological interest and landscape design are concerned.

Certain facts have to be faced, however: most conifers grow much more productively than most hardwoods and also mature at a much earlier age. Thus, at fifty years old, a beech crop can still be only producing pulpwood or firewood, whilst a neighbouring crop of larch of the same age, consisting mainly of quality sawlogs, can be ready to clearfell. By the time the beech has reached maturity, two larch crops could have been produced and have yielded more than twice as much timber.

In order to grow timber successfully one must not only match choice of species to the type of site, but also speculate on what might be the market requirements many years in the future. With some species taking over a hundred years to grow to maturity, trying to guess the state of future demand involves a great deal of optimism. With the wide variety of soils on the estate, and the many species that can be successfully grown there, it makes sense to spread the risks.

The distribution of woodland type, as between conifer, broadleaf, coppice and scrub at Cowdray is shown in Figure 8.2 and for both the proposed National Park area and for Cowdray.

It will be seen from this that conifers are the most abundant species used, amongst which are:

- **Douglas Fir** (*Pseudotsuga menziesii*) (Plate 121), a native of north-west America, grows at its best on Weald Clay soils, but is satisfactory on sandier areas that were traditionally thought to be the preserve of pines. It grows mostly on sixty to seventy-year rotations, and also does well on the chalk downs, albeit with lesser productivity. With

Plate 121 (*right*)
Fifty-three year-old Douglas fir (*Pseudotsuga menziesii*) on the Cowdray Estate at Minepits, near Fernhurst, West Sussex.
Photo: Val Carver LRPS.

Plate 122 (*centre right*)
Fifty-eight year-old Corsican pine (*Pinus nigra* var. *Calabria*), near Easebourne, West Sussex, 1987, for which the Cowdray Estate was awarded a Gold Medal in the Royal Agricultural Society of England competition.
Photo: Val Carver LRPS.

Plate 123 (*below left*)
Large Corsican pine sawlogs for ultimate use as building timber awaiting transport.
Photo: Val Carver LRPS.

Plate 124 (*below right*)
Small round fencing material; products of an early thinning of larch (*Larix x eurolepis*) at Poors Common road on the Cowdray Estate, 2003.
Photo: Val Carver LRPS.

Plate 125 (*bottom left*)
Oak timber (*Quercus robur*) of a quality for potential use in joinery or furniture, ready to be extracted for roadside collection.
Photo: Val Carver LRPS.

Plate 126 *(above)*
A typical downland scene at West Dean; a beech (*Fagus sylvatica*) hedge fronting a beech shelter belt. Photo: Val Carver LRPS.

Plate 127 *(above far left)*
A mini-swipe weeding a 5 year-old plantation of Corsican pine in Goldballs Plantation, Cowdray Estate, West Sussex, 2005. Photo: Donald Macdonald.

Plate 129 *(left)*
Lonesome pine: the woodland devastation near Midhurst, West Sussex, after the 1987 storm. Photo: Val Carver LRPS.

Plate 130 *(far left)*
A mobile sawmill preparing Douglas fir sawlogs to be converted into 'rustic' sleepers for the garden trade in Cocking Forest, Cowdray Estate, West Sussex, 2005. Photo: Donald Macdonald.

Plate 128 *(left)*
A timber harvester carrying out thinning work in a 40 year-old Norway spruce (*Picea abies*) plantation, Cocking Forest, Cowdray Estate, West Sussex, 2005. Photo: Donald Macdonald.

a good weight-to-strength ratio, allied to a certain amount of natural durability, it is much sought after in large dimensions where it is greatly valued in heavy construction. Its absence from the Baltic countries has meant that its sales price has not suffered compared with other softwood species in recent years.

- **Norway Spruce** (*Picea abies*), is a native of mainland Europe (Plate 128), best suited to soils where moisture retention is high. It grows at its best on the Weald Clay where rotations just in excess of fifty years are all that is required to maximize yields. Although never as valuable, ultimately, as Douglas fir, its virtue lies in the quality of its form, lightness of branch and straightness of stem, leading to early high returns from thinnings. Its greatest use is as a source of carcassing timber in building.

- Both the above-mentioned species create a very dark woodland, with little development of a ground layer of plants once establishment has taken place. A less dense canopy is associated with **Corsican Pine** (*Pinus nigra* var. *Calabria*), a species capable of performing well on a wide range of sites (Plates 122 and 127) but at its best on the Lower Greensand. As a sawlog it is valued for its straightness and roundness (Plate 123), and has supplanted the slower-growing Scots Pine in many instances. Its most common end-use is in fencing.

- **Scots Pine** (*Pinus sylvestris*) is now so naturalized (Plate 72), and seems such a characteristic feature of the southern landscape, that it would be one of the first species to take advantage of any withdrawal from agriculture on the relatively lighter sandier soils, as has been the case on abandoned heathland. It is, however, poor in form and productivity in comparison with its cousin (above).

- **Larch**, particularly in its hybrid form (*Larix x eurolepis* – a cross between the European *L. decidua* and the Japanese *L. kaempferi*), is greatly valued because of its speed of establishment, which can normally be accomplished in three years as opposed to the six years usually associated with pine and spruce. It performs well on the more fertile, yet free-draining, soils of the Lower Greensand. It is valuable as fencing-material, and for cladding and other external use in building (Plate 124).

- Other conifer species that have been planted on the Cowdray Estate include **Western Red Cedar** (*Thuya plicata*), **Western Hemlock** (*Tsuga heterophylla*), **Grand Fir** (*Abies grandis*) and **Sitka Spruce** (*Picea sitchensis*).

Turning now to broadleaves, the main species used at Cowdray tend to be oak and ash on the lower ground with beech on the Downs. This follows the natural pattern that was evident in the pre-human natural forest.

- **Oak**, at Cowdray mostly **pendunculate** (*Quercus robur*), grows best on the heavier soils where its lack of productivity is balanced by its better quality. It is the commonest component of ancient semi-natural woodlands, but as little use was made of it in planting schemes throughout most of the twentieth century, there is an imbalance in age, more than 80 per cent being over 100 years old. It has a wide variety of uses, the very best trees being kept for furniture and joinery (Plate 125), although around a third of the volume of a mature oak-tree is likely to be used as fuel.

- **Ash** (*Fraxinus excelsior*) grows in association with oak as a minor component of the forest canopy. On the north face of the chalk Downs, where conservation and landscape are the main priorities, it grows in mixture with yew and beech. Its main use today is as firewood.

- **Beech** (*Fagus sylvatica*) performs best on the clay-with-flint soils of the Downs where it has been planted extensively (Plate 126). Like ash, it has lost out on the timber market recently, and only the biggest, whitest and cleanest is now used for timber. It is a favourite species for hardwood pulp, and finds a ready use as firewood.

- **Sweet Chestnut** (*Castanea sativa*) is mostly grown as coppice on fertile acid soils where it is now commonly grown on a rotation of between 15 and 25 years (Plate 119). A combination of fading markets and unavailability of harvesting labour has seen its importance diminish over the years, but it still has a market as walking-sticks and fencing.

Other species in Cowdray's woodlands include **Willows**, **Poplars** and **Alder** on wetter ground, with **Birch** present throughout. Most of these species occur naturally and are rarely timber-producing.

FORESTRY OPERATIONS: ESTABLISHMENT, THINNING AND FELLING

Visitors to the countryside often are unaware of the nature of forest operations, and may therefore be concerned when they see work in progress, fearing drastic change to the landscape. Continuous management is, in fact, an essential part of a very complex long-term process of maintaining woodland resources, and it is done with great care for its ecological impact. A short explanation of what is involved on the ground is therefore given here.

As most planting at Cowdray nowadays is in established woodlands, ground-preparation for the next generation concentrates on disposing of the lop and top of the previous one, with very little ploughing ever undertaken. **Burning** or **chipping** of these residues not only prevents pests and diseases but also allows for easy passage, later, of any necessary weeding-machinery. The conditions that encourage good tree growth are also appreciated by competing weed species, and it is not unusual to have over a hundred such species on a site at the start of a rotation, all competing with trees for nutrients and moisture. It is, however, very rare for any overall chemical weed control to be carried out prior to planting.

Planting usually makes use of transplants grown in commercial nurseries. The degree of protection deemed necessary varies according to site and sometimes to the chosen species. Most conifers, particularly on light land, need safeguarding against rabbits, usually by way of fencing; many hardwoods are nowadays planted in tubes which helps protect them from rabbits, hares and deer, provides sheltered conditions for young trees, and allows safe application of herbicides. With fencing adding up to 50 per cent to the costs of planting, and tubing more than doubling it, these are costs which are not lightly borne, but failure to protect some sites can make it impossible to get any trees established.

Bearing in mind that survival is best when using smaller transplants, young plants can soon be swamped by much larger competing vegetation. Some form of **weed control** is therefore necessary; in former times this would have been carried out by men skillfully wielding hand tools, but it is now largely done by tractor-mounted machinery, the manual input being restricted to weeds in actual contact with the plants. Although the light sandy soils of the heaths may have a narrow range of weeds – mostly bracken and birch – they are vigorous, and it is not unusual to have six-inch trees trying to grow amongst three-foot tall bracken. The chalk Downs, on the other hand, have more weed species, many of them of a woody nature. In most cases mechanical weeding is likely to continue for at least three years after planting, normally in late summer to minimize disturbance to nesting birds (Plate 127).

Some years after summer weeding becomes no longer necessary, one final clean is carried out, at perhaps eight to ten years old. The crop is now in what is called the thicket stage, and is then given a period of rest so that it is rarely disturbed until in its late teens. It is then ready for **brashing**, a process that removes the lower branches of the crop to facilitate access for measuring, marking, and other

management. The opportunity is also taken – hopefully for one last time – to get rid of the last of those stubborn woody weeds. The crop has now entered what is called the pole stage.

Thinning is one of the more obvious operations likely to be encountered when visiting a woodland a (Plate 128). It provides more room for the trees that remain, thus increasing the total yield of timber over the lifetime of a stand and providing earlier flows of income. As a general rule, in well-stocked stands, it will be undertaken for the first time in conifers at around age twenty; in broadleaves, thirty years is more likely. In conifers, a cycle of five years is most common and thus a crop is likely to be subject to thinning at ages of roughly twenty, twenty-five, thirty, thirty-five and forty, before perhaps being allowed a period of consolidation in the years leading up to its final felling. In broadleaves, where growth is generally slower, the cycle is more likely to be ten years. Volumes removed at thinning should never be allowed to jeopardize the underlying growth in the capital value of a crop.

Thinning also involves the **selection** of trees of quality, so that only the best are expected to last for the full rotation. This is vital in hardwoods, where the range of quality is wide and where the rewards for quality are great. In an oak plantation, for instance, it is common to start a stand with 1600 trees to the hectare and to end up, one hundred and twenty years later, with only 100. It is therefore essential to ensure that the trees chosen to last the full term are the best. The same applies, albeit to a lesser extent, to conifers, although the differences in reward are not as pronounced as in broadleaves.

In the South Downs, early thinnings of conifer produce mainly round fencing-material. With the absence now of any particle-board mills in the region, poorer-quality wood is often left behind to rot on the forest-floor, although increasing volumes of this type are being chipped in the woods for use in mulches, paths, equestrian surfaces and occasionally as boiler fuel. Subsequent thinnings see an improvement in the size and quality of timber being harvested, with small sawlogs, known as **bars**, coming on stream and ultimately larger sawlogs. Bars are mainly processed into panel-fences with larger logs more likely to produce timber for building.

The main produce from hardwood thinnings is pulpwood or firewood. Until its closure in 2006, around twenty-five thousand tonnes, mostly beech, from the National Park area went each year to the St. Regis pulp-mill in Gwent for paper-making. Despite a series of mild winters there has been a steady growth in the demand for firewood, and many merchants are now equipping themselves with purpose-built machinery. It often takes 50 years in a hardwood crop before any sawlogs can be produced.

When the great expansion of Britain's forests took place in the mid-twentieth century it was assumed that thinning would be commonplace. What had not been anticipated was the effect of wind on newly thinned crops. Trees which had hitherto spent all their lives sheltered by their neighbours were found to be very vulnerable to being blown over. As a result, most of the country's new forests, situated as they are mainly high up in the regions with heavier rainfall, are less likely to be thinned, and in fact are often felled prematurely as a preventive measure. Forests in the South Downs are fortunate in that they are located in an area of low rainfall with less exposure to high winds. Foresters can therefore carry out thinning without constantly worrying about possible windblown damage – though few can forget the storms of 1987 and 1990.

Thinning, in opening up the canopy, allows more light to reach the forest floor and brings about a return of ground flora that may have been completely suppressed during the thicket-stage of a crop. Some species, such as beech, however, form such a dense overstorey that only springtime species like bluebells can thrive. The woodland floor in sweet chestnut crops can also be very bare due to the inhospitable nature of its leaf-mulch.

In some cases the opportunity is taken after early thinnings to high-prune those trees which can be expected to form the final crop, removing all the branches up to a height of around five metres so as eventually to produce sawlogs with as few knots as possible. While this may have a great impact on the appearance of the stand, the rewards for undertaking it seldom justify the expense, except in the most valuable of stands.

The ultimate stage of forest-management, *felling*, when between half and three-quarters of the total production is likely to be realized, is about as traumatic an event as could be imagined. It is liable, therefore, to arouse much public concern, even hostility, born of misunderstanding. Advance planning is essential, and well-run woods should have a minimum programme covering at least twenty years. At Cowdray a twenty-five year felling-plan operates. Prior to felling, any special conservation features are identified and plans put in place to protect and enhance them; opportunities for landscape improvements are noted, possibilities for introducing more varied species considered, and design-improvements to the layout of open ground, streamsides and semi-natural habitats are looked at. Areas suitable for retention (for example, near Wolverstone Farm, west of the A286 road between Cocking and Singleton) are also noted. In such places groups of trees can be allowed to grow beyond normal maturity, perhaps eventually becoming veteran trees with many advantages to biodiversity. In areas of particular sensitivity, a full ecological survey is done, and plans altered if necessary. To minimize the harm to wildlife, all clearfells at Cowdray are undertaken in the winter months when the fauna is more mobile and birds are not nesting.

Ideally, adjacent areas should have at least a ten-year interval between felling, so as to give a patchwork age-class structure to a woodland. Nature, unfortunately, has a habit of spoiling the best-laid plans, and great care has to be taken when exposing new areas to winds that they never had to face in their previous sheltered life (Plate 129).

Most thinning work is now done using purpose-built harvesting-machines which fell, delimb and crosscut individual trees (Plate 130). The larger tree-sizes associated with clearfelling are the preserve of manual chainsaw-operators. The major output is of course sawlogs, but tops and branches must be disposed of if the next crop is to be established successfully and managed properly in its early years. Even after firewood and other minor co-products have been accounted for, there is still a great deal of work to do in disposing of the remainder, usually by burning.

THE FUTURE, AND IMPLICATIONS FOR NATIONAL PARK MANAGEMENT

This chapter has briefly illustrated the complex and finely-balanced process of forest management, illustrated by a case study of a large, well-run private estate. The economic benefits are important in terms of local employment and trade; and good management enhances landscape and ecological values, which also, to an extent, provide opportunities for recreation and tourism. The amount of woodland within the proposed National Park as a whole is high, and it is not thought that there will be any great expansion of forestry except in the unlikely event of agriculture going into a very steep decline at the same time as timber prices greatly improve. Any modest increase that might occur would probably be in the form of woodlands where conservation, game-cover, and quiet recreation is deemed to be the main priority. Like Cowdray's, most private woodland-owners will continue to run their woodlands as businesses and react, in the main, to commercial pressures. It will be primarily to conservation groups such as the Woodland Trust, with the benefit of legacies, donations and corporate support, and to public authorities with recreational or conservation landholdings, that we should look for any expansion.

The importance of conservation, however, is likely to pull strongly in the other direction, with moves to restore heathland and downland in order to improve biodiversity as a major priority. Most of the heathland that has been lost has become woodland, either through planting or through the natural invasion of pine and birch. Although clearance has so far mainly concentrated on scrub-control, there are increasing pressures on well-established woodlands adjacent to restored areas. Most downland that has been lost has remained in agriculture, although there are notable exceptions such as Friston Forest and Queen Eliabeth Forest in Hampshire. Thus any reversion to the more flower-rich pastures of the past is unlikely to affect forestry. Nevertheless, it is a burden forestry has to bear that many woodland sites were originally used for some other purpose, be it heathland, semi-natural woodland or downland, all of which have well-funded supporters seeking change for specific reasons of conservation.

As mentioned earlier, government policy, applied through the Forestry Commission, has changed over time, and is now concentrating on only directing financial support to where there is a perceived public benefit, such as providing recreational opportunities or encouraging biodiversity. Given the long-term nature of forestry, these changes have not always been helpful to woodland management. As recently as the 1980s the Commission was still grant-aiding the felling of ancient woodlands and targeting planted woodlands for replacement with conifers; yet who then would have thought that it would one day be approving the removal of good-quality mid-rotation pines in favour of heather. Clarification may come with the implementation of the English Forestry Strategy of 1998 which sets out how the Government expects to deliver its forestry-policies over the next few years. In it the Government observes that 'Woodlands and forests can provide timber, enhance the beauty of the countryside, revitalise derelict and degraded landscapes, reduce pollution, improve health and enhance wildlife. Woodlands can also generate employment, provide opportunities for sporting and recreational activities, and improve the quality of life in and around towns and cities by screening development and improving the setting for housing and industry. Few other land uses can boast such a diverse range of benefits.'

Reflecting these changes in emphasis, there is an important opportunity for land-management strategies in the National Park area to explore further the ways in which forestry could help to increase benefits to the local economy through employment. This might be through finding new markets, by including the possibility of re-establishing local sawmills, and in other modest improvements to infrastructure, production of high-quality local products, game-cover, tourism and recreation. There could also be benefits to the environment through wildlife conservation and landscape enhancement, and bringing neglected woodlands into proper management.

Drawing on the high standards of practice which this chapter has endeavoured to describe, the aim of such strategies should be towards integration of economic forestry with provision for access, improvement of biodiversity and habitats, and maintenance of local character in the landscape. The Forestry Commission has been active in support of the requirements of National Parks and Areas of Outstanding Natural Beauty, but there is always a need to 'fine tune' the co-ordination of national and local advice and financial incentives to improve the quality and quantity of woodland. The strategies should originate from and relate essentially to the needs of a National Park, and be sensitive to other aspects of management by the Park Authority and landowners, especially in terms of landscape, agriculture, wildlife and recreation.

Forestry is a great exercise in optimism, sometimes misplaced, from the oak-planters of the mid-seventeenth century confident that the results of their labours would be used to build ships, to the Sitka spruce-planters of the mid-twentieth, assured that numerous sawmills and pulp-mills would sprout up in depressed locations throughout the country. Yet one thing has remained constant, and that is the overall demand for timber. Despite growth in recycling there is an ever-increasing use made of timber and timber-products, with over 50 million cubic metres being consumed in the UK in 2004 (Forestry Commission, 2005b). Thus even if all the Park's woodlands were to be fully productive we would struggle to supply one-twentieth of the needs of the population of the South East alone.

Our woods could never be expected to compete with the, as yet, barely-tapped resources of the former Soviet empire. Nevertheless, proximity to markets and the qualitative advantages of British woodlands, along with the potential for added value that exists, must surely offer benefits and commercial underpinning to woodland-owners, encouraging them to create forests that are not only productive but able to fulfil all the other demands made of them in the present.

REFERENCES

Cowdray Estate (1922) Report on the Cowdray Woods. Unpublished.

Forestry Commission (2000) *National Inventory of Woodland Trees, Great Britain.* FC, Edinburgh.

Forestry Commission (2005a) *Forestry Facts and Figures.* FC, Edinburgh.

Forestry Commission (2005b) *Forestry Statistics.* FC, Edinburgh.

Ministry of Reconstruction, Reconstruction Committee (1918) *Final Report of the Forestry Sub-Committee.* F.D. Acland, Chairman. Cmd 8881. HMSO, London. **('The Acland Committee'.)**

Royal Forestry Society, Website www.rfs.org.uk

CHAPTER 9

Water Resources Management

JASON D. LAVENDER

What would the world be, once bereft,
Of wet and wildness? Let them be left,
O let them be left, wildness and wet;
Long live the weeds and the wildness yet.

G. Manley Hopkins

The main rivers of the South Downs, the Arun, Adur, Ouse and Cuckmere, have headwaters well outside the proposed National Park, to the north, and only the Cuckmere reaches the sea within the area itself (Fig. 9.1). Nevertheless, their valleys through the chalk are major features of the Downs landscape, as has been noted in earlier chapters. In the west of the area, the Meon and the Rother (which flows into the Arun) originate in the area itself, and have rather longer stretches within it. The fact that the Downs form only part of each catchment area means that it would be of limited value to consider the condition of, and policy for, these rivers in relation to the proposed National Park, other than in a general sense. There are, however, two other very important reasons for this chapter to be written at a conceptual, rather than a strictly practical level. Despite the new mood of enthusiasm for better management of water as a natural resource, the present unsatisfactory condition of rivers and options for their future are still poorly understood by society and need explanation. Furthermore, the techniques of river-basin improvement are still very much in their infancy. Thus it would be unrealistic to examine in a short chapter the complexities of the situation facing the Downs rivers, and possible courses of remedial

action. It would be better, therefore, to outline in general what has been happening to rivers such as these, and the habitats they provide, and to look at ways in which damage inherited from previous action can gradually be repaired. In doing so the rivers of the Downs will be used, as necessary, to illustrate a general point.

Riparian landscapes

The expressions 'riparian landscape' and 'wetland landscape' are of fundamental importance to the understanding of river-basin management, but precisely what constitutes a riparian landscape or a wetland landscape is the subject of debate. Much of this revolves around questions of definition. For example, are the terms riparian and wetland interchangeable or are they mutually exclusive? Suffice to say, for the purposes of this chapter, the term riparian landscape will be used throughout and, informed by Graf's definition (1985), it is taken, firstly, to refer to a landscape that is in, and directly influenced by, the aquatic environment, predominantly the river-related processes, and secondly, to imply a broader ecological zone. It is not, therefore, used in the restrictive sense of being solely within the banks of a watercourse; it includes the ecosystems adjacent to the river and within the river valley, which are influenced by the aquatic and marine environment (Malanson, 1995).

The result is the use of the term riparian landscape as a definition that includes the broad floodplains,

109

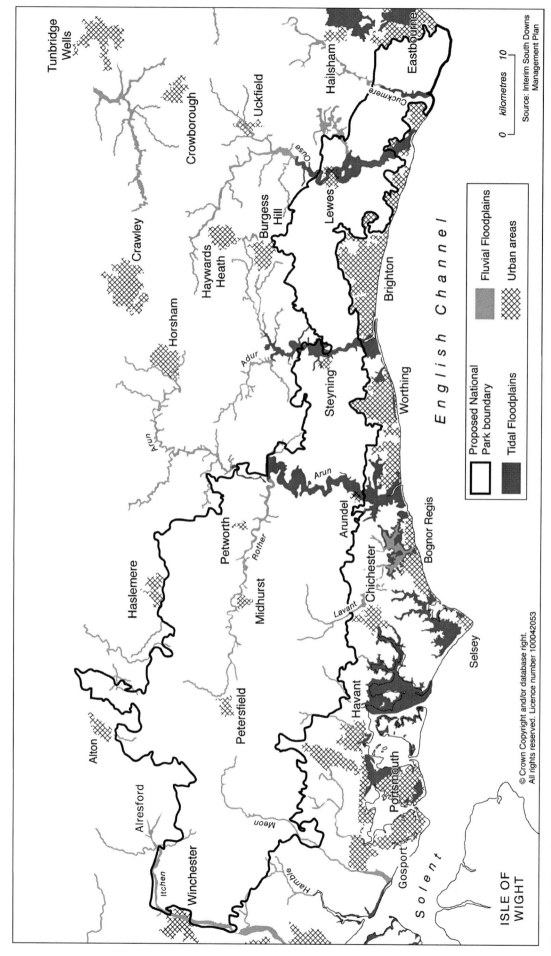

Figure 9.1   The main rivers and flood plains of the South Downs area.

the river channels, the estuaries and islands, as well as the variety of wetland habitats found within it. In a natural context this is a landscape that is continuously reproduced as processes which create patterns that, in turn, control those processes. In a highly modified and artificial context common to most of Britain, the landscape still attempts to reproduce itself, although the degree of artificial modification inevitably affects and limits this.

Wetland habitats

It is important to recognize that wetland habitats within a riparian landscape are variable. They are influenced by the aquatic environment of the river channels to a greater or lesser degree by maintaining natural vegetation and soil structure distinct from the surrounding higher and drier areas. Some habitats may be flooded frequently, others not. Some, depending on the depth of the rivers and tributaries, may have a low water table resulting in drier soils; others may be more characteristic of true aquatic and saturated conditions. Wetlands rarely develop in isolation or as individual types, but are more commonly found in clusters of different habitats linked together to form a complex or mosaic of habitats. When found in isolation, a wetland habitat-type is likely to be the result of modification undertaken in the past, causing the destruction and loss of the other wetland habitats that were once present on some scale. Although a detailed description and examination of wetland habitats is beyond the scope of this chapter, they can be broadly grouped into three types, each supporting a distinctive collection of plants and other wildlife. The term 'naturally-functioning riparian landscapes' used in this chapter refers to a combination of the wetland

Table 9a Naturally-functioning riparian and artificial landscapes

1) *Freshwater*
- Permanent or seasonal rivers and streams
- Riverine floodplains
- Permanent or seasonal lakes and ponds
- Permanent or seasonal marshes and swamps
- Forested floodplains and swamps and peatlands

2) *Estuarine*
- Subtidal estuarine waters
- Intertidal mudflats, salt marshes and reedbeds
- Lagoonal
- Salt lake

3) *Artificial*
- Aquaculture (e.g. fish ponds)
- Agricultural (e.g. farm ponds and reservoirs)
- Urban and industrial (e.g. gravel pits, sewage farms)
- Water storage (e.g. reservoirs and balancing ponds)

Artificial wetlands are not considered further here.

features listed in 1) and 2) in Table 9a below that have not been subjected to artificial modifications caused predominately as a result of civil engineering.

THE CURRENT POSITION

Land drainage – a policy of vandalism

Several commentators have noted the attitudes to the drainage of land in the last thirty years or so. David Baldock of Earth Resources Research wrote that 'the drainage of wetlands has been seen as a progressive, public-spirited endeavour, the very antithesis of vandalism' (Baldock, 1984), whereas Professor David Bellamy exclaimed that 'the continued destruction of wetlands by drainage, exploitation and pollution is the worst act of environmental vandalism being committed on a world-wide scale today' (Bellamy, 1993). Waterhouse (1982) noted the 'intriguing thing about water is that it touches upon pretty well everybody and everything'. Water is indeed a very usable commodity, and yet it has long been undervalued and appallingly misused and mismanaged as a direct consequence of human demands and influence.

Society's ambivalence to, and ignorance of, water, rivers and the riparian landscapes they sustain is puzzling. Human society has developed by the waters' edge. It is often commented that major towns and cities were established on riverbanks and coastlines; the best farmland was on the floodplains, the most productive having been in the estuaries where they were fed by tidal and alluvial deposition. For much of our history, human societies made use of riparian landscapes and wetlands by adaptation, making sustainable use of the tremendous productivity of the resources they provide (Williams, 1994).

Riparian landscapes and the wetland habitats within them historically provided people – directly and indirectly – with an immensely-large range of products and services. Staple food-plants, fertile grazing land, support for coastal and inland fisheries, flood control and protection, breeding grounds for waterfowl, fuel from peat, important plant-harvests and a resource to drink and with which to wash. There are numerous examples of this dependency on, and adaptation to, riparian landscapes in England: the grazing brooks and water meadows of the Downs in Sussex and Hampshire; the Fens of the English midlands; the marshes of Romney and Pevensey and the Somerset Levels; the Essex estuarine salt marshes. Similar adaptations can also be seen throughout the world: the seasonal floodplain agricultural system of the Niger Valley; the adaptations of the people of the Kafue Flats in central Zambia, and the culture and lifestyle of the Marsh Arabs of Iraq.

Despite this general ability to adapt to, and thrive on, sustainably-used wetland habitats, Rackham (1986) tells us that wetland communities, through the centuries, have often been depicted by people from the 'uplands' as a race apart: a people that remained unwilling and unable to conform with the rest of society, and who lived solely on birds and fish, had webbed feet and suffered from bouts of intermittent malarial fever marked by uncontrollable fits of shivering, burning, and sweating. Rackham also tells us that as early as the eighth century, Felix, in his *Life of St Guthlac*, was describing the fens of the English midlands as a place where 'no settler had been able to dwell there before…because of the fantastic demons living there' (Rackham, 1986, p.374). This type of persuasive propaganda stressed that wetland people required rescuing from themselves and from precarious and impoverished indolence to save them from their unprogressive state. And in order to save them, their land required 'improving' by removing the water and increasingly, particularly from the seventeenth century onwards, land drainage and the conversion of wetland into dry land gained momentum and political favour.

As a result, the notion of human communities adapting to riparian landscapes and harvesting their natural wetland resources in sustainable ways gradually became more untenable until the catastrophic collapse of this way of life seen in the last two hundred years. This was, as Williams states (1994), heralded by the arrival of a newer concept derived from the Industrial Revolution when utilitarian views of nature demanded and promoted the exploitation of resources for economic development.

In the context of riparian landscapes this utilitarian concept was increasingly implemented as a policy of land 'reclamation'. This concept was, in part, both informed by, and imbued with, negative depictions of wetlands and wetland-communities, a view that still enjoys widespread and deeply-held credence in many areas today; for example, the current debate exploring the options for the estuarine and coastal restoration for the lower Cuckmere Valley, in which the restoration of inter-tidal habitats has been described by those opposed to it as a re-creation of a landscape reminiscent of the Battle of the Somme (Plate 131). It is no coincidence that in the years since the onset of the Industrial Revolution subscribers to this utilitarian concept of nature have used a policy of land 'reclamation' (i.e. land drainage) to facilitate progressively larger-scale wetland destruction through the use of land-drainage technology and river-system modification. As such, the recent history of riparian landscapes and their wetland habitats and river systems in England is largely one of destruction and loss.

Williams noted that the move away from a concept of adaptation to one of 'reclamation' occurred when particular interest groups became powerful enough to expropriate a communal and societal resource. In this instance and within the context of riparian landscapes and wetlands, this interest group originally consisted of landowners and farmers who have, more recently, been joined by land-developers. As the industrialized world embraced its revolutionary definition of economic progress (i.e. exploit resources for economic development), this definition when applied to riparian landscapes has been implemented as a policy of land drainage that heavily modifies river and coastal systems and destroys complex wetland habitats in an effort to convert wetland to dry land. The benefits to the narrow range of interest groups were quickly realized, easy to identify and highly visible – public funds paid for the widespread land-drainage programmes that made it possible to cultivate marginal land supported by yet more public funds in the form of artificial price-supports for crops grown on drained floodplains. Once the large-scale drainage schemes of freshwater floodplains and coastal marshes were completed, industrial food production and agricultural intensification were encouraged and furthered by industrial technology through increased mechanization, for example, and the use and reliance on pesticides and fertilizers.

The political climate and the huge financial incentives handed out between the end of World War II and the 1990s proved irresistible to the proponents of land drainage. The cumulative effect of a dominant land-drainage policy, housing and road-development pressures and increasing agricultural mechanization and intensification, dramatically altered the pattern of land use in the riparian landscapes with scant regard to the wider economic, hydrological, environmental and societal benefits wetlands once provided.

The affair of the Amberley Wildbrooks, referred to in Chapters 4, 5 and 7, is an example of this, when, fortunately, proposals in 1978 by the Southern Water Authority, a public agency, were rejected following a Public Inquiry, as being contrary to the long-term potential for nature conservation in the area. This, and the well-known issue of the Halvergate Marshes in Norfolk (George, 1992), was the beginning of a turning point. It is only recently that society generally, and policy-makers specifically, have attempted to understand the complexity of the wider economic and environmental costs and their root cause.

Thus we are currently living and attempting to deal with a significant and complicated (and at times seemingly intractable) legacy of river and coastal modification and wetland destruction inherited as a consequence of a land-drainage policy. This legacy has caused, and continues to cause and incur, staggering environmental and economic costs. Before one can fully appreciate the scale of this legacy it is necessary to consider briefly the beneficial role that wetlands and naturally-functioning riparian and coastal systems play for the good of society as a whole.

WATERLOGGED WEALTH – THE ROLE OF WETLANDS IN A RIPARIAN AND COASTAL LANDSCAPE

Edward Maltby, a remarkable and tireless campaigner for the protection and enhancement of wetlands, and the man most responsible for rehabilitating the image of wetlands throughout the world, once wrote that the traditional and widespread view of wetlands is that they are wastelands. He noted (Maltby, 1986) that words like marsh, swamp, bog and fen imply little more than dampness, disease, difficulty and danger, words that consolidated in the minds of many that such waste can only be put to good use if the wetlands are 'reclaimed' (i.e. drained) for agriculture and building development. Nothing could be further from the truth. Far from being wastelands, they are among the most fertile and productive ecosystems in the world. They are essential life-support systems playing a vital role in controlling water cycles, taming floods by absorbing and slowing down floodwaters, providing valuable water resources, cleaning up the environment by trapping sediments and filtering out pollutants, ensuring high productivity of inland and coastal fisheries, providing natural coastal defences that protect us against surges of storm-water and the longer-terms effects of sea-level rise, providing vital breeding and feeding areas for wildlife, and providing fertile grazing land and staple food-plants.

Land-drainage schemes have relied on significant modifications to the riparian and coastal landscape in an attempt to lower the water table of the freshwater floodplains, to move water as quickly as possible out to sea, and to prevent tidal inundation of land seized for intensive agricultural production or built development. As a result, land drainage has largely eliminated the natural characteristics, natural processes and functions of river systems and estuaries, and destroyed the wetland habitats in much of England. Whilst many English riparian landscapes are predominately relict features that are hugely degraded versions of their former selves, particularly in urban areas, this is more pronounced in central and southern England as a consequence of the marked east–west rainfall pattern, together with the uneven distribution of the country's population, all of which results in an over-exploitation of the water resource (Petts, 1988). The South Downs area provides an excellent example of this. The inheritance

from the land-drainage policies of previous years has left us with highly degraded and artificially-functioning river and coastal systems, all characterized by excessive modification and artificial maintenance. Look at any riparian landscape in England, but particularly in the South Downs, and one will fail to find the complex range of wetland-habitat features one would expect, eliminated as a result of a desire to facilitate land drainage on a catchment scale.

Take a walk along the escarpment of Itford Hill, Beddingham Hill and Firle Beacon and look to the west into the Ouse Valley, and then turn to look north into the Glynde Reach and on across to the former wetlands of Laughton Levels. Or stand at either High and Over looking east into the Cuckmere Valley, or at South Hill looking down into the Seven Sisters Country Park. One will be staggered at the overwhelming evidence of excessive artificial modification and manipulation of the river and coastal systems, and the destruction of naturally-functioning rivers and once complex wetland habitats due to land drainage and navigational policies: over-deepened, widened and straightened watercourses, artificially constructed by-pass channels to cut off and isolate meanders, large earth embankments to cut the river from its floodplain and to prevent tidal inundation of former estuarine inter-tidal mudflats and saltmarshes, complex networks of land-drains and ditch-systems to drain water ultimately out to sea, installation of pump-drainage schemes, concrete and sheet-piled river banks and sea walls, treeless river-valley landscapes as a result of the almost complete removal of floodplain woodlands.

HOW IT COULD BE

The position need not be like this but, in order to understand it, policy-makers and the general public first need to recognize that the cycle of droughts and floods, the continuing expense and effort required to clean our drinking water, the degraded landscapes, the remnant fisheries and poor wildlife interest of riparian and coastal landscapes, are the direct legacy of misguided river and coastal management that, in turn, has allowed the expansion of inappropriate and environmentally-damaging land use. There is a desperate need to accept, and celebrate, that natural riparian and coastal landscapes containing a complex and diverse range of wetland habitats have natural functions and economic uses, both of which have economic values, and which deliver tangible benefits to society as a whole. It is the combination of functions, products and ecosystem-attributes that make natural riparian and coastal landscapes important to society (Hughes, 1993). Policy-makers need to examine seriously the benefits that wetlands and naturally-functioning riparian and coastal landscapes can provide in order to ensure the sustainable utilization of our land and water-resource.

THE BENEFITS OF NATURAL RIPARIAN LANDSCAPES

Ten thousand river commissions…cannot tame the lawless stream, cannot say to it 'Go Here' or 'Go There' and make it obey.
Mark Twain referring to the Mississippi River.

Flood alleviation

A quarter of all the rainwater falling on Earth each year runs off as flood flow (Goldsmith & Hildyard, 1984) and routinely results in billions of pounds' worth of damage and regular loss of human life to the world's over-used and over-populated floodplains. In England and Wales, for example, the Environment Agency had a budget of £805 million for 2003/4, one half of which was spent on flood defence. Forty-five per cent of this annual flood-defence expenditure since the 1990s has been spent on capital investment in the existing flood-defence infrastructure (Environment Agency website, 2006) It is this significant annual financial commitment, among other things, that has gradually begun to shift attention away from the traditional river-engineering approach of getting rid of the water fast, draining it from the land and down to the sea in deepened, widened, straightened and embanked rivers. This ever-increasing financial burden, when coupled with the overwhelming evidence that the traditional engineering approach has often failed to protect flood-risk areas (the very thing it is designed to do) (Plate 132), has led to a gradual consideration and investigation of alternative options for flood control.

Take, for example, the Sussex Ouse (or either the Cuckmere, Adur or Arun, for that matter), a heavily engineered and artificially modified river: for two centuries engineers have erased its backwaters, drained its floodplains, cut it off from its floodplains and destroyed its wetland habitats. Known as channelization (see Petts, 1988; 8504 km of rivers were channelized between 1930 and 1980), this was done partly to manipulate the Ouse for navigation and partly to speed floodwaters out to the English Channel to facilitate land drainage. When it rains hard in the High Weald, the peak flows from all the Ouse tributaries rush together in the main river, where once they arrived separately and gradually. With all of the lower Ouse floodplain barricaded from the river, the floodwaters cannot be temporarily stored, having no opportunity to spread out. Consequently, water levels rise ever higher, constrained within artificial channels, resulting in sudden and dramatic over-topping, and creating millions of pounds' worth of damage to homes,

offices, industrial estates, shops and roads in the floodplains of Lewes and Uckfield (adapted from Pearce, 2004) (Plates 133 and 134). Today, here and throughout the country, this situation occurs as the direct result of the land-drainage policy.

Wetland habitats and naturally-functioning river systems and floodplains can alleviate flooding in several ways by capturing surface and groundwater flow. In rivers that take a more tortuous path to the sea, floodwaters lose impetus and volume while meandering through sinuous tributaries. Floodplains that temporarily store them, can allow the water to spread out and slow down. Added to this, the presence of a complex of different wetland habitats, such as floodplain woodlands, reedbeds, seasonal or permanent marshes, can ensure a greater hydraulic roughness to flood-flows thereby increasing the retention and storage of floodwaters. In addition, the reinstatement of a naturally-functioning river and coastal system would release funding from the need to drain farmland, and which could be targeted instead at genuine flood-risk areas (i.e. built property).

Coastal protection

The management of the coast has also occupied the energies of human communities for hundreds of years, and has often included the conversion of estuarine wetlands, predominantly intertidal salt marshes, into dry land in a piece-meal fashion for agricultural, industrial and urban use to meet short-term needs and expectations (Leggett & Dixon, 1994). In places where former salt marsh had been destroyed for agriculture, significant effort went into changing the soil chemistry and structure, and also the installation of field-drains to create grazing-marsh. Considerable public expenditure has been spent on building and maintaining sea walls and, since the 1940s, converting most of the land behind them to arable production. Notwithstanding the increased questioning about the economics and wisdom of continuing to use public funds to protect relatively small areas of land claimed from the sea, taxpayers' money continues to be spent for this very purpose. Taxpayers have provided £200 million between 1954 and 1997 in Essex alone, which equates to a spend of more than £14,000 for each hectare (Dixon, 1997).

It has become increasingly apparent that artificial coastal defences, such as concrete sea walls or maintained shingle embankments, not only require substantial public expenditure to build and maintain, but, because they are poor at dissipating wave energy, they fail to withstand the wave action and storm surges from the sea in the longer term, the forces being much greater than their design capability. As a result they require continual strengthening, rebuilding and maintenance. Also, there is a realization that sea-level change is an issue requiring serious attention.

DEFRA figures record a sea-level rise or an increase in tidal range at a rate of three millimetres each year (Elliott, unpublished). When this effect is considered in combination with the isostatic readjustment from of the last major Ice Age causing southern England to tilt downwards by three millimetres each year exacerbating relative sea-level rise, it quickly becomes obvious that change is inevitable. Simply employing the flawed policies of the past of shovelling money to maintain or build ever-higher sea defences to protect agricultural land created on former estuarine wetlands without considering potential alternatives, is no longer tenable.

One alternative approach is to promote the role that intertidal wetland habitats such as mudflats and salt marshes can play by providing natural buffers to the sea, absorbing the effects of wave erosion and storm surges so that, in effect, they act as coastal stabilization and erosion control. The impact that salt marshes have on the dissipation of wave energy has only recently been identified (NRA Salt marsh management guide, cited in University of Newcastle, 1998), but early work has shown that intertidal wetlands tend to maximize energy dissipation so that tidal and wave energy is damped within the channel and not exported (Pethick, 1994). Also, in a naturally functioning system, salt marshes and mudflats are capable of self-repair and maintenance, and because of the expensive cost of building and repairing artificial sea defences and tidal flood embankments, no-cost natural alternatives begin to look very appealing (Maltby, 1986). The potential these wetland habitats have to provide coastal protection cannot be dismissed, and in localities where they have not been destroyed this role is increasingly recognized.

Water supply

The increased use and uses of water – for drinking, irrigation and industry – is putting an ever-greater pressure on the water-resource provision in England. Southern England in particular is likely to face considerable problems in the near future in coping with the supply of water for these uses. In 2005 the Environment Agency undertook assessments of the availability of water resources in order to understand better the public water supply in this part of the country. Its assessments suggest that water abstraction from both surface watercourses and groundwater aquifers are at the sustainable limit, and would therefore be unlikely to support additional water abstraction. Yet again the policy of land drainage with its aim of draining the land and watercourses as efficiently and quickly as possible means a loss of a valuable water resource to the sea.

The rivers of the South Downs are linked inextricably with their groundwater aquifers, the layers of underground rock or soil that hold the water which swells the springs and wet flushes that feed into the headwater tributaries (Sussex Biodiversity Partnership, 2004). In turn, the aquifers should be re-charged by the rivers where there is a connection with the underlying geology and also when water seeps down from the wetland and floodplains above following periods of rainfall. But, as a result of land-drainage policy, the capacity and ability for the river systems flowing into the South Downs naturally to re-charge the aquifers are currently strictly limited due to a lack of complex wetland habitats and naturally-functioning rivers.

Instead, where the riparian landscapes of the South Downs and the Weald are capable of retaining and slowing down floodwaters, using natural wetland floodplain habitats and sinuous watercourses, the enhancement of low river flows is potentially significant. The retained water, in the form of surface pools and shallow groundwater, could be gradually released into the river system (Kerr & Nisbet, 1996), augmenting levels. In addition the trapping of rain and floodwater by wetland habitats, in the same manner as a giant sponge, would allow for the gradual release and percolation of surface water down into the underground aquifers, not only cleaning the water but also making it available via boreholes for drinking, industrial, and agricultural water supplies.

Pollution control and water quality

The recent successes of water regulatory authorities and the water companies in controlling pollutant discharges of sewage and trade effluents at source, are commendable. They have drawn attention away, however, from the pronounced and detrimental impacts on water quality resulting from the diffuse pollution of sedimentation, eutrophication and elevated levels of agricultural chemicals and pesticides. Again, the policy to remove water from the land as rapidly as possible and out to sea to enable arable and salad cropping adjacent to and on floodplains, has resulted in runoff water loaded with sediments and artificial agricultural chemicals entering both surface watercourses and groundwater reserves. This potential source of drinking water is then contaminated and is likely to require expensive treatment before it can be used for human consumption. In addition, the often gradual seepage and the occasional sudden large-scale input of suspended sediments into water courses via agricultural ditches and field drains has contributed to the detrimental effects on fish and other aquatic wildlife by, among other things, smothering riverbed breeding habitats, such as gravels.

All forms of wetland habitats within a riparian landscape have a role in reducing both diffuse and point-source pollutant inputs to groundwater and surface water supplies. In addition to the obvious benefits of replacing intensive agricultural land use (Kerr & Nisbet, 1996), wetland habitats also offer significant advantages by filtering out soil sediments (including absorbed pesticides, nutrients and heavy metals), soluble forms of nitrogen and phosphorus and oils draining from adjacent agricultural and urban land. Slowing the velocity of water flow with sinuous, meandering natural watercourses increases the 'residence time' of water in a catchment, and as the water passes through dense stands of wetland habitats, sediments are deposited and collected thereby, cleaning the water of suspended material.

Wetland habitats also improve water quality by providing the means for breaking down nutrients in the water, including fertilizers. Wetland soils, with their characteristically low permeable soils, and neutral pHs, have been shown to immobilize, transform and fix trace and toxic metals (Gambrell, 1994), preventing high proportions of these contaminants from entering groundwater or the food chain. Wetland plants in conjunction with wetland soil microbes use an elaborate process to break down complex chemical nutrients, such as nitrates and phosphates, into less harmful forms of nitrogen and phosphorus that are used in plant growth.

The result of the beneficial role wetland habitats perform in controlling diffuse pollution is cleaner water, without requiring the considerable construction, operating and maintenance costs associated with conventional, artificial and engineered water-quality systems.

Wildlife and fisheries

Strongly influenced by water, riparian landscapes support a specialized natural vegetation and maintain soil structure that is distinct from the surrounding drier uplands. This in turn affects the type and diversity of wildlife and fisheries. Maltby (1986) stresses that naturally-functioning watercourses and wetland habitats host, among other things, a rich and diverse collection of plants, fish, birds, mammals, insects and other invertebrates. They offer wildlife, including fish, different ecological niches, not only from one place to another but also at different times. A floodplain with a complex mosaic of wetland habitats, for example, may be flooded at one time of year and dry at another, so fish, birds, and mammals will use the same area at different times. In addition, the rich productivity of wetlands allows them to sustain large populations of organisms dependent on one another, and is responsible for the rich resource of species endemic (i.e. restricted) to wetlands or geographical areas. Natural riparian landscapes are a vast genetic resource, only a fraction of which has been studied, and a still smaller fraction tapped for human use. They have already yielded economically important plants such as rice, plant

products like sago, and fish of various species. They may yield even more important genetic material as yet undiscovered, particularly in the field of medicine.

It is precisely because wetland plants and animals have adapted to their landscape, and depend on wetlands, that they are particularly vulnerable to changes caused by human efforts to artificially manage rivers, coastlines and floodplain areas. Many species are specialized, needing to live exclusively in wetland habitats; others are only able to utilize a particular type of wetland, or to spend only part of their breeding cycle there for specific purposes, such as over-wintering or spawning.

It has already been shown that all English riparian landscapes have experienced significant and long-standing artificial modifications due to the land-drainage policies of the past. It is no exaggeration to state that natural riparian landscapes are relict features in the current English landscape, including the South Downs, and that the diversity and abundance of wildlife and fisheries of these landscapes is poor and best described as remnant. What little is left of the South Downs' natural riparian landscapes and their wetland habitats harbours species formerly more abundant prior to their destruction and loss caused by a combination of land drainage, intensive agriculture, road-building, housing and industrial development within the riparian landscape.

Economic uses

Natural riparian landscapes can be regarded as having natural functions that provide society with a range of benefits and, while not claiming to be exhaustive, these have been outlined above. It is obvious then, that the functions of natural riparian landscapes and their wetlands have economic uses to which economic values can be applied. This was recognized intuitively by England's wetland communities of the past, and in more recent times has been acknowledged following research (e.g. Pearce & Turner, 1990; Barbier, 1989). However, even today, policy-makers at national and local levels have failed to recognize the benefits to society of wetlands; as a consequence, the economic uses and values of wetlands are not understood. It is within this context that Hughes (1993) implores decision-makers to undertake assessments of the economic values of wetland habitats to ensure their sustainable utilization and conservation.

Hughes states that wetlands are important to society precisely because of: the combination of wetland functions – groundwater recharge, flood control, coastal erosion control and protection, sediment and pollutant retention, nutrient retention, water-resource provision; wetland products – timber resources, wildlife resources, fisheries, water supply, agricultural resources; and wetland ecosystem attributes – biodiversity, cultural and landscape diversity and interest. These have economic values. Some are direct-use values derived from the economic uses made of wetland resources, for example, fishing, tourism, and water supply. Others are indirect-use values provided by the wetland resources, such as groundwater recharge, flood storage, sediment trapping, and coastal protection.

SUSTAINABLE USE OR SUSTAINED ABUSE? – THE NEED FOR CHANGE

Observe always that everything is the result of change and get used to thinking that there is nothing nature loves so well as to change forms and make new ones like them.

Marcus Aurelius

Buisson and Bradley (1994) have examined the concept of sustainable use and abuse, but it is worth examining their remarks in the context of naturally-functioning riparian landscapes.

The reinstatement of naturally-functioning riparian landscapes

The legacy we have inherited has left us with a series of highly complex, inter-related and seemingly intractable problems. As members of society we need firstly to recognize these problems by understanding them and accepting that they exist and, secondly, to lift our heads from out of the sand, and to face and deal with them.

The mid-1980s saw the beginnings of a major shift in the approaches to the management of rivers, floodplains and coasts. This was largely seen in mainland Europe, particularly in Denmark and Germany, and in the USA, advances not reflected in Britain. England, in particular, has witnessed only a gradual and a rather reluctant shift in approaches to the management of rivers and coastlines in the last six years, a shift that has almost exclusively been driven forward by wildlife-conservation groups and individuals. The ambivalence to riparian landscapes including their coastal zones and the antagonism to integrated policies appears to be largely political and institutional. Witness the reactionary attitude of national and local government and their agencies, and of non-government organizations, against fully-integrated policies. This frame of mind is only just beginning to be challenged.

Take for example the policy for flood defence. Only now is it beginning to be recognized in some organizations that we have inherited fundamental problems that should never have been addressed by piecemeal and ad hoc works that have little or no regard for natural river or coastal processes (Leggett & Dixon, 1994). By failing to address these and in

continuing predominantly to accommodate the interests of the proponents of a land-drainage policy, these problems were not solved but were diverted elsewhere, eventually to multiply, and which then increased local economic pressure for yet more piecemeal works.

The ecological, hydrological and economic advantages to society of naturally-functioning riparian landscapes have been outlined above. Likewise the disadvantages of a land-drainage policy to ecology, hydrology and economics have also been highlighted. The management of riparian landscapes, therefore, requires a flexible approach. It needs a new philosophy that accords fully with the wider geographical area and its effect on the environment, and which relates to national and societal interests rather than solely to local economies and the wishes of individual pressure groups. This approach's primary mission needs to be the restoration of natural resources, and it has to be fully integrated and holistic and take the longer-term view; something decision and policy-makers are now beginning to acknowledge.

River restoration and coastal managed realignment

Time canonises what earlier seemed an act of wildness. Time chooses.

Vincente Tolodi

Water management has been defined as the art of resolving conflicting demands upon a natural resource, and at the same time it attempts to define and conserve the essential features of that resource (Wood, 1981). Our spectacular failure to do so has led to a shift in the approaches to the management of rivers, floodplains and coasts which, although gradual, have followed the realization that conventional types of river engineering, land drainage and coastal defence are having undesirable ecological, hydrological and economic consequences. The first tentative steps to address these consequences saw the development of new methods of river management used to reduce the impacts of maintenance and capital schemes, which were then followed by adaptation of mitigating works to off-set unavoidable damage (Holmes, 1995). Now, with the advent of heavyweight policy in the shape of the Water Framework Directive (WFD), considered by some as the most significant piece of European water legislation to have been produced, it has been recognized that genuine riparian landscape rehabilitation and restoration works need to be undertaken to reintroduce natural process to our degraded rivers, floodplains and estuaries.

The WFD aims to introduce an integrated and co-ordinated approach to water management in Europebased on the concept of river-basin planning, and this has been transposed into UK legislation; as the sole competent authority for England and Wales, the Environment Agency has been charged with its implementation. Its key objectives are to achieve good ecological and chemical status of all water bodies by 2015, to prevent further deterioration and to enhance the status of aquatic ecosystems and associated wetlands, to promote sustainable water consumption, to reduce the pollution of surface and ground waters and to mitigate the effects of floods and droughts. River Basin Management Plans will be produced by 2009 and reviewed every six years thereafter to ensure, strategic, integrated and (for the first time) ecologically-driven water management. It sounds wonderful, and one trusts the WFD may indeed be the piece of legislation that recognizes riparian landscapes as providing a combination of functions and products important to the whole of society. As an integrated environmental policy the WFD will be the appropriate piece of legislation that puts the concept of river restoration into the heart of the water-managerial decision-making process. This will allow us to reconcile and deal with the legacy of past irresponsible river and coastal management and the destruction of our natural wetlands, and to ensure that future policies for water management benefit the whole of society's requirements.

To ensure a more integrated and holistic water management policy – where connectivity between river (or estuary) and floodplain is seen in tandem with influencing activities within the catchment – it is essential that the concept of river restoration and coastal managed realignment are embraced as vital tools in this process.

River restoration and coastal realignment use conventional engineering techniques to restore the floodplain or estuary as a major component of flood conveyance, as well as for temporary storage of water. Put simply this means that as members of society we need to be promoting and pursuing policies and employing engineering techniques that reclaim freshwater and estuarine wetlands. We need to rehabilitate riparian landscapes by adapting or removing artificial modifications to rivers and streams and estuaries, that is, by rehabilitating rivers and tributaries which are straightened and deepened, removing embankments that prevent tidal inundation of former estuarine landscapes, decommissioning drainage pumps, land drains and ditch networks (all of which require continual maintenance, repair and replacement) and allowing the re-creation of, for example, saltmarsh, mudflat, naturally-functioning rivers, floodplain forests, reedbeds, marshes and wet grasslands. The presence of these restored and naturally-functioning wetland habitats and riparian landscapes would, in turn, bring the type of benefits to society outlined above. It would address the direct legacy of a history of irresponsible river and coastal management that has in its turn allowed the expansion of inappropriate and environmentally damaging land use promoted and encouraged by a long-established land-drainage policy.

Inevitably not everywhere will be suitable for river restoration. Where road and housing development currently exists in floodplains, it is likely that these will always be protected locally by conventional civil engineering flood-defence solutions, for example, the flood-alleviation scheme on the River Ouse through the centre of Lewes, completed at the end of 2004. Undeveloped freshwater and former estuarine floodplains, however, are likely to be very appropriate candidates for river restoration and coastal realignment policies.

The implications for the South Downs of a more integrated and holistic water-managerial policy employing the concept of river restoration and coastal managed re-alignment remain unclear at this point, as to date there has been a general reluctance by policy-makers to move away from conventional policies for river engineering, land drainage and coastal defence. Recognition that the concept of river restoration and coastal realignment is a legitimate alternative or complement to the conventional water managerial techniques is relatively recent. As a result, applying it to specific reaches of river, to river sub-catchments or to entire river catchments has not yet undergone detailed and rigorous research. Policies for river restoration and coastal realignment for the degraded riparian landscapes of the South Downs will be informed following detailed design and the needs of the catchment, and they will need to be tailored to individual reaches under consideration (Brookes, 1990). The potential restoration options for the South Downs will be influenced by a variety of factors such as the existing physical environment, the wider objectives and the extent to which the degraded landscape can be restored.

Although there are few detailed studies of river restoration for all the catchments within and upstream of the South Downs, it is possible to envisage the type of modifications to the existing policies for water and river management that could be appropriate – the setback of artificial embankments to allow tidal inundation and the restoration of inter-tidal habitats, the restoration of sinuous watercourses and of freshwater habitats such as reedbeds, floodplain forests and so forth, to provide the range of benefits outlined above. It is important to stress, however, that these observations are at this stage largely subjective in content, relying on judgement and experience of river management, and not upon any detailed technical appraisal. As such, it is vital that these observations are considered with caution, at least until they might be more fully investigated and understood. The key at this stage is to raise initial awareness and understanding of some of the issues affecting the future policies for water management.

Plate 131

Part of the lower Cuckmere Valley; the artificial embankments can be seen which, if removed, could allow water to disperse across the floodplain, thereby providing a natural and temporary storage of flood water.
Photo: John Tyler, courtesy of SDJC.

Plate 132

Floods at Bramber, West Sussex, c.1931; from an old postcard, photographer unknown, courtesy of Rendel Williams.

Plate 133

Bell Lane, Uckfield, East Sussex, at 10.30 a.m., 12 October 2000; land-drainage policy has encouraged building on floodplains, the catastrophic results of which can be seen. Uckfield is in the catchment area of the River Ouse just outside the proposed South Downs National Park. At times of heavy rainfall, flood water cannot remain within artificially deepened river channels, altering dramatically the amount of overflow the results of which can lead to misery for local residents and millions of pounds worth of damage to built property.
Photo: Alan Thompson, the Symonds Group, courtesy of the Environment Agency.

Plate 134

The centre of Lewes, East Sussex, at 2.00 p.m., 12 October 2000. Typical of many lowland rivers, the Sussex Ouse has been heavily engineered and artificially modified, resulting in the loss of wetland habitats in naturally functioning floodplains. This has robbed the river catchment of the ability to cope with flooding; downstream towns suffer as a consequence.
Photo: John Gower, courtesy of the Environment Agency.

Plate 135
Mountain bikers on an 'open access' section of the South Downs Way west of Ditchling Beacon, March 1996. Photo: Phil Belden.

Plate 136
Guided walks are also popular, often organized through groups such as the Ramblers' Association. Photo: Mark Brookes, courtesy of SDJC

Plate 137
Walkers on the Hampshire Hangers. Access and recreation are key uses of the Downs. Photo: Nick Heasman, courtesy of SDJC

Plate 138
Visitors to the South Downs peacefully enjoying the scenery; the Long Man at Wilmington, East Sussex, is in the background. Photo: Peter Greenhalf, courtesy of Natural England/SDJC.

Plate 139
The extensive bridleway network and underlying dry chalk geology make the South Downs particularly popular with horse-riders, though not necessarily with hikers, who suffer from interrupted walks and churned up and often muddy pathways; here riders are pictured just south of Wilmington, East Sussex, c. 1985. Photo: Paul Millmore.

Plate 140
The bridleways up the steep scarp-slopes of the Downs can suffer from severe erosion if not properly maintained. Here rangers repair a deep gulley in Bridleway Westmeston 33 – an expensive procedure. Photo: Paul Millmore.

Plate 141
Paragliding, a more recent development from hang gliding using a cheaper, specially-designed parachute wing, has become increasingly popular. The scarp-slopes of the Eastern Downs provide ideal launch-sites for this sport. Photo: SDJC.

Plate 142
A mountain biker on the South Downs Way, west of Lewes, c. 1996, negotiating and, importantly, closing the gates. Design improvements to the humble bicycle have made the Downs accessible to this form of sustainable recreation. Photo: Paul Millmore.

Plate 143
This extreme example of pressure on the South Downs trackways speaks for itself; the four-wheel drive 'Southern Hill Rally' on the escarpment at Kingston, near Lewes, East Sussex, August 1995. Photo: Phil Belden.

CONCLUSION

Going up that river was like travelling back to the earliest beginnings of the world, when vegetation rioted on the earth and the big trees were kings.

Joseph Conrad

River restoration is clearly one of the more pressing needs facing natural-resource management in the Downs, and is readily justifiable in environmental, social and economic terms. This challenge, however, is not one to be tackled solely in the Downs; the headwaters of most rivers flowing through the area arise at a considerable distance inland, and, with the exception of the Cuckmere River, the outflows to the sea lie outside to the south. For the proposed National Park, therefore, the action required could be summarized as:

- Ensuring that all policies of land management and recreation are fully attuned to the requirements of river restoration, flood defence, aquifer protection, and the related ecological opportunities; this needs to be pursued and monitored under the require-ments of the Water Framework Directive;

- Helping to inform landowners and farmers, public authorities, the general public and schools of the aims and methods of river restoration;

- On all matters affecting water as a resource, working in close partnership with the Environment Agency, other public bodies and local authorities within and adjoining the area;

- Demonstrating the importance of landscape design in management of the sections of river basins and the coast within the area.

REFERENCES

Barbier, E.B. (1989) *The Economic Value of Ecosystems: 1. Tropical Wetlands.* IEED & Environmental Economics Centre, London.

Brookes, A. (1990) Restoration and Enhancement of Engineered River Channels: Some European Experiences. *Regulatory Rivers: Research and Management* **5**, 45–56.

Buisson, R.S.K. & Bradley, P. (1994) Human Pressures on Natural Wetlands: Sustainable Use or Sustained Abuse? In: Falconer, R.A & Goodwin, P. (eds) *Wetland Management.* Thomas Telford, London. pp. 35–46.

Dixon, M. (1997) The Rising Tide. *Natural World.*

Elliott, M., *A Guide to the Tidal Floodplain of Sussex and its Potential for Restoration.* Unpublished.

Gambrell, R.P. (1994) Trace and Toxic Metals in Wetlands – A Review. *Journal of Environmental Quality.* **23**.

George, M. (1992) *The Land Use, Ecology and Conservation of Broadland.* Packard, Chichester. pp. 282–304.

Goldsmith, E. & Hildyard, N. (1984) *The Social and Environmental Effects of Large Dams.* Wadebridge Ecological Centre, Cornwall.

Graf, W.L. (1985) *The Colorado River.* Association of American Geographers, Washington DC.

Holmes, N.T.H. *(1995)* Rehabilitation of Floodplains. In: Linnean Society of London, *A Symposium on UK Floodplains. 25–27 October 1995.* Abstract of Papers. Linnean Society, London. p. 20.

Hughes, J.M.R. (1993) The Use and Abuse of Wetlands. In: Mannion, A.M. & Bowlby, S.R. (eds) *Environmental Issues in the 1990s.* Wiley, Chichester.

Kerr, G. & Nisbet, T.R. (1996) *The Restoration of Floodplain Woodlands in Lowland Britain – A Scoping Study and Recommendations for Research.* Environment Agency, Swindon.

Leggett, D. J. & Dixon, M. (1994) Management of the Essex Saltmarshes for Flood Defence. In: Falconer, R.A. & Goodwin, P. (eds) *Wetland Management.* Thomas Telford, London. pp. 64–73.

Malanson, G.P. (1995) *Riparian Landscapes.* Cambridge University Press.

Maltby, E. (1986) *Waterlogged Wealth. Why Waste the World's Wet Places?* Earthscan, London.

Pearce, D.W. & Turner, R.K. (1990) *Economics of Natural Resources and the Environment.* Harvester Wheatsheaf.

Pearce, F. (2004) We Can't Hold Back the Water Anymore. *New Scientist,* 10 January.

Pethick, J. (1994) Estuaries and Wetlands: Function and Form. In: Falconer, R.A. & Goodwin, P. (eds) *Wetland Management.* Thomas Telford, London. pp. 75–87.

Petts, G.E. (1988) Regulated Rivers in the United Kingdom. *Regulatory Rivers: Research and Management.* pp. 201–20.

Rackham, O. (1986) *The History of the Countryside.* Dent, London.

Sussex Biodiversity Partnership (2004) *The Habitat Action Plan for Sussex Rivers and Streams.* Sussex Biodiversity Partnership, Chichester.

University of Newcastle (1998) *North Sea Camp Realignment.* University of Newcastle.

Waterhouse, J. (1982) *Water Engineering for Agriculture.* Batsford, London.

Williams, P.B. (1994) From Reclamation to Restoration – Changing Perspectives in Wetland Management. In: Falconer, R.A. & P. Goodwin, P. (ed) *Wetland Management.* Thomas Telford, London. pp. 1–6.

Wood, T.R. (1981) River Management. In: Lewin, J. (ed) *British Rivers.* Allen & Unwin, London.

CHAPTER 10

Countryside Recreation in the South Downs

PAUL MILLMORE

In a sense the importance of recreation on the Downs has been governed by only a few factors – some of which are interlinked. These are the amount of leisure time available to the people of this nation, the amount of disposable income available to the general population, the prevailing fashions for how individuals wished to spend their leisure time, and the proximity (in terms of time and cost) of the Downs to centres of population.

Historically, the well-off have always had the time and the money to treat the Downs as a place of leisure, and hunting, in all its forms, has been their pastime for hundreds, if not thousands, of years (Brent, 2004). It is only since the industrialization of Britain, from the eighteenth century onwards, combined with the first turnpike roads, then railways and more recently the development of the automobile, that the wider population has been able to have both the finance and the time truly to 'enjoy' the Downs. An example of this trend can be read in Dr Gideon Mantell's introduction to a small publication of 1846 entitled *A Day's Ramble in Lewes:*

> In one of the most beautiful river valleys of the south-east of England, and spread over the terminal slope of a range of chalk hills that stretches along inland, in a direction nearly parallel with the Sussex coast, is the interesting town of LEWES, which the Railway, recently completed, has brought within a two hours journey of the Metropolis . . . That Lewes will speedily rise in importance and regain its former prosperity, there can be little doubt; for the beautiful and salubrious situation of the town, the

invigorating influence of the climate, and the objects of natural and antiquarian interest with which the environs abound, render it a most desirable resort for visitors of every description, and a charming retreat from the ceaseless turmoil of the Metropolis.

While one recognizes that this is a Victorian 'puff' for the town, it highlights how easily the Downs could be reached from London, even in 1846. Now the journey time is a little over an hour, and in real terms the fares are probably significantly lower.

The varying attitudes towards this chalk landscape are best explained by Dr Peter Brandon in the first chapter of this book and in his other book *The South Downs* (1998). Suffice it to say that the recreational value we now place on the South Downs is one of the key reasons why the area is presently being considered for National Park status. So what makes the area so special in recreational terms? Again Brandon covers this aspect extremely well, but in essence it is the openness of the views, the sense of space, the fascinating history, wildlife and archaeology that all combine to form a quintessential 'English' landscape that is particularly easy for the people living in the region to reach.

A DETAILED LOOK AT THIS 'ACCESSIBLE' LANDSCAPE

Local information on recreation in the South Downs was not readily available until recently, because no particular body was given the task of gathering data

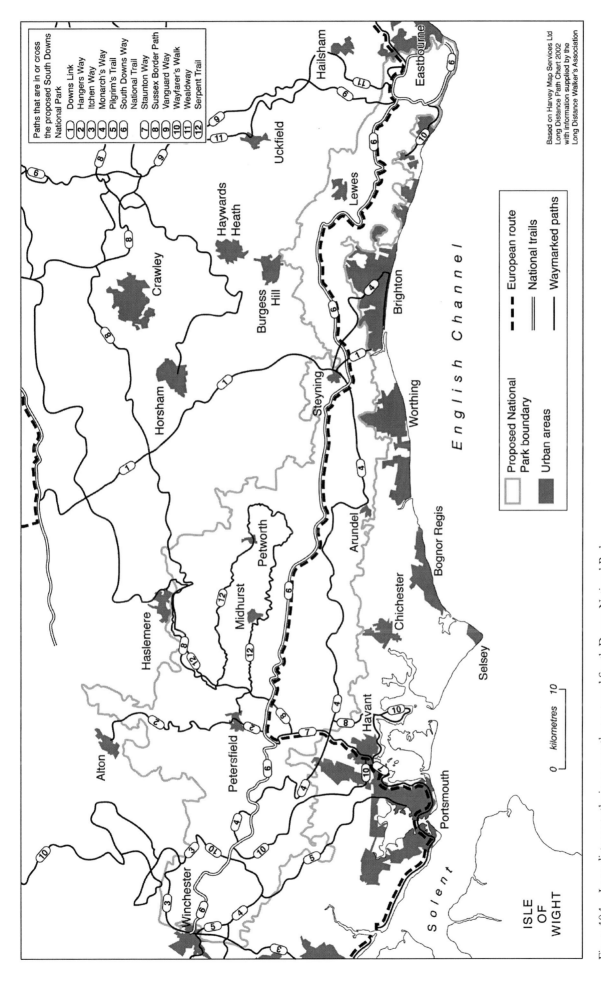

Figure 10.1   Long-distance paths in or near the proposed South Downs National Park.

for this specific area. Fortunately the pressure of the National Park Public Inquiry (see Chapter 13) led the South Downs Campaign to gather together some of the relevant data and to analyse their importance for future management. The Countryside Agency also commissioned a survey of recreational use (Broom Associates, 2003) to help its officers put their case. This chapter uses both the Campaign's and the Agency's work to give the most up-to-date South Downs-focused picture of recreational activity. Many of the references refer to documents that had been submitted to the National Park Inquiry, and at the time of writing these were lodged in the Inquiry library (but see references on p.129).

SOME RECREATIONAL DATA

Paths and rights of way

For the south-east of England, the South Downs area contains an exceptionally rich network of *paths* complemented by substantial areas of publicly accessible land (Appendix 10A, p.129). The two Areas of Outstanding Natural Beauty (AONBs) of Hampshire and Sussex have 2745 kilometres of rights of way (figures supplied by the East Hampshire AONB Joint Advisory Committee and the the Sussex Downs Conservation Board), with the designated National Park area having 3244 km (see Appendix 10B, p.131, and South Downs Conservation Board, Inquiry document CD178), the highest length and density of *rights of way* of any National Park (Appendix 10B). The Downs themselves have a significant number of recreational routes crossing them. This includes the South Downs Way, among the country's most popular National Trails if judged by sales of its National Trail Guide (Burnett, pers. comm.) and its website receiving the highest number of 'hits' of any National Trail website (Jenman, pers. comm.). Between 10,000 to 20,000 people per annum – a mixture of walkers, riders and off-road cyclists – complete the 100 miles of the whole trail (Jenman, pers. comm.) and many more use sections of it. The Trail is also part of the E9 European Walking Route between Dover and Plymouth, going along the South Coast (Fig. 10.1).

The South Downs area also has one of the best networks of *long-distance footpaths* in the country (*Out and About*, Inquiry document CD178), including the Vanguard Way, the Weald Way, the Monarch's Way, the Pilgrim's Trail, the Downs Link, the Sussex Border Path, the Itchen Way, the Hangers Way, the Staunton Way and the Wayfarer's Walk (Fig. 10.1). As can be seen by their names these are historic paths, many of which are bridleways, which for centuries have been used by travellers, pilgrims and those walking for pleasure. More recently, parts of the National Cycle Network (NCN) have been established within and across the proposed National

Park (Routes NCN 2, 20, 22, and Regional Routes 88, 89 and 90) (Plate 135).

To put the significance of the path network in context, it has been calculated that in the last three years over 4500 *guided walks and rides* (see figures in Appendix 10C, p.133) have been organized by local ramblers groups, the Society of Sussex Downsmen (now the South Downs Society) and the three county councils within the proposed South Downs National Park. Each walk has attracted up to 40 people and covered downland, weald and river valleys (Plate 136). This, of course, excludes the far more numerous walks undertaken by individuals or other groups, and going for a walk was by far the most popular recreational pursuit identified by the survey commissioned by the Countryside Agency with 25 per cent of visitors giving this as their main reason for visiting the South Downs. Walking (Plates 136 and 137) was closely followed by a visit to a tourist attraction or place of interest (24%) and relaxing (Plate 138) or enjoying the view (19%) as the primary motivations for visiting (Broom Associates, 2003). It is worth noting that there was very little participation in these rambling activities by the ethnic minority population – an issue that any new National Park Authority will have to tackle.

Importantly, there is a vast array of *books and maps* available, documenting and describing walks (Channer *et al.*, 2005; Perkins, 1996, 2000 & 2001; Price & Price, 2001) and cycle rides in the Downs, as well as routes published in local newspapers (Evans, 1995; Hancock & Toms, 2004; Perkins & Walsh, various dates) which help to ensure that both local people and visitors are provided with the available information. The Broom Associates report noted that Ordnance Survey (OS) maps are a particularly important source of information with 27 per cent saying they used them and 41 per cent of staying visitors doing so. Additionally, OS maps now are the only source of information about the Countryside and Rights of Way Act (CRoW Act) open-access land, and their importance is likely to grow. The South Downs Way National Trail Guide has sold over 20,000 copies since its first publication in 1990 (Burnett, pers. comm.), and is among the best selling of all the National Trail Guides in the UK. The substantial sales of all these South Downs guides are a clear reflection of the popularity of the area for quiet recreation.

The many river valleys within the South Downs (see Chapter 9) not only offer level riverside routes for those less able to cope with steep terrain but, in many cases, also access to water for canoeing, kayaking, and boating, as well as more leisurely pursuits such as *fishing*. Nevertheless, the recreational *boating* use of the rivers has declined during the twentieth century. For example, prior to World War II there was a small paddle-steamer plying a trade between the Golden Galleon Pub (at the A259 crossing over the Cuckmere River) and Cuckmere Haven as well as boating and canoeing facilities upstream at both Alfriston and close to Drusillas; all of these have now gone.

Horse-riders consider that the South Downs offer superior conditions for riding and that the **bridlepath** network is one of the most important in the country (Parker & Payne, pers. comm.) (Plate 139). The Downs themselves are important because of the undulating nature of the ground and the free-draining chalk supports a turf which remains relatively dry in winter and springy in summer. Horses can therefore be ridden at speed without straining their tendons. It is worth noting that much of the downland between Eastbourne and Brighton was a military training ground, particularly for cavalry up to World War I (a detailed map of this military training area is available in the library of the South Downs Society).

The South Downs Way is the only National Trail open to horse-riders along its entire length. Its route acts as a spine to the dense network of bridleways, and thereby provides innumerable, much valued, local circuits. In addition, much of the arable land on the Downs is free of gates, and even where livestock are kept, the fields are of a size that requires fewer gates to be negotiated than elsewhere.

The Western Weald is also of great importance for recreational horse-riding because of the combination of a high density of interconnected bridleways interspersed with areas of open access, particularly the heathlands. These areas are especially significant because they afford natural sand tracks which provide good un-poached going whatever the weather conditions. It is possible to spend a morning, or even a full day, in the saddle without recourse to riding along roadside verges, which is an exceptional experience for a horse-rider in this country.

The sheer cumulative volume of planning applications for new **stabling** facilities within and around the South Downs over the last decade (approximately 30 per annum) is a reflection of the area's growing popularity for riding (figures provided by Martin Small, and see Chapter 11). This continued growth in the popularity of riding is leading to an increased need for bridleway maintenance and in some areas landscape degradation (Plate 140).

The extensive bridleway network – close to centres of population – has also seen a spectacular growth in **off-road cycle use** over the last two decades (Plates 135 and 142). As this tends to be an individualistic rather than a club sport the best reflection of its popularity in the South Downs are the numbers of bicycle shops within easy reach of the South Downs Way (Millmore, 2004).

Road-cycling in this superb landscape should not be discounted from the recreational picture. The Cyclists Touring Club, by way of example, organized 25 *randonnées* in and around the designated National Park in 2004, which on average attracted 150 participants per event (Green, pers. comm.). The London to Brighton Bike Ride, which passes through the Downs at Ditchling Beacon, has on average 50,000 participants each year.

Opponents of the proposed South Downs National Park have made much of the lack of access land. This, however, ignores the fact that when the first National Parks were established, they were also created in the absence of any formal access land. That was because there was no legal requirement for a National Park specifically to have access land before designation can occur. It should also be noted that National Park Authorities have had 50 years in which to secure many access agreements and the resources to follow them up. While the South Downs may have less formal access land than the existing National Parks, its rights-of-way network is far superior (Appendix 10B), and a South Downs National Park Authority would be able to build from this very strong position. Nevertheless, as the South Downs was one of the first areas in England to have its open-access land mapped under the CRoW Act there is now a detailed picture of the extent of this new 'right to roam'.

There are 8155 hectares of land identified as **open-access land** within the South Downs (Plate 135). This is somewhat fragmented, however, consisting of 322 separate parcels. Approximately half lies in West Sussex (3902 ha), a quarter in East Sussex (2145 ha), and a quarter in Hampshire (1952 ha). Brighton and Hove City has only 156 hectares (figures supplied by SDCB, October 2004). The bald figures give a rather skewed picture, as quite a substantial area of existing access land has not been mapped. This is because of the very tight definition of 'unimproved chalk grassland' that meets the requirements of 'downland' under the Act. Thus much of the 300 ha of the Seven Sisters Country Park, which has actually been public access land since 1971, is not mapped under the CRoW Act as the land was previously 'improved'. Only 35 ha, or 12.5 per cent of all access land in the Country Park is actually mapped under the Act (Beattie, pers. comm.). Woodland with public access, such as Friston Forest, is of course also excluded, as is all of the foreshore. Overall only three per cent of the South Downs is open-access land and only one-third (1%) of that has been created by the new CRoW Act.

A glance at the new Ordnance Survey Explorer maps, which show designated access land, reveals that most of the new access rights on downland are on very steep slopes – not really ideal for roaming freely! In terms of geographical distribution the concentration of access land in the South Downs is at its eastern end. This is because much of the remaining 'unimproved chalk grassland' is on the steepest slopes, which are also concentrated geographically in the eastern half of the Downs. Historically, purchases or gifts of land for access by public and charitable bodies have also been focused on the most spectacular landscapes, especially where the Downs meet the sea. Nevertheless, the CRoW Act designations are the start of a process that, combined with agricultural change, could over time restore to the public at least part of the Downs that so enthralled writers like W.H. Hudson (1900) or Arthur Beckett (1909).

Perhaps the greatest future opportunity for increased public access, combined with landscape enhancement, lies in the landholding of Brighton & Hove City Council. Over 12,000 acres of downland, surrounding this city by the sea, have been owned by the local council since the 1930s. However, the financial pressures to generate income from farm rents, combined with post-World War II agricultural production-subsidies, has unfortunately led to most of this land being ploughed for arable cultivation. Fortunately the City Council is presently reviewing its managerial policy for the downland it owns, and one hopes this will lead to greatly improved access.

Charitable landholdings on the Downs have not been immune to this financial pressure to maximize rents, and even the National Trust owns land at Telscombe and at Chyngton Farm in the Cuckmere Valley that is still under the plough. Similarly Eastbourne Borough Council bought 4000 acres of downland for 'public enjoyment' in the late 1920s but has yet (despite real but temporary improvements in the 1990s) to permanently return access to all of this land back to the people who paid for it!

One hopes that the impetus of the CRoW Act, combined with changes in agricultural subsidy, may generate sufficient political will for most, if not all, of this land to be returned to grassland. If the local councils and charitable trusts then dedicate it in perpetuity as access land, it could provide the local population (almost 500,000 people between Eastbourne and Shoreham) with a permanent 'green lung'.

It should be noted that the CRoW Act even allows for additional rights to be granted – to cyclists and horse-riders for example. How much extra land, and what greater rights will be added over the coming years, will depend in some part on the generosity of future (and existing) landowners, and to some extent on how much more the landowning community becomes financially involved in the tourist industry. The closure of the countryside during the Foot and Mouth outbreak between March and May 2001 highlighted how financially important public access is to the downland communities, but whether this will make an impact on the decision-making process of individual and public landowners remains to be seen.

VARIETY OF LANDSCAPES

Part of the reason for the exceptionally high use of the South Downs by walkers, cyclists and riders is because of the wealth of landscapes and experiences available (see Millmore, 2004, pp. 18–28). From the feeling of being alone, remote and free on top of the Seven Sisters with the sea air and the gulls swooping and screeching, to the intimacy of the river valleys with their historic market towns and villages, the South Downs offers landscapes of great variety and splendour. These landscapes also present many opportunities for people to cycle, ride or walk miles and miles, or just for a short distance, and yet still be able to experience the area's beauty and uniqueness. On much of the chalk Downs, the paths are not only numerous, but also broad – even undefined (such as over the Seven Sisters) – creating a feeling of freedom and space similar to 'access' land.

Some of the land within the proposed National Park is not a chalk landscape, but a key part of the lure of the area is that from these equally beautiful low-lying surroundings one can gaze on the undulating beauty, skylines and shadows that the shape of the hills generate (sunrise and sunset are the best times to appreciate the special qualities of the downland landscape).

The ***heathlands*** within the South Downs are not only important for wildlife but are also extensively used for recreation. They provide superb opportunities for those seeking access to open country. In many places it is possible to walk or ride for long distances across extensive tracts of open country surrounded only by heather, birch and pine, often with views of the Downs or Hangers. These provide a different sense of wildness not available on the chalk Downs themselves. At points, such as on Older Hill, Iping Common, Woolmer and Longmoor there are breathtaking views of semi-natural countryside (Plate 25). In April 2005 the Sussex Downs Conservation Board opened a 60-mile long-distance footpath, 'The Serpent Trail', which links nearly all these special heathland sites together (Fig.10.1).

From high points, it is possible to see far out across the sea, down the river valleys, over the High Weald and even to the Isle of Wight and the the North Downs. Clearly, the scale and remoteness of these varied landscapes provides a context within which it is possible to 'escape', avoiding traffic noise, other people and built development to enjoy tranquillity, nature and peace.

There is no doubt that the sheer diversity and scale of the landscape are of great appeal to those living in Britain and particularly in the crowded South East. The day-to-day experiences of this nation's population are most likely to be of town or city life. Hence it is unsurprising that so many want to be within the South

Downs, making use of this 'superior recreational' experience.

ACCESS FOR ALL – DISABLED, YOUNG, OLD

Not only does a huge number of people want to use the South Downs for quiet recreation, but most people actually can. This is partly due to the generally underlying 'dry' geology of the chalk, which allows year-round access, but also its proximity to urban centres, with a good network of public transport both within and around the South Downs – even from as far afield as London. Walking, cycling and riding opportunities are many, and the psychological as well as the physical freedom that can be gained from simply stepping out of the nearby urban areas into this splendid countryside should not be underestimated. The easy, low-cost accessibility combined with the network of gated (rather than stiled) paths (Plate 142), make the South Downs particularly attractive to the disabled and socially or economically excluded. While a number of north–south transport corridors can have an impact locally on the tranquillity of the countryside, the fact that they also provide access to the area for visitors should not be dismissed. Indeed, the rich network of paths has been accommodated in their design by including numerous safe crossings (for example in the six miles between Liss and Petersfield there are ten or more crossings over the A3 (T) so ensuring that the roads do not in any way prevent long-distance walking, cycling or riding).

Nevertheless, there is still much room for improvement over safety – especially at some of the road crossings of the South Downs Way (Plate 160) and the South Downs Campaign would expect the National Park Authority to be able to raise the priority of these much-needed works. Equally, the preparation and implementation of imaginative Rights of Way Improvement Plans should significantly enhance the accessibility, functionality and safety of the downland path network. Perhaps even the Roman Road network and the navigable rivers might become open to all.

Historic and cultural opportunities

The South Downs have become an iconic landscape. Chapter 1 recounts the stories and visions that many writers, poets, composers and artists have produced of the area: these are both inspiring and alluring. With so much literature, art and history embodied in this landscape, it is not surprising that visitors are drawn to the area. Not only can one visit some of the historic houses, barrows, tumuli, hillforts, castles, windmills, dewponds, mansions and parks, old pubs and tea shops, but most of the villages have Saxon or Norman churches, interesting artefacts, stories

and landmarks all of which help the visitor enjoy and understand the historical context of the South Downs (South Downs Campaign, 2003).

Other recreational opportunities

The South Downs offer many other recreational opportunities including canoeing, sailing, diving, painting, gliding, hang-gliding, paragliding, bird watching, plant hunting, metal detecting (once derided by archaeologists but now far more acceptable since the introduction of the Portable Antiquities Scheme), kite and model-aircraft flying, fishing, shooting (a vital income earner for many downland farms and estates; rough shooting alone is worth about £5 per acre per annum, and managed game shoots far more; for an in-depth study see Cobham Resource Consultants, 1997), jogging and photography, as well as more leisurely pursuits such as visiting gardens and nurseries or just country pubs. All these activities help to revitalize the spirit and provide rest from work.

The educational value of sites within the South Downs should also be recognized – places such as the Weald and Downland Open Air Museum, Queen Elizabeth and Seven Sisters Country Parks (Plate 161), Local and National Nature Reserves, youth hostels, Regionally Important Geological Sites, river valleys like the Cuckmere and the Marine environment are all used as part of the learning experience by both teachers and individuals.

This is an area that is already being used by the people of Britain as a de-facto National Park and has been for over a century since the dawn of the coach, railway and car.

THE RECREATIONAL PICTURE – A FLUID SITUATION

Historically the South Downs have been perceived as a place for principally only two sorts of quiet recreation – walking and horse-riding. Whilst these may have been the main types of recreation many years ago, it is quite clear that technological innovation has been the driving force behind change in the overall picture. Two case studies illustrate this thesis.

Hang gliding and paragliding

Whilst Leonardo de Vinci may have designed the first flying machine in the fifteenth century, it was not until the 1970s that the development of the early Rogallo-type Hang Glider in the USA led to a new quiet recreational activity that particularly suited the topography of the South Downs. The simple textile wing on an aluminium frame led to the rise of an extreme sport – hang gliding.

The Southern Hang Gliding Club (SHGC) has over 500 members who could not enjoy the free spirit of flying without the natural breezes and topography of the South Downs. Their sport also gives a great deal of pleasure to the many who come and just watch. SHGC is one of the larger clubs of its kind in the UK. The steep scarp-slope with its smooth grass-covered slopes is perfect for safe take-off with these relatively low-cost, colourful gliders that can be stowed on a modified roof rack and driven anywhere in the Downs that had a road to the top of the hill. In the early years of hang gliding, however, the equipment was particularly dependent on wind direction for take-off.

Initially this was a sport for anarchists. No consents were sought from landowners, and participants would just turn up and fly when the wind-strength and direction on a particular slope was suitable. New businesses sprang up to manufacture and develop the equipment, and the early UK pioneers were concentrated in the South Downs. Many died while testing flying machines or techniques.

The reaction of the public authorities to this new sport at first was entirely negative. Local Authorities did their best to ban it, instead of trying to regulate and control it. They objected to the distraction of this daredevil activity to motorists driving along the roads that were in sight of the flying. Cars would line the verges when any flying took place, and the police and highway authorities were terrified that serious road-traffic accidents would occur. Myths and scare stories abounded. Most local authority staff had no idea how the sport functioned and what the realities were. They thought that flying from any particular site could happen on any day of the year, and did not understand that all flying activity was completely dependent on wind speed and direction. They hated the fact that high accident rates were leading to expensive call-outs of the ambulance services. They were paranoid about traffic accidents and potential risk to the traditional downland users, the walkers and riders.

Fortunately five things happened. First, the pilots became better at flying and fewer people were killed. Second, the design of the equipment was improved, which helped safety. Third, people became used to hang gliders on the Downs and stopped driving erratically when they saw the sport taking place. Fourth, the sport became better organized with rules, and club membership was developed. Fifth, and probably most importantly, two local authority officers (the author and Jack Wilkinson at East Sussex County Council) decided that they should engage with the participants and try to understand the requirements of the sport. In 1977 they produced the pioneering *A Recreational Guideline No.1 – Hang Gliding* (covering the AONB in East and West Sussex) which dispelled the myths that had developed, and set a template for the ordered management of this quiet, non-polluting sport.

The local hang-gliding club (SHGC) started to licence flying sites from landowners and develop management plans for each one. Not surprisingly most of the perceived problems went away, and the sport has gone from strength to strength with the South Downs becoming one of the key areas for training pilots – many local pilots like Johnny Carr became successful in World Championship flying events. New businesses thrive, and hang gliding or paragliding training centres, like the one at Firle, generate a substantial income for Downs tourism.

New developments in technology have led to the growth of ***paragliding*** (using a cheaper specially designed parachute wing to glide over the Downs) (Plate 141), and despite the previous concerns, the very small growth of motorized hang gliders, paragliders and micro-light aircraft has not brought the destruction of tranquillity that many feared.

All in all, this is a success story for the Downs, and hang gliding and paragliding are now a permanent part of the South Downs scene. The technological changes that have taken place in the sport now demand an update of the original Hang Gliding Guidelines document with its extension to cover the East Hampshire Downs. One hopes that a new South Downs National Park Authority would undertake this task in a positive manner and help the sport to develop and grow.

Mountain biking

Until the mid-1970s only a handful of cyclists bothered to explore the off-road possibilities of the South Downs. They were known as the 'Rough Stuff Fellowship' and hardly anyone noticed them. Then in Marin County, California, the Mountain Bike was developed. Basically the only differences from ordinary bicycles were thicker, knobbly tyres, very low gearing for steep slopes, and a stronger frame to resist shocks.

These few design changes in the traditional bicycle had a huge impact. Another anarchic sport took off and the dry, extensive bridleway system of the South Downs was the perfect place for it to take hold in the UK. Further refinements in the design of mountain bikes have included lightweight aluminium frames, first front suspension and later rear, hydraulic disc brakes, 21-gears with hyperglide teeth and chains that allow for easier gear changes, thorn-proof tyres and generally, lighter and better engineered components.

It is hard today to go for a walk on the Downs and not see a mountain bike (Plates 135 and 142), and there are dozens of new shops servicing this activity in all the surrounding towns. However, unlike hang gliding, participants in this sport have no real incentive to join a club (like the insurance offered to hang gliders) so it remains particularly individualistic and thus more difficult to manage.

The potential for conflict between users of the bridleway network, the possibilities of additional erosion and illegal use of footpaths, does cause some concern amongst countryside managers. Many traditionalist ramblers loathe mountain bikers with a vengeance. This may be something to do with the different age structures of the two recreational activities. Yet mountain biking has brought a new breed of younger people into contact with the pleasures of the South Downs, where the rambling and riding communities had become used to an almost private enjoyment. The latter disliked the hang- or paragliding communities sharing 'their' space beforehand, but they seem to have become used to them!

Clearly the two new sports highlighted are not short-lived and are unlikely to disappear. On the other hand they seem to have reached some sort of equilibrium in terms of growth, and the various parties will have to learn to live with each other. The hang-gliding experience shows, that with time, existing users become accustomed to new activities – so long as the participants exhibit respect for each other's needs. Insurance requirements seem to have been the key to the regulation of the new aerial sports, and perhaps some moves in that direction for mountain biking might be the answer to a more settled relationship with other downland users.

Despite the above-mentioned activities, it should be recognized that the number of visitors to the South Downs found by the 2003 survey of recreational visits (Broom Associates, 2003) to be involved in 'very active outdoor pursuits' was low – less than five per cent. This is somewhat surprising but may be partly due to the methods of collecting data – mountain bikers are not particularly keen to stop and fill in questionnaires! Nevertheless, walking is still the main quiet recreational activity and the principal reason for visiting the area – between 50 and 60 per cent of respondents.

Clearly there are opportunities for private enterprise to service active outdoor pursuits, and the mountain-bike hire centre and canoe facilities at Seven Sisters Country Park are examples of what can be done. Certainly riding horses is a growing activity. More could be made of the recreational canoeing or boating opportunities of the river systems within the Downs, and even the cliffs offer rock-climbing opportunities outside the bird-nesting season. A quick glance at the accommodation occupancy figures in the Tourism South-East report (Broom Associates, 2003) bear these suggestions out.

The picture of downland recreational use is not entirely rosy. In particular, there are serious problems on the urban fringes with anti-social and illegal use of motorbikes disturbing the generally tranquil scene. On byways and Roads Used As Public Paths (RUPPs)

increased use by four-wheel-drive vehicles is causing damage, conflict with other users, and further loss of tranquillity (Plate 143).

Far too many people still travel to the Downs by car – despite initiatives like the 'Tourism without Traffic ' project piloted by East Sussex County Council and the Sussex Downs Conservation Board. Recent changes in the rail network rolling stock have set back progress by strictly limiting the space on trains to two bicycles.

The new access land created by the CRoW Act has been extremely limited in the South Downs – principally due to the very strict interpretation of what constitutes 'downland'.

Ethnic minorities don't use the Downs much and social inclusivity is not helped by the shortage of youth hostels at the western end of the South Downs Way National Trail.

CONCLUSION

There is no doubt that the variety and quality of opportunities for quiet recreation are seemingly endless in the South Downs. They are easy to get to and accessible. There is a huge variety of things to do, places to go and experiences to be had. All this recreational activity in the South Downs has a major economic impact in the region, generating 8000 jobs and £333 million per annum (Broom Associates, 2003, para 5.6, p. 49).

There are also superb views, dense intimate woodlands, splendid seascapes, beautiful river valleys, windy hillsides and pretty villages. The fact that it already gets so many visitors a year (39 million – Broom Associates, 2003) is an indication that the experiences offered by the South Downs are exceptional. The South Downs have much to offer the recreationalist, but its special qualities need special management to cope with the pressure of visitor numbers. Nevertheless, despite the large numbers of visitors, anyone using the South Downs in the winter will experience almost total solitude.

Any new National Park Authority for the South Downs will inherit responsibility for managing an intensively-used yet beautiful landscape. However, whilst the area copes pretty well with the recreational pressures at present, those tensions are unlikely to diminish. If the South East continues to be the economic powerhouse of the UK, then not only will population growth lead to more recreational use of the Downs, but this will be compounded by increased wealth and leisure time combined with the effects of a growing retired cohort. So what might the recreation policies and priorities be in a South Downs National Park?

Certainly policies cannot be developed in a vacuum, and will have to be integrated within both the socio-economic and conservation contexts. While the 'Sandford Principle' (Department of the

Environment, 1974 – see Chapter 12) would apply in a new National Park, it is thought that the South Downs have yet to meet their full recreational carrying capacity. This is especially so during the winter months and would also be the case if visitors start to reach the area by the more sustainable means of bicycle, bus or train. However, the present national trends in car ownership and use do not bode well for the future. The challenge will be to ensure that pilot projects like the Tourism without Traffic initiative are expanded to cover the whole of the Downs between Eastbourne and Winchester. It has to become cheap and easy to participate in recreational activities without first jumping into a car (see Plate 104). Achieving such a major change in personal behaviour will not be a simple task. Nevertheless, if any National Park in the UK is capable of doing this, then it is the South Downs.

The immediate challenges and priorities that a new South Downs National Park Authority will face when considering recreational management might therefore be:

- To integrate CRoW access land with other access land, and develop an imaginative Rights of Way Improvement Plan. This should consider the growth in horse-riding and its implications for increased maintenance and landscape degradation; carriage driving; mountain biking; hang gliding and paragliding; motorized use of the rights of way network and the need for specialist off-roading sites; managing the path network and access land in the context of an ageing population; and ensuring access for all social and ethnic groups.

- To develop practical management policies and action for the marine area (see Plates 163 and 164) which cover such issues as jet-skis and power boats; fishing; protection of shipwrecks; collecting geological specimens; sea-kyaking; beach cleanliness; and cliff climbing.

- To update and refine the Interpretive plan for the South Downs.

- To make sure that the local tourist authorities do not over-promote the area, and to consider ways of helping them shift visitor patterns towards the off-season.

These four challenges deserve priority, but there are others that also need to be pursued:

- To produce an updated Hang gliding and Paragliding Recreation Guideline and consider the production of further guides covering such new activities as 'mountain-boarding'.

- To develop policies and action for maximizing the recreational opportunities on the South Downs river and canal network in the context of changes in policy for flood protection.

- To get a clear understanding of how tourism and visitors affect the socio-economic aspects of local residents' lives – including the demand for local produce, agricultural diversification into tourism, the economic stability of village shops and post offices.

- Find ways of ensuring that local distinctiveness is appreciated, maintained and enhanced.

- To consider what to do about the market for second homes and how this relates to local rating.

- To look at visitor taxation-schemes and voluntary payback to fund visitor management and interpretation.

There are going to be some interesting times ahead for recreation managers of the South Downs. One hopes that this chapter will help them to gather their thoughts and rise to the challenge of conserving and enhancing a nationally treasured landscape, whilst enabling people both to enjoy and understand its special qualities. Clearly, with 39 million visits per annum, the people of Britain already are using the South Downs as a de-facto National Park. What the recreational picture highlights is the need to formalize this situation and get a National Park Authority in place quickly, with sufficient staff and funds to manage and enhance this valuable and threatened landscape, so that future generations can enjoy it as much as we have.

REFERENCES

Beattie, A., Seven Sisters Park Manager. Personal communication.

Beckett, A., (1909) *Spirit of the Downs.* London.

Brent, C. (2004) *Pre-Georgian Lewes c. 890–1714. The emergence of a county town.* Privately published.

Broom Associates, Geoff and Tourism South East Research Services (October 2003) *A Survey of Recreational Visits to the Proposed South Downs National Park.* Final Report for the Countryside Agency. South East England Tourist Board, Eastleigh.

Burnett, P., Editorial Director of Aurum Press. Personal communication.

Channer, N. et al. (2005) *Pub Walks and Cycle Rides – The South Downs and the South Coast.* AA Publishing, Farnborough.

Cobham Resource Consultants (1997) *Countryside Sports. Their Economic, Social and Conservation Significance – Review and Survey.* Standing Conference on Countryside Sports, Reading.

Department of the Environment (1974) *Report of the National Park Policies Review Committee.* HMSO, London. (The 'Sandford Principle'.)

Evans, J. (1995) *Great Cycle Routes: the North and South Downs.* Crowood Press.

Green, A., Cycle Lewes. Personal communication.

Hancock, D. & Toms, B. (2004) *A Mountain Bike Guide to the Highways and Bridleways of Hampshire and the New Forest.* Power Publications, Ferndown.

Hudson, W.H. (1900) *Nature in Downland.* London.

Jenman, W., National Trail Officer. Personal communication.

Millmore, P. (2004) *National Trail Guides – South Downs Way.* Aurum Press, London.

Parker, M. and **Payne, P.,** British Horse Society. Personal communications.

Perkins, B. (1996) *Pub Walks in the South Downs.* Countryside Books, Newbury. Sales of 9000+ copies.

Perkins, B. (2000) *On Foot in the East Sussex Downs.* SB Publications, Seaford. Sales of 1500+ copies.

Perkins, B. (2001) *On Foot in the West Sussex Downs.* SB Publications, Seaford. Sales of 1200+ copies.

Perkins, B. and **Walsh, P.** (1990 *et seq.*) Articles in the *Evening Argus.* Approx. 1000 published.

Price, J. & V. (2001) *Family Days in the Countryside Around Portsmouth and the South Downs.* Way Ahead Publications, Frome.

South Downs Campaign (2003) *Support for a South Downs National Park.* 'In Principle' support paper for the South Downs National Park Inquiry. Inquiry document no. 3275/3/3.* SDC, Brighton.

* Note: all documents for the South Downs National Park Inquiry are held by the Sponsorship, Landscape and Recreation Division of the Department of Environment, Farming and Rural Affairs (DEFRA), Temple Quay House, 2 The Square, Temple Quay, Bristol, BS1 6EB. Telephone: 0117 372 8655.

Appendix 10A

Publicly accessible land in the South Downs

Sites are either local authority, charity, Quango and Crown Estate owned, or land available under agri-environment schemes such as Countryside Stewardship and the Environmentally Sensitive Area (ESA), commons and CRoW Act access land. Details of ownership are as up-to-date as possible; there was no requirement to notify registration authorities of changes of ownership under the 1965 Commons Registration Act, a situation which DEFRA expects to rectify by 2012 under the Registration Authorities Act, 2006.

Name of site	*Owner*
The entire foreshore	mostly the Crown Estate
(including various tidal river banks)	(some leased to local authorities)
Additional CROW Act Land	Various
Countryside Stewardship Land	Various
Eastbourne Downland	Eastbourne Borough Council
Crowlink Estate	National Trust
Friston Forest	South East Water (leased by Forestry Commission)
Seven Sisters Country Park	East Sussex County Council
Lullington Heath NNR	English Nature
Frog Firle Estate	National Trust
Chyngton Farm Estate	National Trust
Hindover	Lewes District Council
Seaford Head LNR	Lewes District Council
Bopeep Bostal	Firle Estate
Firle Beacon	Firle Estate
Mount Caburn NNR	Glynde Estate (leased by English Nature)
The Malling Downs LNR	Sussex Wildlife Trust
Ambrose Goreham Trust Land	Ambrose Goreham Trust
Telscombe Tye	Telscombe TC
Ditchling Beacon	National Trust
Ditchling Beacon LNR	Sussex Wildlife Trust (leased, but open to the public)
Battle of Lewes Site (Landport Bottom)	Lewes District Council/Lewes Town Council
Blackcap & Mount Harry	National Trust
Lewes Railway Land	Lewes District Council/Lewes Railway Land Wildlife Trust
Bollens Bush	Lewes District Council
Stanmer Park & Woods	Brighton & Hove City Council
Hollingbury Castle & Wild Park LNR	Brighton & Hove City Council
Bevendean Down	Brighton & Hove City Council
Benfield Hill LNR	Brighton & Hove City Council
Southwick Hill	National Trust
Wolstonbury Hill	National Trust
Newtimber Hill	National Trust
Saddlescombe Farm	National Trust
The Devil's Dyke	National Trust
Fulking Escarpment (includes Edburton Hill)	National Trust

(continued overleaf)

Name of site	Owner
Bramber Castle	National Trust but managed by English Heritage under 'Guardianship scheme' Cissbury Ring National Trust
Durford Heath	National Trust
South Cissbury Ring	Worthing Borough Council
Mill Hill LNR	Adur District Council
Lancing Ring	Adur District Council
Goodwood Country Park	Goodwood Estate
Selhurst Park	Goodwood Estate
Slindon Park Wood	National Trust
Amberley Wild Brooks	Sussex Wildlife Trust/RSPB
Fairmile Bottom LNR	West Sussex County Council
Whiteways Lodge & Houghton Forest	Norfolk Estate (Leased Forestry Commission)
Burton Mill Pond	West Sussex County Council/Sussex Wildlife Trust
Bignor Hill	National Trust
Barlavington Estate	Anstruther Trust
Petworth Park	National Trust
Swanbourne Lake & Arundel Park	Norfolk Estate
Graffham Down	Graffham Down Trust
Heyshott Down	Murray Downland Trust
Stansted Park	Stansted Trust
The Mens	Sussex Wildlife Trust
Levin Down	Sussex Wildlife Trust (leased)
Harting Down LNR	National Trust
Catherington Down	Hampshire County Council/Hampshire Wildlife Trust/ Horndean Parish Council
Petersfield Pond (Heath Common)	Petersfield Town Council
Queen Elizabeth Country Park & Butser Hill	Hampshire County Council/Forestry Commission
Old Winchester Hill NNR	English Nature
Beacon Hill, Exton NNR	English Nature
Blackdown	National Trust
St Catherine's Hill	Winchester College/Hampshire & Isle of Wight Wildlife Trust
Eartham Wood	National Trust – leased by Forestry Commission
Noar Hill	Hampshire Wildlife Trust
Speltham Down	National Trust
Chappets Copse	Hampshire Wildlife Trust
Ashford Hanger NNR	Hampshire County Council
Magdalen Hill Down	Butterfly Conservation Trust
West Walk	Forestry Commission
Woolmer Forest	Ministry of Defence
All Village Greens	Various

Commons (see below)

Ambersham Common	Cowdray Estate
Iping Common	West Sussex County Council, Cowdray Estate, RMC
Lavington Common	National Trust
Ebernoe Common	Sussex Wildlife Trust
Woolbeding & Pound Commons (includes Older Hill)	National Trust
Stedham Common	Sussex Wildlife Trust
Chapel Common	Mr Mir
Henley Common	Cowdray & Dickinson Trusts
Linchmere Common/Marley Common	National Trust/Linchmere Society
Selborne Common	National Trust
Shortheath Common	Hampshire County Council
Waltham Brooks	Sussex Wildlife Trust

Appendix 10B

Comparison of the designated South Downs National Park rights of way provision with existing National Parks

East Hampshire AONB:
RUPPs 26 km
BOATs 53 km
Bridleways 117 km
Footpaths 404 km
TOTAL = 600km

NB. RUPPs are Roads Used as Public Paths
BOATs are Byways Open to All Traffic

Designated South Downs National Park in Hampshire:
RUPPs 31 km
BOATs 56 km
Bridleways 158 km
(Total RoW available for cyclists and horse-riders = 245 km)
Footpaths 572 km
TOTAL = 817 km

Sussex Downs AONB:
RUPPs 136.3 km
BOATs 16.48 km
Bridleways 932.87 km
(Total RoW available for cyclists and horse-riders = 1085.65km)
Footpaths 1059.2 km
TOTAL = 2144.85 km

Designated South Downs National Park in Sussex (total rights of way figures by county – breakdown of different types not provided):
West Sussex – 1800 km
East Sussex – 548 km
Brighton & Hove – 79 km
(Total RoW available for cyclists and horse-riders (assuming same proportion as in Sussex Downs AONB) = an estimate of 1228 km)
TOTAL = 2427 km

Total Rights of Way in the designated South Downs National Park = 3244 km

Area of the designated South Downs National Park (including Variation Order land) = 1639 km²

Therefore the length of rights of way per square kilometre = 3244/1639 = 1.98 km per km². This is significantly higher than that for other National Parks (see Table 10a – second to last column). Only the Peak District comes close, but even then the South Downs has 270 metres more rights of way than the Peak District for every square kilometre of National Park.

From the breakdown above it can also be seen that the length of rights of way open to cyclists and horse-riders (bridleways, BOATs and RUPPs) in the South Downs is estimated at 1473 km. This is far superior to any existing National Park in both length and density of network (estimated 0.90 in the South Downs) and perhaps underlines why the area is so important for horse-riding. The South Downs has 500 metres of bridleway per square kilometre more than most National Parks which have less than a 0.4 km of rights of way suitable for cyclists and horse-riders per square kilometre (see last column in Table 10a overleaf).

Rights of Way figures kindly provided by the East Hampshire AONB Joint Advisory Committee and the Sussex Downs Conservation Board (now jointly called the South Downs Joint Committee).

Table 10a Existing National Park Rights of Way (RoW) statistics (England & Wales)

National Park (year of data)	Area (sq. km)	Length of public footpaths (km)	Length of bridleways (km)	Length of other RoW (km)	Total RoW (km)	Length of RoW per square km	Length of RoW for cyclists and horse-riders per square km
Dartmoor (01)	953	352	353	19	724	0.76	0.39
Exmoor (03)	693	438	464	64	966	1.39	0.76
Lake District (03)	2292	2133	844	33	3010	1.31	0.38
Northumberland (03)	1049	529	369	2	900	0.86	0.35
North York Moors (03)	1436	1506	749	14	2269	1.58	0.53
Peak District (03)	1438	2136	293	30	2459	1.71	0.22
Yorkshire Dales (03)	1773	1459	617	28	2104	1.19	0.36
The Broads (99)	303	293	17	0	310	1.02	0.06
Brecon Beacons (04)	1347	-	-	-	1983	1.47	-
Pembrokeshire Coast (99)	620	-	-	-	938	1.51	-
Snowdonia (03)	2132	2316	186	211	2713	1.27	0.19
South Downs	1639	1771 (est)	1213 (est)	260 (est)	3244	1.98	0.90 (est)

Note 1: Figures come from the useful data section of the Association of National Park Authorities' website (www.anpa.gov.uk) or, where the information was not available, from the individual National Park Authority websites. While collating this information it was noticed that some figures did occasionally appear to vary somewhat, but not enough to undermine the overall accuracy of the table. All figures used have been cross-checked as much as possible.

Note 2: South Downs estimates are due to the fact that a full breakdown of rights of way was not provided for land included in the National Park but outside the AONB in Sussex. The figures are likely to be fairly accurate as the breakdown was known for the Sussex Downs AONB, which covers most of the designated National Park in Sussex. The percentage split between the different types of rights of way was extrapolated from the known AONB figures for Sussex to give an estimated figure for the designated National Park in Sussex. This was then added to the known figures for the designated National Park in Hampshire to give the above estimates.

132

Appendix 10C

Walk Figures from Ramblers' Association and other Groups

Walking Group	*Dates of programmes provided*	*Number of walks within designated National Park boundary*
Andover RA	January 2000 – December 2003	9
Ashdown Rambling Club	July 2001 – June 2003	21
Brighton and Hove RA	March 2001 – February 2004	171
Countryside Amblers	January 2001 – December 2003	116
East Surrey RA	January 2000 – December 2003	17
Eastbourne Rambling Club	2001 – 2003	190
Eastleigh RA	January 2000 – December 2003	111
Farnham and District RA	April 2000 – November 2003	77
Footpaths Conservation Society	January 2000 – December 2003	72
Godalming and Haslemere RA	November 2001 – October 2003	48
Hailsham Ramblers	December 1999 – December 2003	23
Hasssocks Field Society	April 2000 – September 2003	28
Horsham and Billingshurst RA	December 2000 – March 2004	104
Lewes Footpaths Group	September 2001 – March 2004	58
Meon RA	January 2000 – December 2003	244
New Forest RA	January 2000 – December 2003	9
North East Hampshire RA	January 2000 – December 2003	31
North Hampshire Downs RA	January 2000 – December 2003	15
Polegate Rambling Club	March 2001 – February 2004	96
Portsmouth RA	January 2000 – December 2003	306
Romsey RA	January 2000 – December 2003	40
Seaford Rambling Club	April 2001 – March 2004	318
Society of Sussex Wealdmen	April 2001 – September 2003	82
South East Hampshire RA	January 2000 – December 2003	336
South West Sussex RA	May 2001 – April 2004	321
Southdown Strollers	January 2000 – December 2002	108
Steyning Ramblers	January 2001 – December 2003	157
Sussex Pathfinders	2003	51
Sutton and Wandle Valley RA	November 2000 – October 2003	31
Waltham RA	January 2000 – December 2003	156
Wealdland Walkers	June 2001 – March 2004	9
Winchester RA	January 2000 – December 2003	98
Woking and District RA	July 2000 – June 2003	16
Worthing Natural History Society	2001 – 2003	10
East Sussex CC Guided Walks	2001– 2003	231
West Sussex CC Guided Walks	2001– 2003	223
Hampshire CC Guided Walks	2000 – 2003	300
Society of Sussex Downsmen	2000 – 2003	600
TOTAL		**4833**

CHAPTER 11
Development Issues

MARTIN SMALL

Preceding chapters have dealt with the quality and character of the South Downs and some of the pressures and threats on this landscape. This chapter now examines the issue of development in and around the area, with both an historical perspective, and a look at the future role of the planning system in conserving and enhancing the Downs.

THE PLANNING SYSTEM

The planning system essentially regulates the use of land in the interests of the public and sustainable development. The current Government believes that 'Planning shapes the places where people live and work and the country we live in. It plays a key role in supporting the Government's wider economic, social and environmental objectives and for sustainable communities' (Office of the Deputy Prime Minister, 2004a).

Good textbooks exist on the evolution of the planning system, and it is not the purpose of this chapter to duplicate them. Some historical context is important, however, in order to understand the development issues in the South Downs. The fundamentals of the planning system, the regulation of the right to develop land and the linkage of plan-making and development control through local planning authorities, were established by the 1947 Town and Country Planning Act. Previous Acts, in 1909, 1925 and, most importantly, in 1932, had enabled local authorities to make 'town

planning schemes' for their areas, but until 1947 they did not have the powers to prevent development taking place when it was not in the public interest. Subsequent Planning Acts in 1968, 1990 and 2004 have revised the system, but the fundamental principles remain, although the Planning and Compulsory Purchase Act 2004 has given the system a wider, spatial remit, encompassing land-managerial and social issues.

The post-war Labour Government considered that the newly established local planning authorities were the appropriate bodies to administer National Parks and Areas of Outstanding Natural Beauty (AONBs) introduced by the 1949 National Parks and Access to the Countryside Act. Indeed, the Hobhouse Committee (see Chapter 13), wished 'our proposals for the planning of National Parks to depart as little as possible from the system of town and country planning in operation over the whole of England and Wales' (Ministry of Town & Country Planning, 1947). AONBs were not thought to justify full management as National Parks, but nevertheless required a very special degree of planning control to prevent obtrusive or alien development. Generally, therefore, it was felt that the new planning powers were adequate to prevent major development and the gradual loss of architectural character in these areas, particularly as it was assumed that agriculture would maintain traditional landscapes. As highlighted in earlier chapters this assumption proved to be ironic.

Today the special qualities of National Parks and AONBs are recognized in national planning policy, set out in a series of Planning Policy Statements (PPSs), first introduced by the Government in the late 1980s as Planning Policy Guidance Notes (PPGs). Current planning policy for National Parks and AONBs is primarily in Planning Policy Statement 7 *Sustainable Development in Rural Areas* (Office of the Deputy Prime Minister, 2004b), that is, that the conservation of the natural beauty of the landscape and the countryside should be given great weight in planning policies and decisions about the control of development in such areas, and that major developments should only proceed in 'exceptional circumstances' where the development is in the 'public interest'. Establishing whether this is the case involves a careful assessment, including the national need for the development and the cost of, and scope of, going outside the area or meeting the need in some other way.

The South Downs provide a very good microcosm of the issue of 'national public interest', a significant consideration in several proposals for major development within the area since the designation of the AONBs. However, there were also development issues before then.

EARLY DEVELOPMENT ISSUES IN THE SOUTH DOWNS

For centuries, building in the Downs, as elsewhere in the country, proceeded at a pace and scale in tune with the environment. Buildings were generally modest, with materials found locally, for example flint. 'Development' was not perceived as any threat to the character of the countryside. Other than the occasional cottage or farm building in the countryside the only significant building was undertaken by the landed estates within the South Downs, such as Goodwood, near Chichester, or Cowdray near Midhurst. The lords of the manor exercised their own control, ensuring that the look and location of their estate-workers' houses did not destroy the beauty of their own particular landscapes.

In common with other areas of the country, though, the towns and villages along the south coast of Hampshire and Sussex experienced a building boom in the mid to late nineteenth century. With the sea forming a natural barrier to expansion, development inevitably took place laterally and to the north. Given the proximity of the Downs to Brighton, it was inevitable that as the city grew it would encroach onto the downland to the north of original settlement, which was happening by 1900. Worthing and Hove also expanded on the lower dip-slope of the Downs, although perhaps the greatest loss of downland was at Eastbourne.

Dr Peter Brandon's book *The South Downs* (1998) gives a full account of the threat posed, and actual damage caused, by development in the first half of the twentieth century. Brandon notes that an unregulated scatter of buildings including shacks, bungalows, tea-houses, road-houses, garages and advertisements had begun to creep over the Downs even before 1914. 'Plotland development', where land was bought speculatively and divided into plots for the building of individual houses, was a particularly serious threat, such as at Denton and Peacehaven (Plate 144), in East Sussex.

Largely in response to this pressure, the Brighton and District Joint Town Planning Committee was established by the Borough of Brighton in 1923. It was advisory and its recommendations merely permissive, but nevertheless it formulated the first planning principles for any sector of the Downs in 1932: the Regional Town Planning Scheme for Brighton, Hove and adjoining authorities, which defined an area of downland above the 300 ft contour to be protected from development. The Scheme was accorded general acclaim, with the then Society of Sussex Downsmen calling for the co-operation of local authorities across the Downs in a single town-planning scheme to cover the whole area of the Sussex Downs on the lines of the Regional scheme. (Now, over 70 years later, notwithstanding the existence of a national planning system and planning policy guidance, the benefits of a comprehensive approach to the planning of the South Downs are still being advocated as an advantage of a South Downs National Park).

Both East and West Sussex County Councils (the Hampshire Downs fortunately not suffering the same pressure from development) recognized, however, that stronger protective measures were needed. East Sussex County Council promoted a South Downs Preservation Bill in 1934, which attracted widespread support from conservationists, though a number of landowners objected to it as an unreasonable and unnecessary encroachment upon the rights of owners and tenants of land. Although the supporters put up a strong case, the Bill was rejected.

In fact, the idea of the Bill had originated with West Sussex. Here, the County Council had intended it to cover the whole range of the Downs from the Hampshire border to Beachy Head. West Sussex favoured a more moderate approach than East Sussex and therefore had not supported the latter's Bill. Instead, the Council took a different approach, most of the District Councils delegating their planning powers (such as they were at that time) in respect of the Downs to the County Council. As a result West Sussex established one of the first planning departments in the country, aiming to protect downland above the 200 ft contour through the West Sussex County (South Downs) Planning Scheme. Under Section 34 of the 1932 Town and Country Planning Act, the Council and landowners could enter

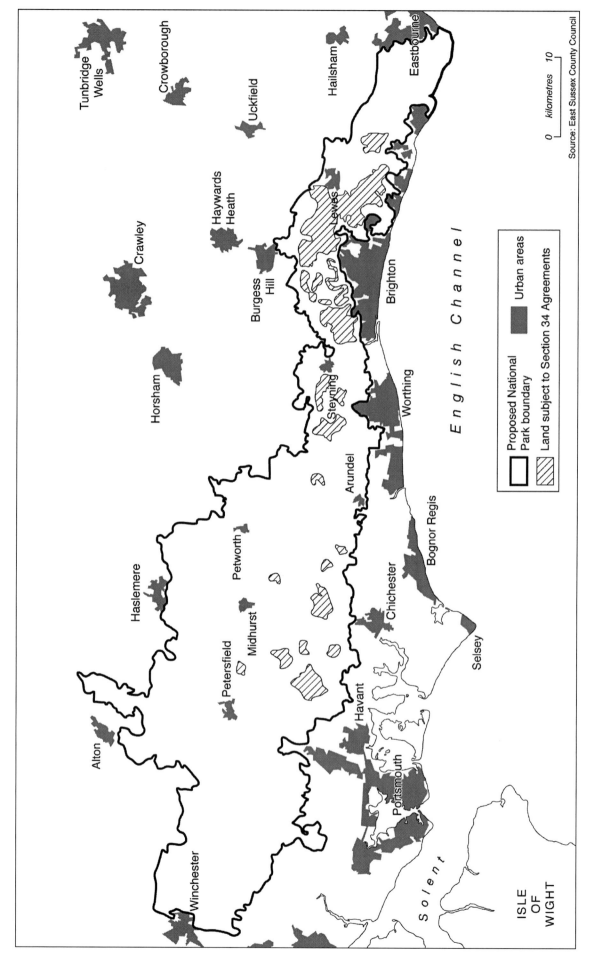

Figure 11.1   Land subject to Section 34 Agreements in relation to the proposed South Downs area and urban conurbations.

into agreements whereby the latter relinquished their development rights in return for a compensatory payment. By this method, with the wholehearted co-operation of more than 100 landowners, some 125 square miles (32,375 hectares) of downland were saved from potential building (see Fig.11.1).

After the failure of the Bill, East Sussex County Council pursued a similar course, although the District Councils remained the executive planning authorities, with the County assuming a co-ordinating role and accepting the obligation to pay any excess of compensation to landowners over the amount a local authority could be expected to bear itself. To avoid expensive compensation, the agreements sought to preserve only downland above the 300 ft contour. As in West Sussex, many landowners proved most co-operative, and more than 85 per cent of the downland covered by the abortive Bill became protected by voluntary agreements.

The 1930s, however, saw a number of proposals for large-scale residential development on the southern slopes of the Downs following the electrification of the railway from London. These may have succeeded but for the protection offered by the two counties' planning schemes. For example, *The Times* (1938) reported on the saving of 26,779 acres (10,845 hectares) of downland between Eastbourne and Brighton, including Black Cap, near Lewes.

Nevertheless, conflict between the needs and desires for development, on the one hand, and the proximity of the Downs to the coastal settlements on the other, continued to exist after the conclusion of these agreements (see Fig.11.2), and continues today. This conflict underlies a number of the significant proposals for development since the designation of the two AONBs.

HOUSING

It is clear that house-building was the earliest and greatest threat to the preservation of the Downs, whether through the expansion of existing towns or by new settlements, such as was proposed at 'Southdown Bay' at Birling Gap or Crowlink Gap in East Sussex. At Denton, west of Seaford, more than 100 plots were sold, although, fortunately, only a small part of this development actually took place. On the cliff-top between Rottingdean and Newhaven, Peacehaven developed as, 'a rash of bungalows, houses, shops, shacks, chicken runs, huts and dog kennels' (Woolf, 1967). The sheer audacity and scale of Peacehaven was roundly condemned, and was seen as symptomatic of all that was wrong with the then laissez-faire attitude to development, not least by Clough Williams-Ellis, in his polemic book *England and the Octopus*, first published in 1928. Williams-Ellis cites Peacehaven (and also Waterlooville, just to the south of the East

Hampshire AONB) as examples of particularly poor planning. He sarcastically refers to a 'mythical' development 'Seaville', built 'on a slice of downland on the coast' and, when attacking bungalows, he cites Peacehaven 'as the classic example of this distressing and almost universal complaint' (Williams-Ellis, 1928). Although the original sporadic layout of Peacehaven has been consolidated, it still has an air of its origins as a plotland settlement (Plate 144).

Housing threats elsewhere led to the National Trust's purchase of Cissbury Ring, near Findon in West Sussex, to save it in 1925, and Worthing Borough Council's acquisition of High Salvington Down north of the town as public open space in 1937, with the support of Worthing residents. Public pressure in 1946 led to the saving of Highdown Hill, west of Worthing, after a notice appeared advertising it for sale. Development on a former Prisoner of War Camp at Rodmell, south of Lewes, was forestalled when the Minister of Health and Town and Country Planning (1948) considered the location unsuitable, and that 'the preservation of the rural area of high scenic value between Lewes and Newhaven was of great importance'.

Plotland housing development, however, did take place north of the Downs, such as at Marley Heights near Fernhurst, divided into four-acre (over one and a half hectare) plots in the 1930s, and even after the 1947 Act on areas of heathland of poor agricultural value, such as Wheatsheaf Inclosure, near Liss. Large residential estates sprawled over downland in the 1960s at Saltdean (Plate 145), just west of Peacehaven; at East Dean, to the west of Eastbourne, on the edge of Seaford; and at Woodingdean, east of Brighton. Although in one sense wasteful desecration of the Downs, Peacehaven and these estates are part of the cultural history of the South Downs.

More recently, with the strict control now available under the planning system, the fear of indiscriminate speculative housing has thankfully passed. The threat of plotlands did return briefly, however, in 2003, when a company purchased land in the Adur Valley, just south of Bramber, West Sussex, intending to sub-divide it into 'leisure plots' for self-build homes. Fortunately this came to nothing. However, there has been housing permitted within the AONBs since designation, some on the edge of urban areas encroaching into the Sussex Downs AONB at Newhaven and Sompting, and in more isolated locations where special circumstances have been thought to apply for the 'greater good'.

Twenty large 'executive' houses were built in the late 1990s at HMS Mercury, a naval training establishment near East Meon in Hampshire (Plates 146 a and b). Permission was granted, contrary to a special local policy for the site, in order to secure the removal of a range of unattractive buildings as 'planning gain'. Around the same time 27 houses

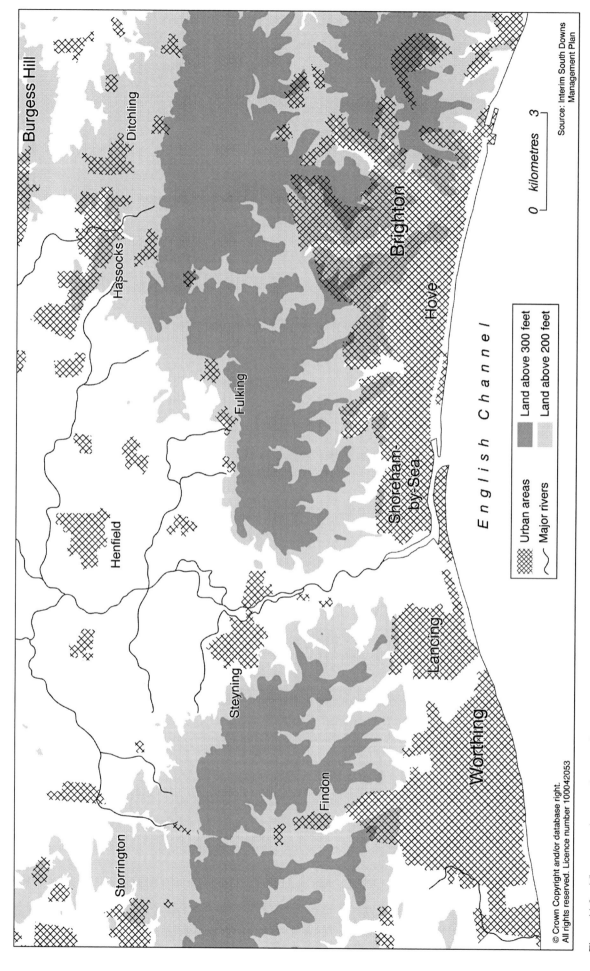

Figure 11.2　The encroachment of some urban areas and conurbations into the South Downs.

Source: Interim South Downs
Management Plan

were built at Burton Park, at Duncton in West Sussex, also as 'enabling development', financing the removal of a number of buildings and the restoration of the Grade I listed Burton House, and the Grade II registered parkland. Conserving an historic mansion was also the justification for planning permission by Brighton & Hove City Council for a new terrace of seven houses at Stanmer House, another Grade I building within Grade II parkland, on the northern edge of Brighton, in 2003.

Perhaps the most controversial proposal for the use of 'enabling development' came the same year at King Edward VII Hospital, located on high ground to the north of Midhurst. In 2003 a new 134-bed hospital was proposed, to be funded by the conversion of the main buildings to 222 flats and the construction of 108 new houses (21 new 'key worker' flats were also proposed). The proposals were opposed by, inter alia, the Countryside Agency and the officers of Chichester District Council as being contrary to policy and with insufficient justification. However, in the face of significant local pressure and the threat of imminent closure, the Council granted permission in May 2004. Nevertheless, no development took place and in August 2006 a new application was submitted for 337 dwellings and ancillary development, but no hospital. This was later reduced to 263 (224 from conversion and 39 'newbuild') and the District Council resolved to grant permission in April 2007, on the basis of the development being the minimum necessary to restore and renovate the Grade II* listed building and Grade II registered grounds.

ROADS

Motorized traffic had been considered a threat to the peace and tranquillity of the Downs since the early days of motoring, allowing access to otherwise unspoilt areas. It opened up areas such as Birling Gap to day-trips, and led to the appearance of tea-houses (Plate 8) and petrol stations. After World War II, specially-made metalled roads on to the Downs, constructed during the war, were opened up to the public, although objections from the Society of Sussex Downsmen led to some closures by the Minister of Transport in 1951.

Nevertheless, the increase of traffic inevitably resulted in pressure for the widening and realignment of roads through the Downs and the construction of bypasses. A bypass was proposed for Petworth in West Sussex in the 1950s, although never built. In the 1960s a cutting was made on the eastern flank of Butser Hill, the highest point in the South Downs, to facilitate the flow of traffic on the A3 trunk road, followed by the Petersfield bypass in 1990.

In fact, the 1980s saw the greatest threats to the South Downs from road schemes. Chapter 1 cites one of them, the infamous M3 cutting through Twyford Down and St Catherine's Hill, just east of Winchester, as a demonstration of 'how to ruin downland' (Plates 3 and 42). The Down and Hill are of national archaeological, ecological and landscape importance. However, when balanced against the desire to complete the M3 link between Basingstoke and Compton, just south of Winchester, these national designations were not considered sufficient. The Department of Transport's cost-benefit analysis did not accord monetary value to environmental and heritage features, and they were sacrificed to the construction of a new road in a huge cutting, gouging through Twyford Down, a decision condemned in *The Guardian*, *The Daily Telegraph* and *The Times*.

Barbara Bryant (1996) believes that 'Nationally, the Government disregarded its own legislation, enacted specifically to prevent loss of heritage-rich sites, and rendered impotent our conservation laws and planning regulations. The Government's obstinate and unintelligent insistence on pressing ahead with its outdated plan for the M3 motorway at Winchester has ensured it a place in environmental history for cynical landscape abuse and muddled thinking'. Bryant's book provides a very detailed account of this environmental vandalism and of the wider consequences that it has had for government and environmental policy.

Also in the 1980s, attention was being paid to the A27 trunk road through south-east Hampshire, West and East Sussex between Southampton and Polegate, near Eastbourne. 'Improvements' to this road have been piecemeal, some sections outside the AONBs, but others within, such as the Shoreham bypass completed in 1968 on a fly-over across the Adur valley, a cutting through Mill Hill north of Shoreham, and the Lewes bypass to the south of the town. A cutting was dug for the A27 at Falmer, east of Brighton, taking through-traffic out of the village, but cutting it in two in the process.

A Brighton bypass (Plates 147 and 148) was first mooted in 1932, but it was in 1974 that the then Secretary of State for Transport directed that an 'Inner Downs' route, close to the urban edge, proposed by consultants, be protected. A Public Inquiry sat for 97 days in 1982, at which the Countryside Commission argued that the road should only be permitted if it was shown to be in the national interest. The Department of Transport replied that although the road would satisfy important national objectives, the suggestion that national interest alone should be considered was unrealistic; local interests needed to be considered too. The Inspector considered that the scheme would cause 'obvious and regrettable detriment to the Downs' (Department of Transport, 1983) but concluded that, overall, the balance of environmental advantage lay with the building of the bypass. Although great care was taken to integrate the road as far as possible into the landscape, such as by using shallower gradients for the embankments to allow them to be grazed, eight miles of dual carriageway cutting across undulating downland inevitably carved up the landscape.

As for Worthing, studies by West Sussex County Council in 1967–1970 and by the Government in 1972–1976 recommended the construction of an 'inner route' at Worthing, following the A27 to the A24 and then a new route, through the AONB, to the north of Lancing, close to the urban edge. This was subsequently abandoned in 1980 because of the cost. Five years later, the proposal re-emerged in government programmes, and the Secretary of State once again opted for the 'inner route'. An 11-month Public Inquiry began in 1993, one of the longest Inquiries of its kind in the area. The Inspector recommended the route with some minor realignment. In 1996, however, the then Secretary of State, Sir George Young, announced that the scheme had again been withdrawn, as it was not popular locally and, as one of the most expensive non-motorway schemes in the country, it could not have been built for a considerable time. Six years later the South Coast Corridor Multi-Modal Study proposed improvements in the form of a tunnel or series of tunnels, but there are still no firm proposals for this section of the A27.

MINERALS

A most controversial form of development anywhere is mineral extraction, given the usual scale of the activity and the effects on the landscape. However, the fact that minerals can only be exploited where they occur leads to particular problems in what are now protected landscapes. As elsewhere, in the South Downs quarrying was small-scale and localized until the nineteenth century, but towards the end of that century, some mineral workings increased in size and commerciality. When the planning system was created in more or less its present form in 1947, it inherited a legacy of mineral workings, proposals for the extension of which often proved controversial, for example at Duncton and Cocking Chalk Pits in West Sussex in the 1950s. An extension to Duncton was allowed after an inquiry in 1950, because of the importance of agriculture (and therefore agricultural lime) to the national economy, but for a smaller area than originally proposed to safeguard Bishop's Ring, a prominent clump of trees, archaeological remains and footpaths. However, the two most significant minerals proposals in the South Downs concerned chalk-quarrying for cement manufacture and sand extraction.

Shoreham Cement Works, in the Adur valley north of Shoreham-by-Sea, developed in the mid-nineteenth century from an earlier chalk pit and lime works, but significantly expanded just after the Second World War. A new works was completed in 1951 (Plate 149). This was considered a perfect example

of its kind, and representatives of the industry came to view it from all over the world (Bushell, 1999). Permission was also given in 1950 for chalk extraction to the east of the works, feeding two newly installed rotary kilns. In 1968 planning permission was sought to extend the quarry over 32 acres (13 hectares) of downland. Although the proposal was a departure from the development plan, West Sussex County Council and Chanctonbury Rural District Council were sympathetic to it, but there was a range of objectors, including the National Parks Commission (forerunner of the Countryside Commission) and the owners of the land, Shoreham-by-Sea Urban District Council, who refused to allow the extension. Nevertheless the application was approved by the County Council. The Shoreham Council maintained its opposition, resulting in a stalemate. In 1971, in order to resolve the impasse, the County Council controversially obtained approval from the Secretary of State for the Environment for the allocation of the land for chalk extraction as an amendment to the development plan. With this allocation and the support of the local planning authority, an application could be made to the Courts for the acquisition of the land. Eventually, in 1975, all terms were settled and mineral-working followed.

In fact quarrying and cement production ceased entirely in 1991. Although the County Council did negotiate the removal of a conveyor that spanned the A283, there was neither a requirement to demolish the buildings nor to restore the site, and no successful proposals for redevelopment. Many of the works buildings and plant remain derelict. Together with the quarry's deep gouge in the Downs, they are forceful reminders of an industrial heritage and the greatest eyesore in the area. Since then alternative uses have been considered, including a major waste transfer and recycling centre, a national winter sports centre, and, in 2002, a business park and 80 houses. At a Public Inquiry in 2003 all parties agreed that the removal of the buildings and the remediation of the landscape would be in the national interest. However, the Deputy Prime Minister rejected the proposals, primarily because the housing element was contrary to the development plan. A more recent suggestion is that it be the site of a new stadium for Brighton & Hove Albion Football Club (see below).

Subsequent minerals policy for the Sussex Downs AONB in West Sussex was largely determined by an appeal decision in the early 1970s. In 1966, the County Council and the then Chanctonbury Rural District Council had agreed a policy to resist sand workings between the A283 and the Downs in the vicinity of Washington, north of Worthing. At a Public Inquiry in 1970, following the refusal of two applications for sand-quarrying on land south of the A283, within the AONB, the County Planning Officer accepted that his Council's policy noted that 'The fact that an

a)

b)

Plate 144 *(top left)*
Clough Williams-Ellis's mythical 'Seaville': an aerial view
of Peacehaven in 1936, showing the gridiron layout and
clifftop position.
Photo: East Sussex County Council, courtesy of Paul Millmore.

Plate 147 *(bottom left)*
Destruction of the downland countryside; construction of the
Brighton bypass, May 1991, which emphasizes the damage done
to the Downs, even after later landscaping, by pushing polluting
traffic into the hills due to the density of the ribbon housing of
the urbanized coastal plain.
Photo: Phil Belden.

Plate 145 *(top right)*
Bungalow city; post-war bungalow development at Saltdean
on the Downs inland from the cliff edge.
Photo: Martin Small, courtesy of SDJC.

Plate 146 (a & b) *(centre)*
A fair exchange? 'Executive' housing a) at the former Royal Navy
establishment, HMS *Mercury*, East Meon, Hampshire, permitted
in order to secure the removal of unsightly MoD buildings b).
Photos: Alison Tingley, courtesy of SDJC.

Plate 148 *(bottom right)*
Construction of the Southwick tunnel on the A27 Brighton bypass.
Photo: Julian Gray, courtesy of SDJC.

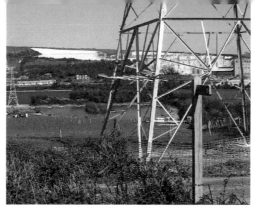

Plate 149
The greatest eyesore in the South Downs: the derelict former Shoreham Cement Works, opened in 1950, closed 40 years later.
Photo: Martin Small, courtesy of SDJC.

Plate 150
How to wreck natural beauty: electricity pylons and the former Shoreham Cement Works frame a right of way, near Coombes, West Sussex, 1996.
Photo: Phil Belden.

Plate 151
Wartime legacy; the twin masts on The Trundle (St Roche's Hill) at Goodwood, West Sussex.
Photo: Martin Small

Plate 152 (left)
'Glorious Goodwood', a site for horse racing on the private Goodwood Estate. This hill-top scene shows the extent of the car parking and crowds attracted to such popular meets, which are serviced by three minor roads through the Downs, often causing extensive disruption to local traffic. The central stands can be seen from miles away.
Photo: Phil Belden.

Plate 153 (below left)
The site of the proposed Brighton & Hove Albion stadium at Court Farm, Falmer, East Sussex, and the University of Brighton, June 1999.
Photo: Phil Belden.

Plate 154 (below right)
Architects' CAD-generated image of Brighton & Hove Albion's proposed new stadium at Falmer.
Image by KSS Design Group Ltd, courtesy of Brighton & Hove Albion Football Club.

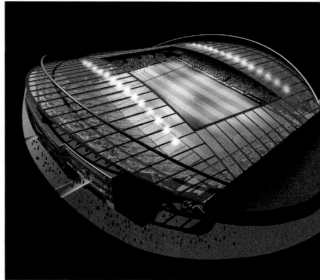

area is within the Area of Outstanding Natural Beauty cannot be the sole reason for prohibiting sand working' (Burrows, 1970). Refusal of the applications was nevertheless fully justified in his opinion by the extreme importance of the area; the beauty of the landscape was not only of local but of national value. The Secretary of State for the Environment, Peter Walker, decided that both applications should be refused, attaching 'great importance' to the fact that the sites were in an area of great landscape value, and within the AONB.

In the early 1980s it was oil that raised concerns. Seismic surveys had identified a number of geological structures across the Downs, including at Lomer in Hampshire, Chilgrove, Singleton and Graffham in West Sussex and Ditchling Beacon in East Sussex, that had the potential to contain oil. Great concern was expressed in Parliament in 1983 at the potential threat to the Downs, and both East and West Sussex County Councils drafted new policies for their Structure Plans in response. After further testing, only Singleton was thought economically viable, and this had to be achieved by means of a long deviation in the borehole (then highly unusual) to allow the well-site to be within Singleton Forest, north of the village and out of sight.

WASTE

Processing and disposing of waste is a major issue for any urban area. The main method of disposal in the past was simply to fill holes in the ground, often those resulting from mineral-working. However, waste production outstrips mineral extraction, and landfill capacity has been diminishing over the years. This is a problem, illustrated at Beddingham, near Lewes. After the closure of the Rodmell Cement Works in 1975, landfilling of the original chalk pit with rubbish began in 1981. By 1991 it appeared that it would be completely full within four to five years, so, in order to provide a further few years' capacity, it was proposed to extend chalk-quarrying over six hectares to the south and to extract limited chalk from the adjacent Asham Valley. It was intended to restore the extended pit to its original contours with landfill, and to infill the valley. This meant the loss of woodland but also, more controversially, the Grade II listed Asham House, built in about 1820, the home of the writer Virginia Woolf for several years. Opposition to the loss of the house came from Woolf enthusiasts as far afield as North America, and from English Heritage and Lewes District Council. However, in 1992, East Sussex County Council gave permission for the chalk and infilling, subject to listed building consent being granted for the demolition of Asham House. Despite the opposition, this was eventually given and Asham House was demolished two years later. In 2005, the lack of landfill space and encouragement for more

sustainable ways of waste management resulted in an application for an energy-from-waste plant at Newhaven, immediately adjacent to the Sussex Downs AONB. The facility would undoubtedly have a significant impact on the AONB, but although there was strong local opposition, no objection was raised by the Countryside Agency.

In addition to domestic and commercial refuse, there is also a need to dispose of waste water. The coastal towns discharge their waste water, after treatment, to the sea. Waste water from Brighton and Hove is piped eastwards from the city to Portobello, a treatment works at Telscombe Cliffs. In December 1997, Southern Water Services Ltd made an application for a new waste-water works, including a new foreshore platform, and the excavation of a recess in the cliff. A significant proportion of the development lay within the Sussex Downs AONB, and the cliff itself was part of the Brighton to Newhaven Cliffs SSSI, being of geological interest. There were significant objections, although not from the Countryside Commission or English Nature. The application was refused by East Sussex County Council in 1998, partly because insufficient evidence had been put forward to justify the proposal, given the national designations and protective development plan policies. Southern Water appealed, and a five-month Public Inquiry was held. The Inspector and Secretary of State considered that the works would have a devastating impact on the AONB, would cause large-scale damage to the SSSI, and that there was at least one alternative site outside the AONB. Therefore, although there was a recognized national need to improve sewage treatment, the appeal was dismissed. Southern Water submitted another planning application in 2005 for a new works inland near Peacehaven, just outside the AONB. The new application was the subject of an appeal against non-determination in 2006.

Probably the most significant waste proposal within the South Downs also came in the late 1990s, when West Sussex County Council sought a permanent waste management complex in the Sussex Downs AONB at Halewick Lane, just north of Sompting. During the 1990s, the County Council had granted itself a series of temporary permissions for a waste transfer station, pending the development of an alternative on the east side of Worthing. However in 1999, the County Council considered that there were serious obstacles to using this alternative site, and therefore opted to seek permission to remain at Halewick Lane permanently. The application was made in 1999 and there were objectors, including Adur District Council and the Sussex Downs Conservation Board. The Board's handling of the application was significant. At its meeting in July 1999 a formal objection was recommended, but West Sussex County Council representatives on the Board spoke strongly in favour of the proposal, despite their remit as Board members to seek the conservation of the AONB. A motion to defer a decision to allow time for further discussion with the County Council was passed on the casting vote of the Chairman. These discussionscould not overcome the fundamental concerns, however, and at the next Board meeting in October 1999 the recommendation to object was agreed, notably without dissension.

Notwithstanding the objections, the County Council resolved to grant itself permission for a permanent waste transfer station, but the application was called in by the Secretary of State, John Prescott, and a Public Inquiry was held over 16 days in 2000. The Secretary of State refused the application in August 2001 partly on the basis that, although waste treatment was in the national interest, a potential alternative site did exist. It has been suggested that this application and the attitude of some of the West Sussex County Council members at the July meeting of the Conservation Board persuaded the Secretary of State that a joint committee of the local authorities (as the Board was) was insufficiently independent, and that a National Park for the South Downs was desirable. Certainly his announcement of the South Downs as a possible National Park came at the Labour Party Conference in October 1999, whilst the application was under discussion after the Board meeting in July that year.

PYLONS AND TELECOMMUNICATIONS

Pylons and telecommunication masts are among the most intrusive and controversial structures on the downland. Even sixty years ago, Hobhouse noted the adverse impact of pylons, radar and radio masts on the landscape.

With regard to pylons, in 1928 the Central Electricity Board proposed a 132KV power line across the Downs between Portslade, near Shoreham, and Offham, near Lewes and thence to Lewes and Eastbourne. Under pressure from the Society of Sussex Downsmen, the Board authorized the expenditure of £15,000 to take the lines off the Downs in the section between Lewes and Eastbourne, but would not spend an additional £30,000 on an alternative route between Portslade and Lewes (Plate 150). In 1966 the Government ruthlessly decided to run a 400kv supergrid line across the Downs in the face of vigorous opposition and against the recommendation of the Inspector that conducted the Inquiry into the proposal.

Radio masts first began to proliferate on the Downs during World War II, with radar installations at Butser Hill, St Roche's Hill, north of Chichester (Plate 151), Truleigh Hill, north of Shoreham, and Beachy Head. After the War, the emergency services sought wireless communications with Sussex Police Authority erecting a 120 ft high steel lattice tower at Burton

Down to the west of the A29 road in West Sussex in 1948, later replaced with two 150 ft masts to allow use by the ambulance service. The Police Authority also proposed a wireless station with two 80 ft steel masts on Beddingham Hill, to the east of Lewes, in 1951. In 1972 the Authority was given permission for a new 150 ft mast on Truleigh Hill, and two years later for two masts for police, fire and local government purposes, each over 90 ft high.

The development of television also led to the need for transmitters, with the BBC using RAF masts at Truleigh Hill (despite opposition from the National Parks Commission) and erecting a 65 ft mast at Newmarket Hill, north of Woodingdean in East Sussex, in 1959. The main controversy over BBC proposals, however, came in 1968, with an application for the erection of a 350 ft transmitter at Bexleyhill, north-east of Midhurst in West Sussex. A year or so later, the Corporation was proposing a 550 ft high mast and, despite objections from a range of amenity organizations, permission was granted.

In 1962 the Post Office proposed to replace a timber 120 ft Ministry of Aviation tower on Butser Hill with a 160 ft steel lattice tower for the Ministry and themselves. After consultation with the Royal Fine Arts Commission, approval was eventually given in 1964 for a 180 ft tower of a design approved by the Commission. Not only is this development notable for the involvement of the Commission, but it also highlighted the archaeological interest of Butser Hill.

In 1979 the Southern Electricity Board applied to replace two war-time radar masts on the western side of St Roche's Hill (also known as The Trundle, the name of the Neolithic hill fort there) with one 80 ft steel lattice mast, higher than the existing ones. Despite opposition, permission was eventually given, the removal of the two masts being seen as planning gain. Four years later British Telecom applied for a mast on the eastern side of the hill. Permission was refused, but subsequently allowed by the Secretary of State on appeal, against the recommendation of the Inspector. This was a particularly significant decision; the Minister considering the national landscape and archaeological interest of The Trundle to be outweighed by the national interest of development of telecommunications. In fact the mast was never erected.

A variation on the telecommunications theme came with the application by NTL Ltd for 21 satellite dishes, an educational building and a 120-bedroom hotel at Morn Hill, to the east of Winchester. The site, formerly a scrapyard and significant eyesore, lies just outside the East Hampshire AONB, but is clearly visible from within it and forms an important part of its setting. Despite objections on the basis of the impact on the AONB, permission was granted in 1999 and the stark white dishes are an incongruous feature in the green landscape.

RECREATION

Brighton's early high reputation in planning and downland conservation was tarnished in 1933 with its proposals to construct a motor-racing circuit on the Downs, close to the Devil's Dyke and Mile Oak Farm. This had originally been put forward in 1927, but financial guarantees were not forthcoming. However, the idea was revived six years later for a track some four and a half miles long, within 450 acres capable of accommodating 500,000 spectators. It attracted great objection, with the issue being reported in *The Times*, demonstrating how important the Downs had become as a national treasure. The proposals were eventually defeated, although motor speed trials were popular on the downland Lewes Racecourse in the 1930s.

In the late 1980s Chichester District Council controversially allowed a stark, eye-catching grandstand at Goodwood Racecourse in a prominent position on the Downs (Plate 152). However, a more significant application came in 2001, when Brighton & Hove Albion FC applied for a stadium on the very north-eastern edge of the city, adjacent to the University of Brighton's Falmer campus and within the Sussex Downs AONB (Plates 153 and 154). The application was supported by the City Council, which had allocated the site in its draft Local Plan for a 'community stadium'. The Secretary of State, John Prescott, called the application in for his own decision, and a Public Inquiry was held in 2003 which also considered the construction of a coach park adjacent to the stadium and the widening of Village Way, the access to the University Campus. The proposals were opposed by a number of bodies including Falmer Parish Council, Lewes District Council, the Countryside Agency, English Heritage and the Sussex Downs Conservation Board.

These applications gave rise to significant issues, particularly their compliance or otherwise with national planning policy as set out in PPG 7, that is, whether the developments would be in the 'public interest'. The Inspector dealing with the Local Plan recommended that the policy allocating the stadium should be deleted, as, in summary, there was no national need for it; there would be significant harm to the landscape; the site was too small; and there were possible alternatives outside the AONB. The application Inquiry Inspector shared his conclusions and recommended refusal of all the applications. However, despite the firm recommendations of two Inspectors, the Secretary of State decided in July 2004 to reopen the Inquiry to consider the specific matter of alternative sites. The reasons for reopening the Inquiry were the subject of much speculation. The more cynical suggested that the Deputy Prime Minister was simply delaying a decision until after the Labour Party Conference, held in Brighton in 2004, and until after a General Election, expected in the spring of 2005.

The reopened Inquiry ran from February to May 2005, and John Prescott's decision came on 29 October of that year. The Deputy Prime Minister accepted that the proposals would be contrary to the development plan and would cause harm to the AONB. However, he also agreed with the Club that the development would meet local social and economic needs, which he considered to be in the national interest, and, despite apparently never having visited Falmer, believed that the proposed site was not as attractive as the two original inspectors had. Accepting the conclusion of the reopened Inquiry Inspector that there were no feasible, practical and realistic alternative sites, Prescott concluded that the development would be in the 'public interest', and therefore granted permission for the development. The decision was particularly notable for the indication that local considerations could be considered to be in the national interest. The decision was described by a past President of the Royal Town Planning Institute as 'a triumph for the power of lobbying over the planning system' (McKay, 2005) and was condemned by objectors to the scheme, some of whom launched a legal challenge. Before the matter reached the Courts, the Treasury Solicitor accepted that Prescott had erred in one respect in his decision – believing the site to be within the built-up area – and eventually Prescott's successor, Ruth Kelly, agreed to the permission being quashed and the application being reconsidered. In November 2006, Kelly invited the major parties to submit further representations on four particular issues, including the interpretation and application of PPS7 to the applications. On 23 July 2007, Hazel Blears, who had replaced Ruth Kelly the previous month, granted permission for the stadium concluding, on balance, that the overall weight of material considerations favoured the development. Incredibly, the Secretary of State considered that, whilst there would be harm to the AONB, the mitigation measures proposed were sufficient to moderate that harm to a degree which was acceptable. Her conclusion inevitably raised the question: 'if the harm caused to an AONB by a football stadium and associated coach park is acceptable, what level of harm would not be?'

EDUCATION

The University of Brighton's Falmer campus is itself within the Sussex Downs AONB, its development having commenced in the early 1960s, thus pre-dating designation, although significant development has continued to take place since. Planning permission for a University College, to be the University of Sussex, on the north side of the A27 was granted in 1959. The main campus, designed by the eminent architect Sir Basil Spence with deliberately low buildings, was substantially complete by 1967. That year, the leading landscape architect, Sylvia Crowe, was commissioned to design landscape improvements within the campus. The quality of the whole design (the original building is listed Grade I and a number of others Grade II*) led to its inclusion within the AONB when finally designated. Subsequent development at the University has been generally acceptable in principle because of the national interest in providing for higher education. The Countryside Agency, however, has excluded both University campuses from the proposed South Downs National Park because, inter alia, they do not meet the statutory criteria and not all the buildings are of sufficient architectural merit.

CONCLUSIONS

It can be seen from this chapter how development pressures on the South Downs led to early moves for their protection, while concerns over unrestrained development nationally led to the establishment of a national planning system. This system was thought to be adequate to protect nationally important landscapes, and even stronger protection has been provided more recently in national planning policy guidance. So, has the planning system been successful in 'conserving and enhancing natural beauty'?

Whilst there can be no doubt that the pre-war excesses of unconstrained development have fortunately been avoided, occasional major proposals have still come forward. Some of these have been rejected by the local authorities, and on appeal, as failing to meet national policy requirements. However, the authorities have allowed, on occasions, local considerations to outweigh the national importance of the South Downs landscape in granting, or seeking to grant, consent. Respective Secretaries of State have intervened to uphold the national importance of the landscape, but not in every case, thus allowing consent by default, and have occasionally allowed other considerations to override it. As a result, major damaging developments have continued to take place.

Yet those major proposals have been relatively exceptional. Perhaps a much greater threat to the character and beauty of the Downs comes from the cumulative effect of much smaller-scale applications and other changes not requiring permission. In 2003/2004 there were over 4000 planning applications within the area of the proposed National Park, nearly four times the number received by any existing National Park. The great majority were for built development, for example, new houses, extensions to houses, domestic buildings, telecommunication masts, large agricultural buildings, and so forth, or changes in the use of land. Despite national and local policy guidances

that fundamentally seek to restrict building to that which is essential in the countryside and would not detrimentally affect the AONBs, over 80 per cent of these small-scale applications are approved. These projects can have an impact on the character, quality and amenity of the South Downs, individually and, more insidiously but significantly, through their cumulative impact. As such, they neither enhance nor even conserve natural beauty. If it was possible to plot all the built development within two AONBs at the time of designation and compare that to the same exercise for 2006, how much of the undeveloped South Downs would be lost?

What about future development issues? There is no indication, nor any reason to expect, a significant decline in the numbers of planning applications each year within the Downs. With limited room in the coastal urban areas to accommodate major infrastructure developments, there is likely to be continuing pressure on the Downs or land immediately adjacent, which will test the resolve of the local planning authorities and the relevant Secretary of State to defend the national importance of the AONBs.

Renewable energy is rightly being promoted at national, regional and local levels, and the high ground of the Downs close to the coast make them suitable, technically, for wind turbines. Opinions of turbines tend to be polarized between absolute eyesores and structures of elegance and beauty, as was found following a tentative proposal for a large turbine at Butser Hill in 2004 (not pursued). However, an application for a turbine 70 m high (to blade tip) to serve the Glyndebourne Opera House was submitted in January 2007. The proposal was supported by Friends of the Earth and opposed by the South Downs Society, the Council for National Parks, the CPRE, the Ramblers' Association, the Open Spaces Society, Natural England, The South Downs Joint Committee, and four local parish councils, but, despite this, and the recommendations of its own planning officers, Lewes District Council approved the application. The Secretary of State, Hazel Blears, has called in the application, but the final decision is likely to set a precedent for the future, similar applications in the South Downs and other protected landscapes, as the turbine would be the largest in any National Park and one of the largest in any AONB in the UK.

The Worthing bypass issue remains unresolved, but is likely to be resurrected at some future, maybe not too distant, date. The A27 at the Beddingham level crossing in East Sussex is being taken over the railway, and there may be bypasses for Selmeston and Wilmington, further to the east.

There will be a continuing demand for minerals, a finite resource, notwithstanding the increasing emphasis on using recycled aggregates. Whilst this may lead to pressure to extend or open up quarries in the South Downs, the working out of some of the pits within or adjacent to the area provides opportunities for their restoration for agriculture, forestry, nature conservation or recreation. The South Downs are not an island; the level of house-building in the South East proposed by the Government and the South East England Regional Assembly will have implications for the Downs: some development will take place in the larger towns in the Downs and development outside will lead to greater traffic and recreational pressure. There will also be a continuing need for infrastructure, for example to manage waste in various ways.

The cumulative impact of smaller-scale applications will continue to be a concern, with particular pressure around the urban fringes and in villages. The need for waste management and disposal will continue, which may affect the Downs. With a desire for an ever-more powerful telecommunications network, there will very likely be further applications for additional masts.

If the designation of the South Downs as a National Park is confirmed, the Park Authority, in consultation with the existing local authorities, will be the planning authority for the area. Interestingly, it appears that a proportion of those supporting a National Park do so because they believe it will stop all development, while some of those objecting to it do so because they believe exactly the same. Both are under a misconception. As explained earlier, the national planning guidance applying to National Parks and AONBs is exactly the same; both are afforded the same level of protection by the planning system.

It may be expected that if a National Park Authority is determining an application it would consistently give greater weight to National Park purposes and national guidance than the current local planning authorities give to AONB purposes, despite their obligations under the Countryside and Rights of Way Act 2000 to do so. But the Park Authority would still have to work within that national policy framework, which does allow development to take place. In fact, an average of 82 per cent of applications for development within National Parks were permitted in 1998/99; National Park Authorities claim that much effort goes into pre-application discussions, thus weeding out most unacceptable proposals and improving the quality of those submitted.

Other chapters in this book have made the point that the South Downs are not a museum to be preserved in aspic: they are a living, working landscape. A National Park Authority would be responsible for preparing a Local Development Framework for the whole area, recognizing that new development will be required in order to meet changing needs, particularly socio-economic ones such as affordable housing, community facilities and rural employment. As has been described in Chapter 6, affordable housing may take place on land outside town and village development boundaries. To support a prosperous agriculture, new, potentially larger, farm buildings may well be required, not easily assimilated into their landscape setting. Planning permission will be needed for such development. The trick is to ensure that it does not detract from the character, quality and amenity of the area. Ideally, such development should contribute positively to the Downs, enhancing their beauty through high standards of siting, design, respect for the local environment, and quality of building. The Countryside Agency promoted a move away from the unwritten but fundamental principle of the planning system: 'Is it bad enough to refuse?' to 'Is it good enough to approve?' (Countryside Agency, 2004) In other words, development should improve rather than merely conserve, through sensitive, locally distinctive, sustainable design. It is unfortunate that this change in approach has not been fully embraced by the Government in its review of the planning system and planning policy guidance, and many consider the current Planning Policy Statement 7 (PPS7) not to be as robust in the protection it offers AONBs and National Parks as its predecessor, PPG7.

There can be no doubt that the control of development and the use of land play vital roles in maintaining the beauty of the South Downs. To be effective, there needs to be robust national policy guidance, a perceptive regional strategy for rural areas, and a comprehensive local policy framework. Equally, or perhaps more important, however, than the written word, is the will of those who make planning decisions, be it at local or national level, to ensure that the right development does take place in the right place, so that it can play its proper part in truly sustaining the South Downs, environmentally, socially and economically.

REFERENCES

Brandon, P. (1998) *The South Downs*. Phillimore, Chichester.
Bryant, B. (1996) *Twyford Down. Roads, Campaigning and Environmental Law*. Spon, London.
Burrows, G.S. (1970) Proof of Evidence.
Bushell, P. (February 1999) Beeding Cement Works and Site. A History. Unpublished.
Countryside Agency (2004) *Towards a New Vernacular. Promoting High Quality Sustainable Development in the Countryside*. Cheltenham.
Department of Transport (1983) *Report of the Inspector into the Public inquiry into the Folkestone to Honiton Trunk Road (A27 Brighton Bypass) Bypass and Slip Roads*. Bypass Side Roads Orders. Department of Transport, London.
McKay, H. (2005) Letter in *Planning*. 18th November issue.

Ministry of Health and Town and Country Planning. Quoted in Society of Sussex Downsmen (1948) *Annual Report*. Lewes.

Ministry of Health and Town and Country Planning. Quoted in Society of Sussex Downsmen (1948) *Annual Report*. Lewes.

Ministry of Town and Country Planning (1947) *Report of the National Parks Committee (England and Wales)*. Cmnd 7121. HMSO, London.

Office of the Deputy Prime Minister (2004a) *Planning Policy Statements*. HMSO, London.

Office of the Deputy Prime Minister (2004b) *Sustainable Development in Rural Areas* (PPS7). HMSO, London. **The Times**, 27 April 1938

Williams-Ellis, C. (1928) *England and the Octopus*. Geoffrey Bles, London.

Woolf, L. (1967) *Autobiography*, Volume 4. Hogarth Press, London. pp. 146–8.

The author of this chapter is very grateful for the help in its initial preparation given by Peter Bryant OBE, former County Planning Officer, West Sussex County Council, and Brian Johnson, former Planning Advisor, West Sussex County Council.

DIDLING

Commentary on Part 2

Clearly, issues arise from each of the land uses (services and jobs, agriculture, forestry, water management, recreation, and development), reviewed in this part of the book. These require the attention, variously, of central government, statutory agencies, local government, landowners, communities and the voluntary sector, and a National Park Authority or area-wide public body with a role similar to that of a Conservation Board.

Chapter 6 gives ample evidence of the growing imbalance of rural community structure and the lack of rural facilities and public transport, which seriously affect the quality of life for less well-off residents in the towns and villages of the area. There is no easy way to solve such problems and, at the same time, to conserve the historic relationship between villages and their landscape setting. It will be a major challenge to local authorities and public agencies in the area, including any future National Park Authority, to integrate their efforts to enable all ages, incomes and occupations to live in rural communities. Success in this will depend on developing a strategic approach in conjunction with Parish Councils, voluntary-sector agencies, landowners and residents. A major feature of the approach will be participation in the preparation of Local Community Strategies and Parish Plans, aiming to get local consensus on policies, priorities, resources for action, and for the necessary research and monitoring.

Agricultural policy has caused dramatic and regrettable change in the landscape over the last 50 years. There is now reason to hope for some reversal of this trend, however, due to public opinion moving in favour of greater priority for the environment rather than for outright food production. The ESA scheme has already been reasonably successful in bringing a better balance into the situation, as indeed has the Sussex Heathland Project, but the coverage of both is limited. There is still much uncertainty, however, about how effective the Government's Rural Strategy will be in encouraging sustainable agriculture and producing benefits to the local economy, and how, in particular, the new Single Farm Payment will complement this. The very convincing case study in Chapter 7 suggests that a high degree of intervention is not necessary, provided that individual farmers can develop robust systems, and that their farms are of a size that allows this to be done. To do so would require a workable partnership, locally, between farmers, nature conservation interests and the National Park Authority or equivalent, supported by finance for environmental improvements. It is unrealistic, nevertheless, to expect a full-scale return to the pre-1939 downland and wealden landscape. More promising would be a campaign to link remaining unspoilt areas, for example small pieces of relatively inaccessible chalk downland, to create cores of greater biodiversity that could gradually extend to make a variety of worthwhile habitats. Above all, however, is the need to encourage diversification in farm development, with its potential benefits to the farmer and to the local economy, provided it is able to improve the condition of the landscape. This could include the development of local 'speciality' products with rural and historical association, in the way that Southdown and Hampshire Downs lamb can make an important contribution to the landscape, to leisure and to tourism.

Forestry, on the other hand, does not appear to have the acute problems that beset farming. Given an increase in economic prospects for good forestry practice, it should be possible to tackle gradually the large expanse of neglected woodland in the area. Much of this is 'ancient' woodland, attractive in the landscape, and potentially a valuable habitat. The case study of a large estate in Chapter 8 reveals the benefits that might accrue from this if owners can be encouraged to take it up. The case study is also a good source of information about forestry operations, a process that is often misunderstood by the public. Foresters have to take a long-term view of investment in woodland management. Given this, the prospect over a period of time might encourage the improvement of infrastructure, especially for timber-processing, and the creation of more receptive local markets, showing that wider economic benefits should be possible from reclaiming the area's woodlands, especially those with recreational potential, including countryside sports.

There is a more pressing problem resulting from the legacy of mismanaged river systems revealed in Chapter 9. The conversion of wetland to farming, for example, has resulted in significant external costs, flood risk, and, in places, an artificial, somewhat unattractive, valley landscape. Here again, as is the case with agriculture, public opinion now looks more favourably at the need for sustainable water management. Perhaps the most far-reaching way of achieving this is through imaginative restoration of rivers, reinstating natural systems, a radical, costly and controversial challenge for public authorities in the area to respond to. Its benefits need to be widely explained, and experience suggests that it can only be achieved through a working partnership between the several interests, public, private and voluntary sector, involved.

The recreational use of land, the subject of Chapter 10, presents another significant challenge. The pressures are immense, are growing rapidly and raise the question of what action is necessary to bring about a more balanced distribution of opportunity. Countryside access, for example, is concentrated at the eastern end of the area. Allied to this is the need to build up the system of rights of way to serve better the new CRoW Act access areas and existing major 'honeypots'. The area's huge variety of landscape, including woodland and heathland, should be a factor in strategic planning for redistribution, as would transport, wildlife, tranquillity and the availability of services. The needs of new forms of recreation should not be overlooked, provided they can be quietly assimilated into the countryside. Landowners and the private sector will have an important role to play in this redistribution, and in ensuring that its economic benefits are widely shared.

Finally, in this part of the book, the control of land use through the planning system is a matter that can make or mar the environment of the whole area. Major developments such as trunk-road construction, mineral-working and waste-disposal have caused much controversy in the past, as recounted in Chapter 11. Hopefully, with designation as a National Park, unpalatable projects of this kind would become non-existent in the future. The risks of damage are great, however, in the cumulative impact of small developments and 'clutter' on local environments, on traffic generation and on the character of the area as a whole. It will be difficult to regulate these satisfactorily (often they do not need planning permission) unless planning policies for the area are consistent, that they require development actually to enhance the landscape, that the highest design standards are insisted upon, and that the plans of adjoining Authorities are compatible. It is important, democratically, that the ability to determine most planning applications remains with the elected Local Authorities. There should be firm guidance from and regular liaison with the Park Authority, especially on design, a willingness to listen to views expressed at community level and to respect the requirements of the Park-wide Local Development Framework, Village Design Statements and Parish Plans.

That these six issues, economic, environmental and social, are inter-related needs to be recognized in policy-making and management. The following themes are suggested:

- Continuing efforts must be made to widen the opportunities for those who need to live in the area's rural communities but cannot afford to do so because of imbalances in the housing market. This is primarily a task for the Local Authority, but needing a flexible approach on the part of those responsible for countryside management. Similarly, steps should continue to be taken to encourage growth of the local economy to reduce job shortages and to stem the decline in rural services, especially public transport. Again, countryside management for recreation and tourism, promotion of nature reserves and for support of farming and forestry, has a role to play in this.

- Decision-makers should understand good farming and forestry practice and its economic context, and should be well informed on the ways in which central and local government, statutory agencies and landowners can work together to influence quality of production, care of the environment, and benefit to the local economy, including by diversification. This knowledge is essential for the successful preparation of the Development Framework and Management Plan for the area, and for a constructive approach to development control;

- Equally, it is essential for those who are responsible for this work to appreciate the kind of action necessary to improve the quality and quantity of water for the natural environment, communities, rural land uses, and recreation, and for them to encourage the management of rivers in harmony with landscape and ecological objectives, and with development of the local economy;

- Knowledge of farming and forestry practice and the process of water management is also of fundamental importance to successful planning for recreation, especially in order to obtain a balanced distribution of opportunity supported by landowners, provided with suitable facilities, and of benefit to the local economy.

All these matters are ones in which public authorities, especially the proposed National Park Authority, could have a positive and innovative policy-making role. Successful action, however, will depend on the relationship they establish with local interests, especially landowners. As can be seen from Chapter 8, large privately-owned estates, of which there are well over a dozen, can be major contributors to this. Indeed they are dominant in the pattern of landownership in parts of the area, especially in the centre, adding much to the character of the landscape. Further east, too, there are extensive public, mainly local authority, landholdings. All these estates, public and private, are large enough to be able to take a comprehensive view of their environmental resource, and to develop its potentail in their own and the wider interest.

With those arising from Parts 1 and 3 of the book, these ideas will be developed further in Chapter 14.

PART 3

Conservation and
Countryside Management

Introduction to Part 3

The idea of a National Park for the South Downs in Sussex and Hampshire is not new. In the face of growing pressure for development, the Society of Sussex Downsmen (SSD but now named The South Downs Society) was advocating one for the Sussex Downs in the 1920s. In the 1930s, evidence by the National Trust to Sir Christopher Addison's Committee (*Report of the National Park Committee*, 1931) proposed a National Park for the South Downs in both Sussex and Hampshire, and the idea was taken further, for Sussex by East Sussex County Council, SSD and the Council for the Preservation of Rural England (CPRE) at the time of the abortive Sussex Downs Preservation Bill (1934). Meanwhile pressure for unregulated development increased further.

Interest in protecting the Downs was renewed after the Second World War by CPRE, SSD and the Commons and Open Spaces Society. With much improved prospects of planning control over development, the main concern then was the fear that downland would be further damaged by continued ploughing. Despite this, a National Park for the Downs was not amongst the recommendations in John Dower's seminal Report (*National Parks in England and Wales*, 1945). Instead, he included them in his list of 'Other Amenity Areas', with the qualification that he would have recommended a National Park if he had not been reasonably satisfied that they would in future be adequately dealt with by the county and local authorities. Two years later, however, National Park status, including the chalk downs in Hampshire, was strongly advocated by the Hobhouse Committee (*Report of the National Parks Committee (England and Wales)*, 1947) on account of the intrinsic beauty and interest of both areas, and their accessibility from London. Plate (map) 162 shows the Hobhouse proposals for England and Wales as a whole.

Eight years later, in 1955, the then National Parks Commission (NPC), having secured the designation of eight National Parks in England and Wales (the Peak District, Lake District, Snowdonia, Dartmoor, Pembrokeshire Coast, North York Moors, Yorkshire Dales and Exmoor) as a priority, turned their attention to other areas. The criteria for designating National Parks in the 1949 National Parks and Access to the Countryside Act specified that they should be extensive tracts of countryside of great natural beauty, affording opportunities for open-air recreation, accessible to centres of population. Within this context, the NPC concluded in 1956 that the South Downs should not be designated: although possessing great natural beauty, readily accessible from London and especially vulnerable to development, the region had a recreational value much reduced by extensive cultivation of the downland. Consequently NPC favoured designation as an Area of Outstanding Natural Beauty (AONB).

This designation followed, separately, for East Hampshire in 1962, and, after extensive and damaging delays due to negotiations with local authorities and landowners on boundary issues, for the Sussex Downs in 1966. In each case, associated parts of the Weald were included. Now, some 40 years later, resulting partly from pressure by the South Downs Campaign (SDC), and by individuals who felt that the local authorities, public agencies and voluntary organizations interested in the Downs needed to be more aware of grass-roots opinion, the idea of a National Park for the whole area is being revisited. The issues arising over this are explored in Chapter 13, but first it is necessary to show the significant progress that has been made in countryside management in the two AONBs.

Thus, in Chapter 12, Phil Belden and Alison Tingley give an account of the setting up of administrative organizations for the Sussex and Hampshire areas respectively, and the achievement of these two somewhat different bodies. They describe the genesis, in 1991, of the East Hampshire AONB Joint Advisory Committee (JAC), and, in 1992, of the more elaborate Sussex Downs Conservation Board (SDCB). The first is an excellent example of what was beginning to become a standard, if somewhat informal, partnership arrangement for AONB conservation; it was strongly encouraged by the Countryside Commission (CC), the successor to NPC, in consultation with County Councils. The second stems from a pioneering move by CC and the two Sussex County Councils, supported by the offer of a generous grant, to encourage a more formal and better-endowed joint administration in the area. It was a model for other AONBs that has now been given statutory recognition in the Countryside and Rights of Way Act, 2000. Chapter 12 then describes the achievements in countryside management in each area, including the completion of Management Plans for both by 1995, the Interim Management Plan for the whole South Downs on which consultation started in 2006, and the formation in 2005 of the South Downs Joint Committee, an important step that combines the interests of the SDCB and the JAC.

In Chapter 13 Gerald Smart looks at the recent moves by CC's successor, the Countryside Agency (CA), to obtain formal designation of the two AONBs as a South Downs National Park. These moves followed a false start in 1999, when the CC, having reviewed the situation at the request of the Secretary of State for the Environment, concluded, as did its predecessor in 1957, that the Downs did not meet the National Parks Act criteria for designation. After strong hints by the Environment Minister that the interpretation of the criteria should be reconsidered, and the announcement at the 1999 Labour Party Conference that the Government wished to create two new National Parks (the New Forest and the South Downs), the CA agreed that the area was, after all, suitable for National Park status, and, in 2000, began the lengthy process of designation. The chapter gives a brief account of this process: the CA's review of a possible boundary, wide consultation on this and possible administrative arrangements; then, in 2002, the making of the Order itself, and the consequent Revocation Order for the two AONBs. Over 5000 representations were received for and against the proposals, including objections from local authorities, and these led to a twelve-month Public Inquiry, starting in 2003. At this, the CA strenuously supported its conclusions in the face of objections in principle, especially from some West Sussex local authorities, and many on details of boundaries (most of which supported the National Park and were asking for more land to be put in). Throughout, they had strong support from the SDC and other organizations, national and local. Amongst the major issues was the question that had exercised minds, even at the time of Dower and Hobhouse, as to whether wealden areas to the north of the chalk should be included. The chapter summarizes the main objections heard at the Inquiry, and comments on their implications for policies in a Management Plan for the whole area.

EAST MARDEN   J Evans

CHAPTER 12

Establishing the Areas of Outstanding Natural Beauty and Their Management

PHIL BELDEN & ALISON TINGLEY

SETTING THE BOUNDARIES

Unusually, the designation of the South Downs as an Area of Outstanding Natural Beauty (AONB) was considered in the light of its rejection as a National Park in 1956, as noted in the Introduction to this part of the book. In the eyes of the National Parks Commission (NPC) at the time, although it was no longer suited for open-air recreation, the area's natural beauty was unchallenged. Further, vulnerability to development due to its proximity to London hastened the AONB designation process. The County Councils were consulted, and in 1957 it was agreed that the South Downs should be designated on a county basis (National Parks Commission, 1957). It was agreed that the designation would include both chalk and wealden landscapes.

Designation of the Sussex Downs AONB

The Sussex part was considered first, and in 1957 the designation process was set in train. Over the next three years various boundary amendments were made, such as excluding the Ouse Brooks south of Lewes, and including Amberley and Parham Parks, an area near Duncton, Bury village and Ebernoe Common. These changes precipitated a procedural debate with the Ministry of Housing and Local Government. The Minister returned the Designation Order unconfirmed 'because a number of persons had not been able to make representations to the Commission in regard to land included in the Order because the submitted

Order deviated from the advertised Order' (National Parks Commission, 1962). This meant that the whole process had to begin again. The rather restrained Commission minute notes their 'keen disappointment'!

The local development plans and a number of classic Downs issues (e.g. Devil's Dyke redevelopment, masts and power lines, excluding or including some key urban-fringe sites) were looked at again, and the new Order, for the 983 square km Sussex Downs AONB, was finally confirmed by the Minister in 1966. It takes in the open and wooded chalk escarpmant and Wealden Greensand, and includes four major river valleys (Countryside Agency, 1999).

Designation of the East Hampshire AONB

In Hampshire the process began in 1958, when the NPC recommended that the Hampshire Downs AONB (as it was then called) should include the Hampshire section of the Hobhouse Committee's proposed South Downs National Park, and be extended westwards from the Meon Valley (Plate 155) to St.Catherine's Hill near Winchester; and northwards to add an area north of Selborne.

The proposed boundary initially excluded Petersfield and Liss. Hampshire County Council (HCC) argued for their inclusion since Midhurst, of a similar size and character to Petersfield, was within the proposed Sussex Downs AONB. If taken north of Liss, the boundary also provided a better match with that for Sussex. The Ministry of Housing and

Local Government objected however, maintaining that the landscape there was of 'ordinary' quality. (It is noteworthy that similar arguments were put forward in 2001 when the Countryside Agency published its area of search for the National Park.) Nevertheless, when the formal AONB designation stages began in 1960, these areas were included. HCC must have made a convincing case (Countryside Agency, 2000).

After public consultation the boundaries were further extended to include Stephen's Castle Down, Corhampton Down and Hambledon, as well as land at Empshott. (It is again of interest that a proposal to include the Itchen Valley was rejected, whereas this was brought in by the Countryside Agency some 40 years later as part of the proposed National Park.) Only one objection was received, and the Designation Order for the East Hampshire AONB (note the subtle change of title) was confirmed in 1962. It covers some 386 km² from the outskirts of Winchester in the west, to the county boundary with West Sussex in the east, adjoining the Sussex Downs AONB. The most southerly village is Hambledon and the most northerly is Selborne. Although the underlying geology provides a degree of unity, the area embraces a variety of contrasting landscapes, from the dramatic open and panoramic views on the chalk downland, to the steep wooded scarp-slopes of 'hanger' woodland, the gentle winding plains of the river valley and the enclosed intimate landscape of the Weald (Countryside Agency, 2000).

THE BEGINNING OF COUNTRYSIDE MANAGEMENT

The 1949 National Parks and Access to the Countryside Act was a seminal piece of legislation. It established the principle of National Parks, and provided a purpose and management framework. Buried deeper in it was provision for AONBs, but with no clear purpose or framework for management. Although it took time to set them up, some National Parks appeared within a decade. For AONBs, without any strict mandate or guidance, it was like being becalmed in the doldrums. This accounts for the time it took for the Sussex Downs Conservation Board and East Hampshire AONB Joint Advisory Committee (see below) to be established: 26 and 29 years respectively after designation.

The exception was planning. Once the lines on the map were drawn, the planners could take into account the national designation. So, from the 1960s, planning policies began to be formulated to guide development control in the South Downs. Chapter 11 explores the impacts of development on the Downs and the effectiveness of planning controls.

Since then there has been growing awareness, nationally and locally, of the impact of agriculture, recreation and development on the countryside. The

issues, so far as the Downs are concerned, are rehearsed in the relevant chapters earlier in this book. Attempts to counteract the slow but sure degradation of the countryside evolved painfully slowly, and each county took a slightly different approach to embryonic conservation action.

Hampshire

In the East Hampshire AONB a pilot project sought to reconcile policies and processes as a basis for later countryside management. In 1968, a report (Hampshire County Council *et al.*, 1968) identified a range of policies relating to settlements, communities, landscape enhancement, recreation, wildlife conservation, woodland management and the spread of glasshouses. This document was applauded as a pioneering effort, but the local government reorganization that followed in the early 1970s meant that little action was taken. To an extent it was superseded by HCC's Countryside Heritage Policy in the mid-1980s. This initiated a record of Countryside Heritage Sites that, although not of national importance, had county if not regional value, and included large areas of ecological or cultural interest with statutory or non-statutory designations. Such sites were being lost at an alarming rate, and the purpose was to promote active interest in their conservation and management, encouraged by advice and grant-aid, coupled with site-management agreements. One such area was the Hampshire Hangers. This was the only part of the AONB to receive special measures, that is, the formation of the East Hampshire Hangers Project to bring the Hanger woodlands back into management (Ockenden, 1991). It ran for six years until funding dried up in 1990, and although it gathered much information about the ecological interest of the Hangers (see Plates 6 and 137), it had limited impact in terms of active management.

Sussex

Meanwhile, a more direct approach was being taken towards countryside management in Sussex. The first project was set up in 1974 by the East Sussex County Council (ESCC) on the newly designated Heritage Coast. It was a generous move, having no pump-priming help from the Countryside Commission. Called the South Downs Conservation Project, it took in the whole of the AONB in the eastern Downs, though the 700-acre (284 hectares) Seven Sisters Country Park, as a result of a lack of 'joined-up' thinking, continued to be managed in isolation to the Heritage Coast (Plate 14). It started with a plan (ESCC, 1976), a steering group, an officer, a car and £500, and within 10 years the success of the project led to its expansion to incorporate the entire AONB within East Sussex, albeit with a staff complement of just two full-time officers. As well as being involved in countryside management, this small team, with the support of other ESCC staff, responded to planning applications in the area.

At this time West Sussex County Council (WSCC) was also considering opportunities for countryside management. Rights of way were being maintained through a cyclical programme across the county, but there was no project dedicated to countryside management, outside the two recreation sites of Buchan Country Park and Pagham Harbour Nature Reserve. The Coombes–Newtimber Project (WSCC, undated) was set up with the aim of getting landowners to manage land for conservation or recreation, encouraged with grant-aid or practical help. There were no project officers; instead, existing staff had to cover this additional work. However, the seeds had been sown, and in 1988 WSCC established the Sussex Downs Conservation Project (WSCC, 1992) (note the title change to distinguish it from East Sussex – never the twain shall meet!).

Both projects were given a boost during the mid-1980s by the Government's bid to reduce unemployment. Funding via the Manpower Services Commission (MSC) allowed the East Sussex project to set up two practical teams, each with a Land Rover, equipment and materials to tackle conservation work, fully manage the rights of way network, and improve access. They were aided by Technical Support and Interpretation teams. Up to 22 people were directly employed at any one time, with other teams called upon to assist at times. For example, over 100 trainees were engaged in a massive conservation project on the chalk grassland at Charleston Bottom. In West Sussex, as part of the Coombes–Newtimber Project, the large Devil's Dyke area was systematically cleared of scrub and fenced to allow a return of grazing – all achieved through MSC teams.

To supplement its meagre resources the South Downs Conservation Project in East Sussex set up a South Downs Volunteer Ranger Service, adapted from practice carried out in National Parks: a well-trained, highly motivated group committed to downland conservation. Work on rights of way was the early priority, but this soon developed into nature conservation and other tasks, such as invaluable public relations at busy sites or in sensitive areas. A parallel Volunteer Ranger Service was subsequently established by the Sussex Downs Conservation Project in West Sussex, taking the cover further west, initially in the Shoreham to Worthing area, then on to the Hampshire border, and finally incorporating the Hampshire Downs by the late 1990s (Plates 156 to 158).

More sensitive agriculture

Countryside management thus was born and gently nurtured in the South Downs. But it could do little to reduce the impact of agricultural intensification, a trend that was never imagined in the 1940s when the main countryside legislation arrived respectively through the Agriculture Act, 1947, Town and Country Planning Act, 1947, and the National Parks and Access to the Countryside Act, 1949. By the 1960s, when the two AONBs were being designated, a few radical voices were heard. Julian Huxley wrote of the 'virtual disappearance of so many butterflies … the chalk downs are almost bare of Blues' (Huxley, 1963). As shown in Chapter 7, the European Union's Common Agricultural Policy compounded the problem: the benign custodianship of the land by farmers had been radically transformed into a one-way process to increase production, but with no account taken of the landscape, wildlife, archaeology and all the negative consequences of the drive for self-sufficiency in food.

The South Downs' first *cause célèbre*, Graffham Down, was publicized by Marion Shoard (1980) where 'uncultivated marginal land, unused capacity for food production' was cleared and ploughed. 'The woodland, scrub and down where nightingales had sung and badgers scuttled became an expanse of barley prairie, like so much of the rest of the South Downs. Its appeal as landscape and its value for wildlife, and humans seeking recreation, has been obliterated.' Like any controversial issue in the Downs, there was a passionate tide of public opinion to save the area; but at the time agriculture had no counterpoints.

As shown also in Chapter 7, 1986 was a watershed: a new Agriculture Act established Environmentally Sensitive Areas (ESAs) to put back some of the hedgerows, ponds and other features lost over the last 40 years (Plate 110). This profound U-turn was conceived in the South Downs: through the ESCC South Downs Conservation Project, a lobby was instigated to 'Save the South Downs', but limited co-operation across the counties proved a problem; and, the Ministry (MAFF) had very modest ideas. The lobby proved essential and it had more support than in all the other potential ESAs put together. However, only the eastern Downs were designated; belatedly WSCC then lobbied, and the ESA was extended in 1988 across West Sussex and into Hampshire. The South Downs was the only area to have such a scheme, not just for maintaining traditional farming, but also offering incentives for restoring grassland landscape (MAFF, 1987).

The battle for the South Downs ESA symbolized the very real problems of trying to run two separate AONBs with different authorities; it galvanized enormous interest, attracting people to fight for the Downs; it emphasized the very real need, not just for maintaining the area, but for the restoration of the landscape. Nevertheless, the three threats of agricultural intensification, inappropriate development and damaging recreation re-surfaced.

A FORUM EMERGES

In an attempt to gather the enormous interest in the Downs and to focus those actively fighting for their protection, the Sussex local authorities in 1986 brought interest groups together into a Sussex Downs AONB Forum. What resulted was a useful talk-shop, but, with no dedicated resources and no executive powers, it was never going to be the saviour of the Downs, and its Statement of Intent (ESCC/WSCC, 1986) never materialized into any really successful action. A South Downs Way Management Plan (Sussex Downs AONB Forum/WSCC, 1986) emerged, but even a common signage policy, to make life easier for the public, proved too much; each County Council clung to its own different, waymarking system.

Meanwhile, out in the real world, as shown in Chapters 1 and 11, dramatic developments were taking place: the M3 Twyford Down cutting in the west and Brighton bypass in the east (Plates 3, 147 and 159), out of town superstores and other damaging infrastructure pressures (Plates 147 and 159). It was not just the physical and visual implications of these that destroyed the landscape, but the consequential urbanization of significant tracts of AONB, reduction in tranquility and the severance of people from their beloved Downs.

The successful ESA lobby had given people hope, but the destructive forces of development could have turned this to despair. Instead, buoyed up by the Norfolk and Suffolk Broads sailing their way to a 'National Park in all but name', people rallied to the cause once more, with many individuals and organizations, though not initially the Society of Sussex Downsmen, coming together in a coalition known as the South Downs Campaign (1990). The cosy, unachieving world of the Sussex Downs AONB Forum was about to come to an end.

It was the call for a National Park that led to the creation of the Sussex Downs Conservation Board. The ghost of Hobhouse (Ministry of Town & Country Planning, 1947) and his list of 12 National Parks appeared; the Broads became the eleventh Park, leaving only the Downs wanting from his list. Demands for real action were made at the Forum. Behind the scenes, the County Councils slowly accumulated information on National Parks, in a region that had no first-hand experience of such a designation, for the Parks were embedded in the mountain rock and moorland of the north and west (see Plate (maps) 162).

A controversial article by Marion Shoard (1989) in *The Times*, stimulated by the fortieth anniversary of the National Parks Act, agitated the musings of local people. She was blunt. 'Our national parks do embrace some fine countryside. But they exclude much that is even more valuable and far more threatened … like the Dorset heaths or the South Downs.' She then turned on AONBs: a 'designation which brings few real benefits'; a status which 'is now perhaps best abandoned'. One of the letters in response, from the County Planning Officer in West Sussex, questioned whether a National Park was 'right for this soft and sensitive landscape' and if this 'status posed a threat to the people who manage the land so well' (Bryant, 1989). These early salvoes fired up local government, MPs, civil servants, national and local organizations and, of course, intense media interest.

At about this time a seminal report was in its gestation: the Smart and Anderson study of AONBs (Countryside Commission, 1990), undertaken on behalf of the Countryside Commission. This recommended the formation of Joint Advisory Committees (JACs). The debate was rapidly hotting up. Hard on its heels was the Edwards Report (Countryside Commission, 1991), a review of the National Parks, which hinted at the possibility of new designations: a point the Minister, Chris Patten, took up, wanting more lowland Parks (Robson, 1990).

The case for National Park status had been fervently debated in both East and West Sussex County Councils during 1989 (WSCC, 1989 a, b, c; ESCC, 1989). Their collective thoughts surfaced at the Sussex Downs Forum in October, when papers from both County Councils were presented (ESCC/WSCC, 1989). WSCC laid out the case with three options: leave things as they are; seek National Park status; find an alternative solution. ESCC delved into the merits of National Park status and asked the Forum's views. The Forum sought a wider consultation with local bodies.

From these debates, two processes seemed to be developing: on the surface, the key issues of recreational demands, agricultural practices and development pressures, together with the need for better protection and more funding, against the fears of a National Park bringing an influx of visitors, increasing bureaucracy and alienating farmers; behind the scenes, issues over power and control if a National Park were created, not least the reduction in influence of the local authorities.

A conference at the University of Sussex in early 1990 brought some 80 people together from the many groups interested in the question of 'A National Park for the South Downs?' (Sussex Rural Community Council, 1990). Addressed by leading national experts in the field, this conference and the Forum's request for views elicited a high and varied response (WSCC, 1990a), generating many column inches in the local newspapers. The idea of the South Downs becoming a National Park was attracting national media interest too (British Broadcasting Corporation, 1990). Questions were asked in Parliament and the Council for National Parks advocated the New Forest and South Downs as potential new Parks.

In May 1990 WSCC published the replies to the Forum's consultation, listing them as 'pro' or 'anti' National Park (WSCC, 1990b). The issue, which hadinitially been more of a fact-finding mission, was maturing and polarizing. Pro-Park groups were beginning to organize themselves, through the new South Downs Campaign network; while some local authority representatives sought better control of the debate. The build-up to a decisive Forum meeting in 1990 had begun. The Forum was being taken seriously for the first time in its existence.

CASTING THE JOINT COMMITTEE MOULD

WSCC conceived the idea of a Joint Committee for the Sussex Downs, working up proposals from the Countryside Commission's statements over 'enhanced AONB status' (to give more bite to the approach suggested in the Smart and Anderson report). ESCC struggled with promoting a South Downs National Park, due to the wide divergence of views, but was sceptical about the chances of any strengthened AONB arrangement. The South Downs Campaign, after much deliberating, started to promote the notion of a single local statutory body 'of equivalent status to a National Park Authority'; an interesting form of words, designed to capture a broad coalition of support.

The two County Councils needed to agree a common proposal, so there was much behind-the-scenes activity over the summer of 1990. They also had to convince the District Councils of this county-led approach. To secure adequate funding, the Countryside Commission was involved in fairly clandestine talks. The mould was being shaped for a Joint Committee under the Local Government Act 1972, but with the type of National Park representation of local authority members and some additional members to be appointed by the Countryside Commission and given powers to vote.

Another matter was the area to be administered by any Joint Committee. WSCC was firm in its view that it should be the Sussex Downs AONB, though there was some debate about chalk only, excluding the Wealden Greensand. ESCC favoured the option of including the East Hampshire AONB.

To set the mould for the 1990 Forum a joint paper was produced by the two County Councils (ESCC/ WSCC, 1990). Several drafts were passed back and forth, including changing the term South Downs to Sussex Downs at the insistence of WSCC. Two options were presented: a National Park, or a 'tailor-made' Sussex Downs Conservation Board. The County Councils recommended option two, but they had not reckoned on the direct lobbying of the South Downs Campaign, which was engaging a wider public, tapping into sources beyond the immediate County

Council-related contacts. But as a late arrival on the scene (only recently formed), was it too late?

Lobbying and media activity increased when the Forum papers were made public. At the meeting the players acted out their parts: councillors generally supported the second option, whilst many of the voluntary bodies wanted to keep the National Park option open, pending the imminent National Parks Review (Countryside Commission, 1991). The *coup d'état* was delivered by the Countryside Commission in a tabled letter (Coleman, 1990). It supported the establishment of a Conservation Board and offered 50 per cent funding for six years, thus dealing a killer blow to National Park protagonists, whose strength lay in the argument that only a Park solution could guarantee adequate funding. The letter stipulated that the Board should take over countryside management from the County Councils, and that the District Councils should delegate development-control decisions. The latter was not so palatable to District members, but the prospect of a National Park alternative meant that they were prepared to consider some form of delegation, perhaps in the upland chalk, and consult on all planning issues across the AONB. Hampshire CC, which had observer status, was neither in favour of a National Park nor a Conservation Board, but wished to be kept informed over progress.

The next six months hastily constructed the various elements, from the right political climate at local and national level, to sorting out the operational and administrative remit of the Board. The Countryside Commission was pleased with this national AONB experiment, and intimated a higher level of funding than originally thought, 50 to 75 per cent. Much hinged on what the Counties' contribution would be, a non-committal figure quoted at the time was £800,000; so the total budget with grant-aid could have been between £1.6 and 3.2 million. Arguments ensued over what the Board would actually do, its political make-up and its tenure (the Countryside Commission wanted to review it after three years, in order to address other AONBs and possibly seek new legislation). The draft agreement eventually stipulated a review after five years of the Board's six-year life.

In April, at Pelham House in Lewes, the AONB Forum (1991) agreed the proposals for establishing a Sussex Downs Conservation Board. These covered the constitution, functions, staffing and funding. Essentially, the two County Councils would delegate the functions of countryside management to the Board and, although not ratified by this time, it was hoped the District Councils would consult on all planning applications outside towns and villages, with a right for the Board to be heard at the relevant planning committee if there was disagreement. True to form, the Countryside Commission tabled a statement supporting the establishment of a Board, pledging 50 per cent funding, and hoping that the District Councils would, in due course, delegate development-control powers to the Board; with the Government's response to the Edwards Panel still awaited, it was requested that the matter of National Park designation be kept under review.

Nationally (aided and abetted by local campaigners) the notion of a South Downs National Park was still simmering. The three main political parties had called for the South Downs to be a National Park at the 1990 local elections, and now the Government's White Paper, *This Common Inheritance,* stated that 'the Government will also consider any case for designating new National Parks' (Department of the Environment, 1990); the Labour Party (in *An Earthly Chance*) proposed 'new National Parks ... early candidates will include the New Forest and South Downs'; and Social and Liberal Democrats (*What Price Our Planet?)* recommended new National Parks.

The South Downs National Park campaign had nevertheless been too late, and although at the time of setting up the Board it was made clear that the matter of designation be kept under review, the move had been out-flanked by the local authorities. However, it had dealt a strong bidding hand that had raised the stakes. Indeed, the Sussex Downs Conservation Board might never have come to fruition, and would certainly have been a shadow of itself, had it not been for the National Park lobby. The Forum's decision had cast the mould, the opposition began to melt away and the local authorities were left to complete the process. A belated conference (Society of Sussex Downsmen, 1991) was the prelude to the swansong, played out in a BBC South documentary (1992), timed to hit the launch of the SDCB, prophetically titled 'Division on the Downs'.

BUILD-UP TO THE AONB CONSERVATION BODIES

The East Hampshire Joint Advisory Committee

After the 'proto-management plan' of 1968 nothing much happened in the East Hampshire AONB for many years. In 1985 the East Hampshire Hangers Project (Ockenden, 1991) was set up, as mentioned above. Although covering only a small part of the AONB, it was perhaps the precursor to the East Hampshire AONB Joint Advisory Committee (JAC) and laid the foundation of joint working between local authorities, government agencies, voluntary conservation groups and local landowners.

The concern in Sussex over inadequate status, power and resources of AONBs did not go unnoticed in Hampshire, but with fewer development and recreational pressures, the call for National Park status by the pressure groups did not extend there. Without the pressure groups, it was East Hampshire District Council (EHDC) that led the way and sought discussions with the Countryside Commission, Winchester City Council (WCC) and HCC. In 1989 a report went to EHDC informing it of the three options being looked at in Sussex (EHDC, 1989). As a result, EHDC informed the Sussex Downs AONB Forum that, whilst recognizing the issues in Sussex , it did not support National Park status.

At a subsequent meeting (EHDC, 1990), the Council resolved to support recent Countryside Commission initiatives promoting AONBs, to consider what Countryside Commission initiatives might be set up in East Hampshire and to consider preparing a Statement of Intent and Management Plan with WCC and HCC. A meeting with the Countryside Commission was then held, to discuss not only the idea of setting up a JAC, but also appointing an AONB Officer and establishing a service for countryside management. The response from HCC was not altogether encouraging (HCC, 1990), expressing concern over the financial implications, although happy for existing staff and work to be co-ordinated by 'someone else'. One thing that was agreed on was the need for a landscape appraisal before setting up a JAC or appointing an AONB Officer. This sought also to prepare the way for the JAC, a tortuous and long-winded process. Whilst HCC was slowly coming round to the idea of supporting the JAC, it wished to delay the appointment of an AONB Officer until the role and activities of the Committee were clarified. It appears that the lack of enthusiasm stemmed from the belief that the officer might 'act independently from the local authorities and possibly challenge them', which the Council believed would be divisive.

The Landscape Assessment (Cobham Resource Consultants, 1991) was published by the Countryside Commission on behalf of the two District Councils and HCC. It was one of a series covering all the AONBs in England and incorporated the development of the landscape, its cultural links, a crude analysis of the landscape character, likely influences and changes, and made recommendations for landscape conservation, and mechanisms to achieve them. Recognizing the role that planning authorities had played in controlling development within the area, it nevertheless sought a more positive approach – to promote change that conserved and enhanced the landscape. The document also supported the Countryside Commission's advocacy of Joint Advisory Committees.

With this backing, local authorities, government agencies, and non-governmental bodies with wildlife, recreation and landowning interests were asked to identify people to represent their organizations on the JAC. The response being positive, it was decided that EHDC should push ahead with the creation of the JAC with or without the County's involvement, and the first meeting took place on 11 November 1991. Minutes of the meeting (EHAONBJAC, 1991) record that neither HCC nor WCC was willing to put money into the AONB coffers; EHDC was the sole funder. Attempts were made later to persuade the parish councils to provide funding, but while they were supportive they were not convinced about an AONB Officer.

Then, in 1992, HCC councillors appeared to change their minds. In a letter to WSCC (HCC, 1992), the Assistant County Secretary informed WSCC that HCC supported the principle of treating the South Downs as a single unit for countryside planning and management, that it would seek to join the Board and negotiate ways to achieve this, and that Hampshire's contribution should be spent in the EHAONB, wholly or partially on an AONB Officer. Indeed, in 1993, HCC agreed to commit £30,000 for the following financial year. WCC agreed to second an officer to write a Management Plan for the AONB. At the next meeting of the JAC (EHAONBJAC, 1993a), the idea of joining the SDCB was aired, with the Countryside Commission representative suggesting that the Hampshire authorities could be brought into the Board at its first review, due in April 1994.

Progress was at last being made, with HCC confirming its support for AONBs, recommending that the post of AONB Officer be filled and welcoming overtures from SDCB. On this latter point, however, there was a subsequent change of mind a month later when the Council decided not to join the Board, but, all the same, to advertise for an AONB Officer (HCC, 1993).

Setting up the East Hampshire Joint Advisory Committee operation

The JAC membership was very different to that of the Sussex Downs Conservation Board. It was not dominated by local authority members. Instead it had a single member from each of the two Districts and the County Council, joined by officers and representatives of government and non-government organizations with an interest in the future management of the AONB from a farming, wildlife, conservation, heritage or recreation point of view.

One of the first jobs for the JAC was the production of the Statement of Intent (EHAONBJAC, 1993b). It set the joint commitment to establish a more co-ordinated and integrated programme of management within the AONB, and provided a vision of 'renewed, vital and sustainable relationships between people, their countryside and their work'. It elaborated briefly on the key management objectives that had been identified by the landscape assessment.

Unlike the Sussex Downs Statement of Intent of 1986, follow-up action was assured, with work starting on a Management Plan. This identified short, medium and long-term action to achieve the key objectives for management. For each action, lead partners were identified, along with the resources needed and by when it should be achieved (EHAONBJAC, 1994). The Plan was launched in January 1994.

The JAC had 38 members. To resolve the difficulty of such a large body with diverse interests, and to engage all the partners, three Panels were subsequently established to consider planning, public transport and agriculture. The remit of the Public Transport Panel was later extended to cover access in its widest sense and renamed the Recreation & Access Panel in 1997. A small Executive Committee was also set up, with a strategic, financial and decision-making role, comprising the funding partners and the chairman of each of the three Panels.

Setting up the Sussex Downs Conservation Board operation

The inaugural meeting of the Sussex Downs Conservation Board, held in April 1992 at the University of Sussex, was memorable, not for the historic occasion, but for the politics, which so often dog the South Downs. After the preambles came the routine business of electing an independent chairman. Baroness Cumberlage waited outside, and waited, and waited. Inside, it was clear that not enough had been done before the meeting to smooth this little procedure. Two Labour councillors cried 'foul' – seeing this as a Conservative political appointment. A Red Card was brandished, threatening to send off the new chairman before she had even been elected (the television cameras had already left by this point, so it is not recorded for posterity). Assurances were made and Julia Cumberlage, somewhat belatedly, took the Chair. Three months later she was off, to a ministerial position in the Government!

There were 36 Board members, made up of six each from the two County Councils, 12 from the 11 Districts – Chichester having two due to its large area in the AONB – to ensure parity, plus 12 nominated by the Countryside Commission (to represent local farming, conservation, recreation, economic and community interests). Proportionality was a key point to be agreed at the meeting, as were the job descriptions for the Clerk (WSCC) and Treasurer (ESCC). The three objectives for the Board were also agreed. Curiously, there was little discussion about actual conservation in the AONB. Still, it was only the first meeting, and there were six years ahead for this national experiment in AONB management. The members were in place, as were the supporting local authority officers and the second chairman, Lord Nathan (Plate 160). As a cross-bencher, there were no political rows to obstruct his election, and he brought with him a great respect in environmental circles.

The 1992–93 financial year was an interesting one for the staff working on the Downs in East and West Sussex and, subsequently, for the Board. With no practical organization in place, the 50 per cent Countryside Commission grant (£500,000) was spent on a single capital programme by the local authorities making up the Board, setting a false premise that the Board was all about delivering 'sexy projects'.

Due to the failure to appoint a chief officer the first time round, it was not until January 1993 that the little gang of rangers, project officers and rights-of-way superintendents, seconded from the County Councils, sat down with the new Sussex Downs Officer and discussed what to do. Within six months, following recruitment of additional staff, four Area offices were put in place, each with a countryside management team, plus an equipped headquarters. For the first time there was a comprehensive countryside managerial service operating across the Sussex Downs AONB. There was also a solitary Planning Officer, to advise the local authorities and seek some form of consistency across the area, initially in development-control decisions and, over time, policy too (see Chapter 11). The main strategic task was to produce a Management Plan for the AONB (SDCB, 1995) an underpinning Landscape Assessment, published as a 'glossy' (Countryside Commission/SDCB, 1996), long overdue since its designation in 1966.

ACHIEVEMENTS

Despite the vulnerable nature of both AONB units, with uncertain and insecure funding, short-term (three-yearly) agreements and stormy politics, much has been achieved across the South Downs. The following Table 12a lists a range of work undertaken in each AONB. It is not an extensive list of achievements, but a selection to illustrate the breadth of work and differences in approach taken and scale between the two organizations. An additional problem with the Board has been the conflict between needing to deliver on delegated functions (priority demand of the local authorities) and needing to show innovation and new projects (Countryside Agency priority).

WRITING ON THE WALL

SDCB, set up as a six-year experiment, had regular battles with reviews and funding cuts. Three years into the New Initiatives Fund, this source was scrapped, and in 1998 funding from the Countryside Commission was halved. As the Board experiment was ending, staff began conducting a number of Land Rover tours for influential, decision-making people – local MPs, Government Ministers and civil servants, plus an array of other VIPs. Before the end of the six-year period the Countryside Commission took on the consultants Green Balance to carry out a review of the Board's achievements (Green Balance, 1996); the ensuing report concluded that the Board had been a success. It should be noted, however, that the promised review of National Park designation never happened, probably because the 1994 local government reorganization diverted attention. Consultations on the Board's future administration (SDCB, 1996) and a Constitution review were started.

Despite the intense activity, these initiatives all amounted to hot air; time ran out and, with no tangible decision about the future administration of the AONB, the Board was extended for three years (1998 – 2001), but with a reduced budget (though the District Councils chipped in to partially offset the Countryside Commission cut). 1998 was a black year, with six staff (out of 30) made redundant. Uncertainty and loss of morale took their toll – a third of the Board staff left in the space of a year. Damage repairs took time, and the Investors in People process proved invaluable in focusing minds positively on organizational and personal values; core staff were given permanent contracts, though the Board had to put aside five per cent of its funds to cover redundancy pay.

After 1998, the Board's role shifted, maintaining its core areas of work, but with an increasing commitment to fund-raising. Much of the innovative management work was dropped, to be resurrected only if and when external fundings were confirmed. The Board was remarkably successful in this venture, but at a price; seeking funds, nurturing contacts, making and re-making applications were all heavy on staff time, and direct delivery suffered as a result. A real problem was the Board's short-term nature; long-term management agreements could not be signed, and the underwriting of grant bids was not possible. WSCC, as the Clerk to the Board, did agree to underwrite those that were in West Sussex, but insisted on guarantees from other local authorities for Downs-wide projects, which rather put paid to any strategic AONB-scale initiatives.

EVOLVING ATTITUDES – THE STORY CONTINUES

The Management Plans for both AONBs specified that the joint management of the two areas be reconsidered. A joint members' working party was set up in 1996 aimed at bringing the two organizations closer together. This spawned joint practical projects, such as the Rother Valley Walks and, more strategically, the development of a Vision and draft

Table 12a ACHIEVEMENTS

1 Strategic Management

	EH AONB JAC	*SDCB*	*Comment*
Primary objective	To protect, conserve and enhance the natural beauty and amenity of the EHAONB, including its physical, ecological and cultural landscape	To protect, conserve and enhance the natural beauty of the Sussex Downs AONB, including its physical, ecological and cultural landscape	
Secondary objectives	• To promote the quiet informal enjoyment of the area by the general public, but only so far as is consistent with the first aim • To improve the liaison with farmers, landowners and other parties, to raise awareness of the AONB and to encourage land management which supports the two aims above • To foster the social and economic well-being of communities within the EHAONB	• To promote the quiet informal enjoyment of the Sussex Downs AONB by the general public, but only so far as is consistent with the first objective • Generally to promote sustainable forms of social and economic development, especially working with farmers and landowners to encourage land management which supports the two objectives above	
Management Plan	January 1994 EH Management Plan	1995 Sussex Downs AONB Management Strategy	Sussex Downs Management Strategy revised in 1996
	September 1999 Draft South Downs Vision and draft South Downs Management Plan		
	March 2004 Interim South Downs Management Plan prepared on behalf of local authorities to meet CRoW Act deadline 2005 Review along with suite of documents (i.e. State of the South Downs Report) June–October 2006 Public consultation South Downs Management, Strategic Environmental Assessment, and South Downs Planning Guidelines		Statutory duty to prepare AONB management plans under CRoW Act 2000

2 Staff and Finance

	EH AONB JAC	*SDCB*	*Comment*
AONB Officer appointed	April 1994	January 1993	
Core Budget year 1	£46,418	£1,000,000*	*less than original £1.6+ m estimate
Core budget year 10	£256,095	£1,500,000	
Funding Partners	Countryside Agency, Hampshire County Council, East Hampshire & Winchester District Council	Countryside Agency, East & West Sussex CCs, Brighton & Hove CC, B/DCs of Adur, Arun, Chichester, Eastbourne, Horsham, Lewes, Mid-Sussex, Wealden, Worthing	
Additional funding		By year 10 – £500,000 external funding	Insignificant in early years, but greater dependency in later years
Number of staff year 1	1	24	SDCB matrix management – Area line management, with cross-Areas delegation of responsibilities
Number of staff year 10	5	50 (inc. part-time and seasonal)	

3 Landscape Conservation & Enhancement	EH AONB JAC	SDCB	Comment
Site Management	No direct site management. Works with partners by providing volunteer help and /or grant aid	42 sites including Seven Sisters Country Park (700 acres), Iping Common and Burton Pond Local Nature Reserves, Telscombe Tye. Maintenance Budget – £50,000/year	
Influence and Advice	Promotion of whole farm plans; lobbying for agricultural policy change. Advice to landowners/ managers	Key influence on SD ESA scheme; lobby for agricultural change. Advice/practical help to farmers	Working towards 'first-stop shop' across South Downs: one on-the-ground contact plus link to funding agencies
Landscape Management	Landscape Enhancement Grants, 1995–2004: Hedge planting 31,080m, 83 sites £69,819; hedge restoration 13,680m 38 sites £25,703; woodland management, 35ha, 50 sites £40,372; tree planting 7196 no, 33 sites £16,682; 33 ponds restored £46,713; grassland management 20ha, 13 sites £18,394. TOTAL=£217,683	New Initiatives fund in 1990s for major landscape enhancement (eg Devils Dyke £30,000; escarpment scrub clearance £120,000/3 years Beachy Head eyesore removal plus buildings rationalization, using 'before and after' photo montages; Birling Gap landscaping; since working with EN to meet government targets to get SSSIs into 'favourable condition' – £40,000/year from EN	
Woodlands	East Hampshire Hangers Challenge Fund (FC); South Downs Woodland Challenge (FC & EHAONB), advice to landowners	Support to coppice industry – help to set up Sussex & Surrey Coppice Group; practical and financial help to encourage management of small woods of importance	
Grasslands	Work in partnership with HCC Grazing Project	Local Grazing Project Lottery and EN funded	'Dating agency' bringing together graziers and land needing grazing
Heathlands	Work with Herpetological Conservation Trust and Ministry of Defence on Woolmer Forest to improve habitat for Natterjack toads	Lottery funded Sussex Wealden Greensand Heathland Project £1.2m/5 years	Very little heathland in EH AONB
Rother Valley Project		Landcare Project providing advice on diffuse pollution, soil erosion; plus biodiversity targeting; otter holts, barn owls, water voles, black poplars; plans to extend Landcare South Downs-wide.	
Surveys – Biological	River Rother* Halnaker Lane* River Meon*	Several innovative Volunteer Ranger surveys, leading to management plans and action	* partnerships with EA, HCC and HWT respectively
Surveys – Archaeological/ heritage	Throughout AONB survey of non-scheduled* archaeological sites plus more detailed surveys of Hen Wood, QECP, Cheriton Wood, Burial site near Chalton	Stanmer Park and Burton Park Historic Landscape Restoration Plans – DEFRA funded New Archaeological Volunteer Rangers	* 2 sites since been scheduled

3 Landscape Conservation & Enhancement (cont.)

	EH	AONB JAC	SDCB
Landscape Enhancement Initiative (LEI) and Lifescapes		LEI brings together a number of partnership projects i.e. Habitat Potential Mapping, Land Management Information System, South Downs Lamb, targeting landscape restoration	
Eyesores		Under-grounding of overhead wires achieved at East Meon	Urban fringe project 2001–04 Various eyesore removal/screening
Trees			Dutch Elm Disease control programme – £50,000/year
Local Distinctiveness		Restoration of tradition road signs 40 signs restored/replaced in past 7 years	Millennium Parish Jigsaw Project (Plate 105) – follow-up local projects (e.g. Pump-house, Up-Marden restored)

4 Planning

	EH	AONB JAC	SDCB
Development Control		South Downs Planning Guidlines 2000	Revised 2006
Influence and Advice		Increase in number of planning applications commented on from less than 10 in 1994/5 to over 70 in 2004/5. In 52% cases where objections raised by the JAC the application was either refused or withdrwan. Where planning permission was granted conditions usually placed to take account of objections raised.	580 planning applications were responded to in 2004/5, with 66% of these objected to by SDCB, either returned to the local authority or withdrawn	Across the South Downs in 2005 some 750 planning applications were commented on; it is estimated that there are in the order of 3500 planning applications a year
Policy		Consultations with Local Planning Authorities	Consultations with Local Planning Authorities
Tranquil Area Study		1997	1997	Targeted Protected Area priority, Regional Development Agency (SEEDA)

5 Access & Recreation

	EH	AONB JAC	SDCB
Sites And ref. 3 Site Management (see page 162)		Support to Queen Elizabeth Country Park through grants and volunteers	1993 Revamp of Seven Sisters Country Park; 1999 car parking charges introduced to fund improvements to area and discourage cars / promote public transpor*	*Lack of staff/structures in first year meant that significant amounts of money went on big capital projects to spend budget (e.g. South Downs Way, Seven Sisters Country Park) see text pp. 159 and 160
		Information boards placed at strategic sites	Welcome Audits: addressed safety, access, interpretation and other issues at sites. Routine management of many key recreation sites	

5 Access & Recreation *(cont.)*	EH AONBJAC	SDCB	Comment
Promoted Routes	East Hampshire Cycle Route 1996	Take the Bus for a Walk (Plate 104), Breeze up to the Downs, Trails by Rail; Disabled Access Trails	
	Rother Valley Walks 1998 14 circular walks between the source of the Rother near Selborne and Pulborough		Partnership between EHJAC, SDCB and EA
Rights of Way	Agreement with Local Authorities to carry out vegetation clearance and minor resurfacing work on 14 unclassified country 'U' roads over 5 years – £42,000	Maintenance of Rights of Way delegated to SDCB. Computerized condition survey and contracts, paths now routinely surveyed by Volunteer Parish Path Rangers. Annual spend – £150,000	EHJAC seek to add value to LA Rights of Way work, not duplicate. SDCB survey and database allows accurate monitoring tied to Audit Commission targets
Open Access	Hampshire – stage II area – launched December 2004	Sussex stage I area (launch September 04) SDCB opened up virtually all areas by March 05 – £200,000 (CA grant)	CRoW Act 'freedom to roam' on down, heath and common land. Job now to create meaningful access from these fragments
South Downs Way	Evidence provided at SDW Public Inquiry	Amberley River Arun bridge, diversion of dangerous road section, 1993 (Plate 160)	See text pp. 158/9 £250,000 from year 1 SDCB underspend due to set-up delays (staff £ saving)
Sustainable Transport	HCC'sIntegrated Access Demonstration Project, partly covered AONB – innovative work, eg support to experimental bus services from Portsmouth – Queen Elizabeth CP, but patronage not sufficient	Devil's Dyke Bus Service UK Bus Industry 'Buses for Pleasure' award, 73,000 passenger journeys in 2003/4 with an average of 600 passenger journeys a day in spring 2004; Cuckmere Rambler bus + Eastern Downs Leisure Map linked in with sustainable transport/access	Proximity of Brighton to Downs compared with Portsmouth appear to be significant in the sustainability of bus routes

6 Social and Economic Well-being

Community Planning	Support for Village Design Statements, Parish Plans, or Market Towns Health Checks; financial or advisory support provided to 9 out of 14 parishes or towns that have carried out VDS, PP or MTHC	Ad hoc work, targeted at individual parish needs, related to priorities in Management Plan	
	Involvement in Community Strategies and Local Area Agreement throughout area	SDCB officers represented on local strategic partnerships and/or community strategy groups	
South Downs Volunteer Ranger Scheme	25 members work on average 131 man days per year on a variety of tasks	Over 300 people midweek and weekend. From practical conservation groups to parish rangers and visitor-centre volunteers. Over 4000 days of work achieved in 2004/5	Work in partnership with a range of organizations involved in caring for the South Downs

	EH AONB JAC	SDCB	Comment
6 Social and Economic Well-being (*cont.*)			
Community Conservation Groups	Provide advice and assistance to local volunteer groups in partnership with BTCV. 7 groups within EHAONB	Over 300 people midweek and weekend. From practical conservation groups to parish rangers and visitor-centre volunteers. Over 4000 days of work achieved in 2004/5 Liaison with and help to a number of 'Friends of' groups, who look after their local patches	
Sustainable Tourism	South Downs Sustainable Tourism Network – over 600 members in 2006		AONB Awareness Walkers and Cyclists Welcome Local Produce
	South Downs Green Accreditation Scheme – 32 award winners in 2005		
Rural Economy	South Downs Lamb – local branding		Environment and economic tie-up
	Research by Oxford Brookes University funded by SEEDA		
Sustainable Development	Natural Light Project – woodland biomass for generation of energy		NB use of local contractors
7 Interpretation, Raising Awareness			
Communications	EH Communication Strategy agreed AONB Leaflet Display boards Annual Reports Regular talks to local groups and societies	SDCB Communication Strategy – Welcome Audits (see 5. Sites p.163) common quality signage policy, with local oak entrance signs and rights of way furniture, etc	
Raising Awareness	www.southdowns.gov.uk – launched 2006		
Community Involvment	Jigsaw 2002 to coincide with 40th anniversary	Millennium Jigsaw (Plate 105) Regular talks + annual update to all parishes on work done in area	Each Parish asked to take pictures of what they felt was special to their area
Education	School Farm Plan Competition: schools were linked to farms within the AONB and invited to complete a farm conservation plan. Over 200 children involved, reaching national curriculum targets through their trips to the farms*	Partnership with Sussex Wildlife Trust in development of educational material and service to schools at Seven Sisters Country Park (Plate 161)	*The idea of linking schools and farms was taken up at County level with the establishment of Hampshire Country Learning
Research and Monitoring	Joint data collection GIS base EU-funded Primavera Project, 'State of the South Downs' Reporting		

165

South Downs Management Plan (Landscape Design Associates, 1999a).

During the late 1990s a number of things were happening at a national level. Although the SDCB management experiment had been judged a success, its short-term, uncertain funding and lack of teeth were great concerns; the EHJAC suffered the same problems. The Countryside Commission (1998) put forward advice to Government, *Protecting our Finest Countryside* on the management of AONBs nationally and, on the back of its bespoke consultation (Countryside Commission, 1997), added specific recommendations for the South Downs. As is shown in Chapter 13, it concluded in 1998 that National Park status was not appropriate for the South Downs, but recommended that the two AONBs be managed as a single unit. This decision, and the fact that both AONB Management Plans were due for renewal, initiated the process for preparing a single Management Plan for the South Downs, as mentioned above.

In 1999 Lord Renton, SDCB's Chairman since 1998, brought a Private Member's Bill (Renton,1999) that sought to improve the position of AONBs by at last providing the formal management framework that they had lacked since the 1949 Act. Parts of the Bill were picked up in the Government's own Countryside & Rights of Way (CRoW) Act 2000 that, for the first time, gave AONBs the potential to set up formal Conservation Boards and local authorities a duty to prepare Management Plans for AONBs. It also gave public bodies the duty to have regard to AONB purposes. These were massive breakthroughs, although sadly there was neither the duty to implement the Plans nor a funding formula; and, no duty to make public bodies accountable for their actions. Cinderella had at last got a toe in the door at the ball!

Chapter 13 notes that in September 1999 the Deputy Prime Minister announced that there should be two new National Parks in the South East: the New Forest and the South Downs (Prescott, 1999). The Joint Members' Group, just about to approve the South Downs Management Plan Vision for public consultation, was thrown into turmoil, and decided that it would be inappropriate to go out to consultation at that time. The move to designate the Downs as a National Park was too much for the local authorities; most opposed the idea vehemently, and the Joint Members' Group became a hot-bed of unrest. It was time for it to be abandoned.

As also recounted in Chapter 13, the newly created Countryside Agency (which replaced the Countryside Commission) was asked to look again at how the National Park designation criteria had been applied to the South Downs, and unsurprisingly came to a different conclusion to its predecessors. So the long process of designation began in earnest in April 2000, four months after the CRoW Act had come into

force. The local authorities and Countryside Agency had assumed that, as the South Downs was in the process of being designated as a National Park, the requirement under the CRoW Act to produce a Management Plan would not be applied to the South Downs. However, in April 2003, DEFRA informed the authorities that in fact a plan would need to be prepared before the deadline of 31 March 2004, as no final decision as to the outcome of the designation process had yet been taken.

So the Vision and Draft South Downs Management Plan, prepared in 1999, were dusted off and revamped. Responsibility for its preparation was delegated to the JAC and SDCB. This was fairly simple in Sussex, as the SDCB, being a legally constituted Joint Committee (which, later in 2005, became part of the South Downs Joint Committee – SDJC see below), was able to adopt the interim Management Plan on behalf of the local authorities. In Hampshire, each local authority had to submit the plan to its own committees for adoption as the JAC was not a formal body.

Although drafted by the SDCB & EHJAC, the Management Plan is a plan for all those with an interest in, or an impact on, the AONB: statutory agencies, local authorities, national and local organizations, voluntary bodies and individuals. It is worth noting, all the same, that one of the main obstacles in its production was the lack of data on a South Downs basis, largely due to the administrative complexity of the South Downs (spanning 15 local authority areas). Due to the tight timescale, only limited consultation was possible. Although the SDCB and local authorities in Hampshire agreed to adopt the *Interim Management Plan,* in order for it to be submitted to DEFRA for the legal deadline, they required that it should be reviewed, prior to wider public consultation – a process that has allowed an intensive period of data-gathering and analysis, which has resulted in a better base of evidence for the revised document when it was submitted for public consultation in 2006.

THE CHALLENGES AHEAD

This is a time of significant change, highlighted in earlier chapters, encompassing three recurring issues. **Agriculture**, where current policy reform is as radical as it was 60 years ago; **development pressures**, with the desire of the South East England Development Agency (SEEDA) that the South East should be one of the top 10 economies in the World (SEEDA, 1999), with all the environmental repercussions; and the **recreation demands**, (39 million visits a year – Countryside Agency, 2004), requiring well-resourced visitor management and a priority for conservation (the 'Sandford Principle' – National Parks Policies Review Committee, 1974). Is this the opportunity to establish the first-stop shop, to provide a local delivery mechanism for advice, information and grant-aid? Will there be the resources to develop projects that put into practice sustainable development within the South Downs, in order to support the conservation and enhancement of the area's special features? Where will protected landscape policies feature within the evolving South East Regional Plan and Local Development Frameworks?

It is vital that the resources and capacity are there to respond to these changes if the landscape, cultural heritage and biodiversity of the South Downs are to be protected and restored. It is vital, too, that there is a strong voice for the South Downs at this juncture, in order to influence core strategic documents such as the South East Plan, Local Transport Plans, agri-environment targets, impact of Common Agricultural Policy (CAP) reform, and so on. All these will have major impacts on the landscape of the South Downs. The work of conserving the Downs must continue unabated, despite the temptation to wait a National Park. The foundations for a future South Downs Authority need urgently to be put in place so that the new body can 'hit the ground running', not prevaricate by re-inventing the wheel.

After nearly a year of negotiation, the 15 local authorities in the South Downs finally agreed to a single South Downs Joint Committee. Based on the model proportionality of the SDCB: 15 County members, 15 District members and 15 Country side Agency (CA) members (Brighton & Hove Unitary has one County and two District seats). To provide for continuity, the SDCB CA nominees were carried forward, and four new Hampshire-based appointments were made. Based on the experiences of the EHJAC, two important changes were made to the proposed agreement: the appointment of CA nominees on the JAC with connetions with parish councils and the formation of a wider Advisory Forum to act as a critical friend to the SDJC. If a National Park is confirmed, an existing 'South Downs Authority' would ease the way towards a National Park; if not confirmed, it provides a single organization for the whole of the Downs, allowing greater co-ordination of action.

The Advisory Forum was launched on 3 November 2005 at the Weald and Downland Open Air Museum. By January 2006 it had nearly 100 members. An Executive Panel was set up to provide a more manageable mechanism for feeding information and views between the wider forum and the SDJC. The Executive Panel meets four times a year prior to each full meeting of the Joint Committee. The chairman of the Forum became an ex-officio member of the SDJC reporting back views from meetings of the Forum.

A South Downs National Park would need to be adequately resourced. The worst position would be if the existing work within the Downs was simply relabeled with no additional funds brought into the area. Some modern, creative thinking will be needed to look at the objectives and essential delivery in the South Downs National Park, such as development control, currently managed by 12 Local Authorities across the area, or access and how best to maximize 'promoting understanding and enjoyment'. It will be important to create an Authority for the twenty-first century, not harking back to the 1949 Act.

The challenge for all interested parties and bodies that have a direct impact on the Downs, will be to form firm partnerships and to add real value to theirwork, to ensure quality results in the interests of conserving the South Downs. The rewards of joint working will provide positive benefits, but there remains the question of holding to account authorities that may not uphold the purposes of National Park designation. If the South Downs had been designated back in the 1950s, the landscape would in all probability look very similar on the surface, though arguably the biodiversity and cultural heritage within that landscape would be greater in terms of both quantity and quality. The challenge ahead is to ensure that the land management of the future does not destroy sites of archaeological interest, is in keeping with the landscape, enhances the biodiversity of the area and is sustainable; and that a programme of landscape restoration can be achieved. Imagination, proper funding and sufficient clout are all that is needed!

REFERENCES

British Broadcasting Corporation (1990) File on Four. (BBC Radio 4 Programme.). 13 February. BBC, London.
British Broadcasting Corporation (South) (1992) *Division on the Downs.* Documentary, 30 April. BBC, Southampton.
Bryant, P. (1989) Letter in *The Times.* 5 April.
Cobham Resource Consultants (1991) *The East Hampshire Landscape – An Assessment of the Area of Outstanding Beauty.* CCP 358. Countryside Commission, Cheltenham.
Coleman, D. (1990) Proposed Sussex Downs Conservation Board. Letter to Sussex AONB Forum. 16 October. Countryside Commission, Cheltenham.
Countryside Agency (1999) *Sussex Downs Area of Outstanding Natural Beauty 1957-66.* Designation History Series. Countryside Agency, Cheltenham.
Countryside Agency (March 2000) *The East Hampshire Area of Outstanding Natural Beauty.* Designation History Series. Countryside Agency, Cheltenham.
Countryside Agency (2004) *South Downs Visitor Survey.* Countryside Agency, Cheltenham.
Countryside Commission (1991) *Fit for the Future.* Report of the National Parks Review Panel. CCP334. Countryside Commission, Cheltenham. ('**The Edwards Report**'.)
Countryside Commission (1997) *Conserving the South Downs – Providing for Their Needs.* Countryside Commission (South East), London.
Countryside Commission (1998) *Protecting Our Finest Countryside. Advice to Government.* CCP 532. Countryside Commission, Cheltenham.

Countryside Commission & Sussex Downs Conservation Board (1996) *The Landscape of the Sussex Downs Area of Outstanding Natural Beauty.* Countryside Commission, Cheltenham.

Department of the Environment (1974) *Report of the National Park Policies Review Committee.* HMSO, London. ('The Sandford Principle'.)

Department of the Environment (1990) *This Common Inheritance.* DoE, London.

East Hampshire AONB Joint Advisory Committee (1991) Minutes of the Meeting held on 12 November 1991. EHAONBJAC, Winchester.

East Hampshire AONB Joint Advisory Committee (1993a) Minutes of the Meeting held on 10 March 1993. EHAONBJAC, Winchester.

East Hampshire AONB Joint Advisory Committee (1993b) *East Hampshire Area of Outstanding Natural Beauty. A Statement of Commitment.* East Hampshire District Council, Petersfield.

East Hampshire AONB Joint Advisory Committee (January 1994) *East Hampshire AONB Management Plan.* Winchester City Council, Winchester.

East Hampshire District Council (1989) Report D5/89 to Development (Policy) Committee, 23 January 1989. EHDC, Petersfield.

East Hampshire Dictrict Council (1990) Report D6/90 to Development (Policy) Committee, 23 January 1990. EHDC, Petersfield.

East Sussex County Council (June 1976) Sussex Heritage Coast Draft Management Policies. ESCC, Lewes.

East Sussex County Council (1989) *A Case for National Park Status for the South Downs.* Report by County Planning Officer, Environment Committee, 13 September. ESCC, Lewes.

East Sussex County Council & West Sussex County Council (June 1986) Sussex Downs Area of Outstanding Natural Beauty – Statement of Intent. ESCC, Lewes; WSCC, Chichester.

East Sussex County Council & West Sussex County Council (1989) *National Park Status?* Sussex Downs AONB Forum, 24 October. ESCC, Lewes; WSCC, Chichester.

East Sussex County Council & West Sussex County Council (1990) *The Future Status of the South Downs.* Report by the County Planning Officers and County Secretaries of East and West Sussex County Councils, 23 October. ESCC, Lewes: WSCC, Chichester.

Green Balance (1996) *The Achievements and Effectiveness of the Sussex Downs Conservation Board.* A Report to the Countryside Commission, September 1996. Countryside Commission, Cheltenham.

Hampshire County Council (1990) Notes of East Hampshire AONB Working Group, 8 June 1990. HCC, Winchester.

Hampshire County Council (1992) Letter to West Sussex County Council by HCC Assistant County Secretary, E.W.Mason , 8 December 1992. HCC, Winchester.

Hampshire County Council (1993) Report to Planning & Transportation Committee by County Planning Officer, 5 July 1993. HCC, Winchester.

Hampshire County Council et al. (1968) *East Hampshire Area of Outstanding Natural Beauty – A Study in Countryside Conservation.* Hampshire County Council., Winchester; Countryside Commission, Cheltenham; Ministry of Agriculture, London; Forestry Commission, Edinburgh.

Huxley, J. (1963) Foreword in Carson, R., *Silent Spring.* Hamish Hamilton, London.

Landscape Design Associates (1999a) *A Vision for the South Downs – Consultation Draft.* Landscape Design Associates, Peterborough.

Landscape Design Associates (1999b) *The South Downs AONB Draft Strategic Management Plan.* Landscape Design Associates, Peterborough.

Ministry of Agriculture, Fisheries & Food (1987) *Environmentally Sensitive Areas.* Information Pack. MAFF, London.

Ministry of Town & Country Planning (1947) *Report of the National Parks Committee (England & Wales).* Cmd. 7121. HMSO, London. ('The Hobhouse Report'.)

National Parks Commission (1957) *Minutes.* 1129. 27 February. HMSO, London.

National Parks Commission (1962) *Minutes.* 2446, 25/26 September. HMSO, London.

Ockenden, J. (1991) *East Hampshire Hangers Project 1985 – 1990.* East Hampshire District Council, Petersfield.

Prescott, J., Deputy Prime Minister (1999) Speech at the Labour Party Conference, Bournemouth. 29 September.

Renton, Lord, of Mount Harry (1999) *Areas of Outstanding Natural Beauty.* House of Lords Bill 46, 13 April. HMSO, London.

Robson, E. (1990) Patten Power – The Great Parks Battle. *The Listener*, 15 February.

Shoard, M. (1980) *The Theft of the Countryside.* Temple Smith, London.

Shoard, M. (1989) Parks with a Difference. *The Times*, 27 March.

Smart, G. and Anderson, M. (1990) *Planning and Management of Areas of Outstanding Natural Beauty.* CCP 295. Countryside Commission, Cheltenham.

Society of Sussex Downsmen (1991) *Planning the Future of the South Downs.* SSD Conference at University of Sussex, 16 November. SSD, Hove.

South Downs Campaign (1990) *A Better Future for the South Downs.* Information sheet and letter. SDC, Henfield.

South East England Development Agency (1999) *Building a World Class Region. Strategy for the South East of England.* SEEDA, Guildford.

Sussex Downs AONB (undated) *Coombes – Newtimber Project.* Leaflet. WSCC, Chichester.

Sussex Downs Conservation Board (1992) Inaugural Meeting Papers. SDCB/WSCC, Chichester.

Sussex Downs Conservation Board (1995) *A Management Strategy for the Sussex Downs Area of Outstanding Beauty.* SDCB, Storrington. (Revised 1996.)

Sussex Downs Conservation Board (1996) *The Future Administration of the South Downs Area of Outstanding Natural Beauty. A Consultation Paper.* SDCB/WSCC, Chichester.

Sussex Downs Conservation Project (1989 –1992) *Annual Reports.* WSCC, Chichester.

Sussex Downs AONB Forum (1988) *South Downs Way. A Management Plan.* WSCC, Chichester.

Sussex Downs AONB Forum (1991) Papers, 24 April. SDAONB, Lewes.

Sussex Rural Community Council (1990) *A National Park for the South Downs.* SRCC/CPRE, Lewes.

West Sussex County Council (1989a) *South Downs National Park.* Report by County Planning Officer, Coast & Countryside Committee, 26 June. WSCC, Chichester.

West Sussex County Council (1989b) *Sussex Downs AONB – Future Status.* Report by County Planning Officer & County Secretary, Coast & Countryside Committee, 11 September. WSCC, Chichester.

West Sussex County Council (1989c) *Sussex Downs AONB – Future Status.* Report by County Planning Officer & County Secretary, Planning Committee, 11 October. WSCC, Chichester.

West Sussex County Council (1990a) *Sussex Downs: Future Status.* Joint Coast & Countryside / Planning Committees, 11 July. WSCC, Chichester.

West Sussex County Council (1990b) *Future Status of the South Downs*.* Result of the consultation process (response of local authorities and other bodies to the Forum's consultation – 'pro' or 'anti' National Park) For Sussex Downs AONB Forum. WSCC, Chichester. (*Updated & amended to Sussex Downs October 1990.)

168

Plate 155 (above)
Looking towards the Meon Valley, Hampshire, from Beacon Hill NNR.
Photo: SDJC.

The participation of volunteers in the conservation of the South Downs is vital

Plate 156 (centre left)
Scrub clearance at Malling Down, October 1986.
Photo Phil Belden.

Plate 157 (centre right)
Volunteers mending fences at the Seven Sisters Country Park.
Photo: Keith Fryer, courtesy of SDJC.

Plate 158 (bottom left)
Enthusiastic volunteer rangers litter-picking on the beach at Seaford Head, December 1985.
Photo: Phil Belden.

Plate 159 (bottom right)
Intrusive superstores at Lyons Farm north of the A27 Sompting bypass near Broadwater and Worthing.
Photo: Phil Belden

Proposed National Parks

Proposed Conservation Areas

0 50km

Plate (map) 162
(left) A relief map showing the location of National Parks and Conservation Areas in England and Wales proposed by the Hobhouse Committee in 1947. Note that the suggested National Parks, though mostly in relatively wild upland areas, did include the South Downs. Map produced by the University of Southampton Cartographic Unit. (Right) National Parks and Areas of Outstanding Natural Beauty at December 2006. Note that the proposed South Downs National Park extends into the Western Weald beyond that proposed by Hobhouse.
Map courtesy of Natural England.

Areas of Outstanding Natural Beauty and National Parks in England & Wales

Area of Outstanding Natural Beauty

National Park

South Downs National Park, designated but not yet confirmed

As at 1.12.06

CHAPTER 13
A South Downs National Park?

GERALD SMART

DESIGNATION: A NATIONAL PARK AS ENVISAGED IN THE 1949 NATIONAL PARKS ACT?

The introduction to Part 3 of the book briefly outlines the long and disjointed history of moves to protect and enhance the Downs. It was towards the end of the nineteenth century that a National Park was first suggested, and the idea was taken further by the Council for the Preservation of Rural England (CPRE) in 1929. Formal recommendations to this effect were made in 1947 by the Hobhouse Committee (Ministry of Town & Country Planning, 1947). For a number of reasons, however, the eventual decision, long delayed until the 1960s, was to designate as Areas of Outstanding Natural Beauty (AONBs) both the Sussex Downs and the chalk hills and hanger woodlands of East Hampshire. Together, these did in fact cover a rather larger area, extending to the Western Weald, than that recommended by Hobhouse, but they were not to be a National Park (see Plate (map) 162). A Joint Advisory Committee for the East Hampshire AONB was set up in 1991. Then, in 1992, came the pioneering move to establish the Sussex Downs Conservation Board. The achievements of both these organizations, and the problems encountered, have been spelled out in Chapter 12.

Five years later, in 1997, things began to move again, partly as a result of wide national and local consultations by the Conservation Board about the future administration of the Downs, and partly through a growing interest shown by government in rural conservation. The Secretary of State for the Environment decided to ask the Countryside Commission to advise on the best type of organization to meet the future needs of the Downs as a whole.

Acting on this request, the Commission carried out a limited public consultation to obtain a background of opinion. This enabled its officers to agree in principle that there was a need for an authority stronger in status than the Board, covering both AONBs, needing secure funding and a statutory remit. The next step was to consider four options for it:

1. a National Park established under the 1949 National Parks Act;
2. a National Park with a tailor-made statutory National Park Authority;
3. an AONB under current administrative arrangements;
4. and an AONB organization with enhanced powers.

The Commission concluded that the Downs did not meet the criteria for designation as a National Park. (These statutory requirements, albeit fifty years old, were that the area should contain extensive tracts of open country, be of great natural beauty, and should afford opportunities for open-air recreation accessible to centres of population.) In its opinion,

169

the reasons for rejecting National Park status given in 1957 by their forerunner, the National Parks Commission, still held good. Of course natural beauty was not in doubt, nor was accessibility to population centres. Nevertheless, due to extensive cultivation of the downland itself, there were no longer sufficient tracts of open countryside, and even more land was now under the plough. If, on the other hand, the criteria were changed to enable the Downs to be designated (i.e. the second option), the Commission feared there would be demand from AONBs such as the Chilterns and Cotswolds to become National Parks. In the light of all this, they decided that a statutory Conservation Board for the whole area, in accordance with legislation being recommended in their paper *Protecting Our Finest Countryside: Advice to Government* (Countryside Commission, 1998) would be more appropriate.

In passing. it should be noted that an analysis of responses to this paper made by the South Downs Campaign, a network formed in 1990 of over 80 mostly non-statutory national, regional and local environmental organizations committed to a South Downs National Park, indicated that 63 per cent supported designation for this purpose (South Downs Campaign, 2004a).

The Environment Minister, obviously not convinced, then suggested that the Countryside Agency (successor to the Countryside Commission) should reconsider its interpretation of the criteria (not the criteria themselves), and the Deputy Prime Minister made a statement in Parliament to this effect (Countryside Agency, 2004a). The wheel was turning full circle.

PREPARATIONS FOR THE DESIGNATION ORDER

Accordingly, in 2000, the new Agency reviewed policy for interpretation. In doing so, it took account also of the emphasis in National Park Policy reports by Lord Sandford (Department of Environment, 1974) and Professor Ron Edwards (Countryside Commission, 1991) on the need for a variety of provision for quiet enjoyment of National Parks by the public. The Agency concluded that a National Park:

- should be an extensive tract of country of highest landscape quality;
- should be capable of providing 'a superior recreational experience';
- need no longer include open and rugged country like the existing National Parks, but should include a sense of wildness;
- should relate well to large centres of population.

With relief, perhaps, the Agency thought that a South Downs National Park would fit this policy, and that, in terms of the Environment Act, 1995, it would be

'especially desirable' to provide for its leadership by a National Park Authority. The Minister responded that the review reached 'very sound and worthwhile conclusions' (Countryside Agency, 2004a).

The saga was by no means finished, however, in that the necessary Order had to be made; only the second one since the original programme of designation in the 1950s. Over the next two years the Agency began the process of making the Order itself. Integral to this was the need to review a possible boundary for the Park, to study possible administrative arrangements, and to consult widely on both. Its very active programme for consultation included widely-circulated newsletters, a three-month round of public consultation, 'roadshows' to get local opinion on the boundary, technical advisory panels, and a three-month statutory consultation with Local Authorities (Countryside Agency, 2002). This consultation document was also circulated to the very many Parish Councils in the whole area.

There was a good response to public consultation, 6700 replies being received. These showed much concern about the future of the Downs and the need to protect them, and there was majority support in principle for a National Park, as indeed there had been from opinion surveys conducted for the Ramblers Association in 1998 and 1999 (Countryside Agency, 2004a). This support was strongly endorsed by the South Downs Campaign (2003), but there were nevertheless some calls for 'tailor-made' legislation, or to maintain the status quo (Countryside Agency, 2004a).

In preparation for the Local Authority consultation, the Agency had defined a proposed boundary (see endpapers (front)), and had set out their views on administration of the Park. The latter included advice on the statutory framework of membership of the National Park Authority, over half being drawn from Local Authority members; advice on its responsibility for forward-planning in the Park; on the need for it to delegate to the existing Local Authorities much of the development-control case-work; on its responsibilities to produce a wide-ranging statutory Management Plan; on its role in land and visitor management; and on the need to work closely with local people. Amongst the issues highlighted by the response to this consultation were the strong feelings of Local Authorities that they should retain control over all planning matters, and that there should be no reduction in local democratic representation. There were also renewed calls for a statutory Conservation Board and for a Public Inquiry (Countryside Agency, 2004a).

Both consultations produced suggestions for changes to the draft boundary. This had been drawn up from an area of search that reflected National Park criteria, starting broadly with the two AONBs (but excluding, in the first instance, the urban areas of Petersfield and Liss, and the A3 corridor), and looking also at tracts of countryside with high landscape-quality immediately outside. The actual boundary was chosen according to a list of considerations: high landscape-value, differing landscape-character, superior recreational opportunity for quiet enjoyment, the needs of the rural economy and community life, and features of scientific or cultural value.

Three major issues emerged from views given on the boundary: the question of whether to limit the Park to chalk landscapes only; whether to exclude towns such as Petersfield and Lewes; and whether to add further tracts outside the AONBs. In response to the first, the Agency decided that the geological, historical, land-use, cultural and visual links between the chalk 'core' and non-chalk areas of the Weald were so important that there was no case for limiting the Park to the chalk. As to the second, they decided that towns with strong landscape, cultural and economic links to National Park character and purposes should be included. On the third issue, they decided that certain areas beyond the AONBs should be designated (see end-papers), especially to the north (Countryside Agency, 2002). Their approach to setting the boundary was strongly supported by the South Downs Campaign (2004a).

THE ORDER IS MADE, AND A PUBLIC INQUIRY IS HELD

To give it its formal title, the South Downs National Park (Designation) Order 2002, made under the National Parks Act, 1949, was submitted by the Agency to the Secretary of State for Environment, Food and Rural Affairs (DEFRA) on 4 February 2003. This was accompanied by Revocation Orders made under the Countryside and Rights of Way Act, 2000, to de-designate each of the two AONBs in the event of the National Park being approved (see below). The orders were given wide publicity. Not surprisingly, DEFRA received 5700 representations on the Designation Order. A further 140 were made on the Revocation Order. Of the 5700, most were on boundary matters; 1300 were in support of the National Park in principle. As the representations included objections from Local Authorities, it was legally necessary for a Public Inquiry to be held, and this was arranged by the Planning Inspectorate.

What should the Inquiry be about? DEFRA advised that it should address the main issues listed below (Planning Inspectorate, 2003).

- Does the area as a whole meet the criteria and purposes of designation set out in the 1949 Act? (As mentioned earlier, the criteria are that National Parks should be extensive tracts of country with great natural beauty and opportunities for open-air recreation having regard to the character of the area and proximity to centres of population. It should be 'especially desirable' that the designation reflects the purposes of conserving and enhancing natural beauty, wildlife and cultural heritage, and promoting understanding and enjoyment by the public of the area's special qualities.)
- Is the boundary properly drawn, having regard to the criteria and purposes of designation?
- Is a National Park Authority, set up within the terms of the Environment Act, 1995, appropriate for the South Downs, and how might it best be established and operate?
- Should the two AONBs be de-designated? (There would be duplication if AONB status were to be retained for land within a National Park boundary. It should be noted, however, that small areas within each AONB might ultimately lie outside the proposed boundary and thus would also need to be included in the necessary revocation of the AONB.)

The Inquiry, held mainly at Worthing, began in November 2003. It dealt first with objections to the general principle of having the National Park, then objections to the boundary in particular areas (more than three-quarters of which wanted to add land to the National Park), and finally looking at the proposed administrative arrangements for the National Park Authority. Big Planning Inquiries can be gladiatorial, expensive, legalistic, repetitive, and very often rather boring to the listener. So, like the recent Inquiry into the proposed New Forest National Park, the degree of formality in the proceedings, and hence the general atmosphere, were rightly varied according to the actual topic being considered, the Inspector dealing with many boundary issues in an informal manner. The Inspector also made it clear that as the purpose of the Inquiry was to hear objections, representations in full support of the National Park would be taken as read but fully recorded in his report. Attendance by members of the public was spasmodic, varying from perhaps 100 to virtually none.

The Inquiry was a marathon, having sat for 90 days over a 16-month period, finishing in March 2005, though the public sessions closed in December 2004.

THE PRINCIPAL OBJECTIONS TO DESIGNATION, AND THE RESPONSE OF THE COUNTRYSIDE AGENCY

At the start of the Inquiry the Agency was given the opportunity to establish the principles of its case. This it did through an introduction by leading Counsel, supported by convincing evidence from Agency officers and a landscape consultant. They outlined the origin and purpose of National Parks and the role of a National Park Authority, explained how the special qualities of the Downs met the 1949 Act criteria and gave the reasons for the choice of boundary (in particular the inclusion of wealden areas). They described the consultations they had carried out, and the degree of public support that the proposals had generated.

The Inquiry then heard the objections by Local Authorities, led by West Sussex County Council (2003), to the very principle of having a National Park. As might be expected, these were:

- ***The statutory criteria for natural beauty and recreational value in a National Park were being misapplied***. The area included substantial amounts of land outside the two AONBs, had no extensive tracts of open country, little access-land, offered no markedly superior recreational experience, and its designation was not 'especially desirable'. If, nevertheless, designation were to be approved by the Secretary of State, the Park should cover chalk downs only, not the weald. (The latter point was further developed later during the Inquiry, West Sussex County Council and Chichester District Council proposing that the wealden area in Sussex and Hampshire should remain as an AONB, conjoined with the Surrey Hills AONB.)

- ***Local Authorities in the area would lose power***. At the outset, and in a later stage of the Inquiry dealing with the administrative role of the National Park Authority, it was clear that this is a major concern to West Sussex County Council. The National Park would divide the county across the middle, making links with other services unduly complex. There would be no saving in cost, and no value added. The problem would be acute in planning, both policy-making and development control, due to the size and shape of the Park, the large number of Local Authorities in it, and the presence of sizeable towns such as Petersfield and Lewes. The planning function should remain with the existing bodies, and this would enable the National Park Authority to concentrate on land management, in partnership with the other organizations whose personnel have the necessary skills.

- ***Information about the cost of running the National Park was inadequate***, and the Agency had not demonstrated that there would be added value.

- ***The constitution of the proposed National Park Authority would be undemocratic***, and its existence as a separate organization would result in additional bureaucracy, especially in planning matters. (This point was also developed further at the administration-stage of the Inquiry.)

- ***Existing protection of the Downs is adequate***. A statutory Conservation Board, set up under the Countryside and Rights of Way Act, 2000, for the whole area of the two AONBs could do the same job as a National Park Authority, and would be more democratically accountable. Not being a planning authority and not being required to promote recreation, the Board could focus on conservation which is the main need of the area.

- ***The Agency should have consulted the Local Authorities when they were reviewing policy for interpretation of National Park criteria***. It is difficult to justify designation in light of the former Countryside Commission's decision in 1998 that the Downs were unsuitable as a National Park.

Other main objections heard by the Inquiry at this stage included concern that the large size of the area would make a National Park unmanageable (in fact, three existing National Parks are larger); that house prices would increase; that recreational pressure would grow; that the promotion of recreation would damage farming; that the rural economy would be stifled; and that there would be undue development pressures outside the boundary.

In response, the three Agency witnesses and their consultants, endlessly patient, dealt with the issues as follows (Countryside Agency, 2004a & b):

- ***The application of National Park criteria***. These had been applied correctly. The proposed boundary embraces landscape of the highest quality, being largely AONB, and offers diversity of landscape-character and recreational opportunity. They argued both in the opening session of the Inquiry, and later when the 'chalk only' issue (see above) was being debated, that there are clear geological, visual and cultural relationships between the chalk and the weald. It would be wrong to place too much emphasis on homogeneity of landscape character.

- ***The concern about loss of power and the need to avoid complexity***. The National Park Authority could delegate planning control to the existing Local Authorities. It should liaise closely with them, especially on cross-boundary issues, in its work on the statutory National Park Plan and the Park-wide Local Development Framework. For a strategic context of the work, it should seek membership of the South East Regional Assembly. Agency agreements could be entered into for other services as necessary. Without an all-embracing Park administration the existence of 15 Local authorities in the area would indeed make countryside management a complex operation.

- ***The question of cost***. It had been difficult to forecast cost accurately at this stage (an annual figure of £5.8 million was quoted in the Local Authority consultation document), but a National Park Authority would have more permanence and significantly more funding than would be possible for a Conservation Board.

- **Democracy**. Planning decisions would remain largely with the existing authorities. Furthermore, the National Park Authority would have a majority of Local Authority councillors as members, would be a statutory consultee, and could be in regular and widespread contact with local opinion. It would not be 'remote'.
- **A Conservation Board alternative**. A statutory Conservation Board could not do the same job as a National Park Authority. The latter has a national perspective, is a statutory body with a wider function in planning, able to relate planning to its recreational and managerial role and its responsibilities under the Countryside and Rights of Way Act. Because the area is suitable for a National Park, an AONB Conservation Board is not an option, although the South Downs Conservation Board and the East Hampshire Joint Advisory Committee have done a good job.
- **Consultation**. In the public and Local Authority consultation documents the Agency had asked very clearly for views on their policy for interpretation of National Park criteria and their application to the designation.

Subsequently, in response to several organizations about the effect on farming and the local economy, the Agency emphasized that it is not the role of a National Park Authority to increase visitor numbers, and the Authority could indeed restrict them in particular locations. The Agency also pointed to the measures taken to support and diversify farming and local economic development in existing National Parks.

This whole stage of the Inquiry was successful in illuminating the position of the objectors, particularly the Local Authorities, and the very nature of their objections. When all the evidence had been heard, leading Counsel for the main Local Authority objectors and for the Agency each summarized his case, clashing swords on interpretation of the evidence, especially on the application of the statutory criteria for designation. Their addresses were frank. Counsel for the objectors was very critical of the Agency's decision to designate, in the light of years of official reluctance to do so, and made much of the lack of hard evidence on key matters such as added-value resulting from designation. Equally, Counsel for the Agency, having pointed to the abundance of evidence on, for example, recreation in the area, reiterated his belief that the objectors' case sprang from their concern

that the National Park Authority would be the sole planning authority. In the light of the explanationsgiven of its role, this was 'neither relevant nor valid'.

The Inquiry then turned to the many objections to the proposed boundary, some of which, for example those of the South Downs Campaign, advocated extension, and some sought reduction. One notable example was the proposal by the CPRE that the boundary should be extended southward to include the lower Arun valley, between Arundel and the coast at Climping. Although these took up much of the time, effort and occasional heat of the whole Inquiry, they tended to focus on necessary detail rather than to have implications for the principle of having a National Park, which is the main concern of this chapter.

One boundary issue of unusual interest was the distance to which a National Park should extend into the sea at its eastern end, which is defined as Heritage Coast. As noted in Chapter 4, the South Downs Campaign, supported by the Sussex Downs Conservation Board, argued that, being tightly constrained by the mean low water mark (MLWM) boundary, the National Park Authority could not exercise its powers in relation to aspects of the rich landscape of the marine area and its wildlife, geological and historic features, and its exceptional recreational value (Plate 163). They drew attention to the successful management of Marine National Parks in the USA and elsewhere (Plate 164). The area should extend approximately two kilometres out to sea, and it is legally possible to do so; or, at the very least , they felt, the marine boundary should be left open (South Downs Campaign, 2004b). The Countryside Agency, while not disputing the value of the resource, argued that, under the provisions of the 1949 Act, it could not legally include a marine area within the Park. It would be outside the statutory limits of planning control (and, indeed, outside 'England'). On the other hand, it would not oppose leaving the sea boundary open, provided it was made clear that the MLWM should be interpreted as the legal limit (Countryside Agency, 2004b). Importantly, the debate on this issue points strongly to a longer-term need for legislation that does allow the inclusion of marine areas in National Parks.

REPRESENTATIONS IN SUPPORT OF DESIGNATION

As mentioned earlier, representations made in support of the National Park were not able to be supported by oral evidence at the Inquiry – an unfortunate fact of life in hearings of this kind – but would be taken fully into account in the Inspector's report. One of the most important of these was that of the South Downs Campaign, and its members often referred to it when giving evidence as objectors on several of the boundary issues, arguing for the inclusion of certain areas.

In its well-researched and hard-hitting 'support paper' and annexes (South Downs Campaign, 2003), the Campaign strongly argued that the South Downs have always met the statutory criteria for a National Park, and that previous decisions were fundamentally flawed. Downland, cliffs, weald and valleys unite to form an outstandingly valuable landscape with important opportunities for open-air recreation in close proximity to millions of people in southern England. This landscape is, however, very vulnerable. While the existing management bodies in the two AONBs had been acting in the best way they could, they lacked the powers (especially in planning), the independence, funding and long- term security that a National Park would bring. Pointing to the ever-increasing pressures on the Downs, the Campaign was under no doubt that the most effective way to conserve and enhance the area for future generations would be to have a National Park Authority. Fulfilment of its statutory duties would include delivering National Park purposes, and seeking to foster the economic and social well-being of the Park's local communities. The South Downs Campaign regarded the Agency's procedure for designation as being open and inclusive, and its members expressed the view, bravely, that the Local Authorities appearing at the Inquiry to oppose the National Park were doing so without the support of their electorate.

THE NATURAL ENVIRONMENT AND RURAL COMMUNITIES ACT, 2006

Since the ending of the Public Inquiry, there have been two related events, one of which may have implications for the final decision on the Designation Order, were this to be approved in principle. The first of these was the High Court judgement known as the Meyrick case, now under appeal by DEFRA, which concerns a small part of the recently designated New Forest National Park. The second was the decision of Parliament, arising from this case, to clarify, in Sections 59 and 99 of the Natural Environment and Rural Communities Act, certain factors to be considered when designating a National Park. The Act allows a broader view of the meaning of the expression 'natural beauty' than was taken in the Meyrick Case. In particular, this enables the wildlife and cultural heritage value of land, and land with potential opportunities for open-air recreation, to be taken into account when applying the criterion of natural beauty. It remains to be seen what the consequences of this will be for DEFRA's consideration of the South Downs Designation Order, in terms of the principle, and, perhaps more significantly, in timing.

WHAT CAN BE LEARNED FROM THIS CHAPTER FOR THE FUTURE MANAGEMENT OF THE AREA?

As has already been noted, the Inquiry finished in December 2004. Allowing time for the completion of the Inspector's report, its consideration by the Secretary of State and other ministers, and the statutory approval of the Designation and Revocation Orders, it is now unlikely that a National Park Authority would be operational before the years 2008 or 2009. Anticipating a successful outcome, several important points that emerge from this chapter should be taken into account in future administration of the area, especially through the Management Plan and its implementation. These include:

- The early establishment by the National Park Authority of a close working partnership with the existing Local Authorities on its planning strategy for the Park and on the related recreation management and transport requirements, ensuring that most development control decisions are taken locally.
- Equally, fostering efforts to establish regular, informal liaison with local communities throughout the area.
- The need to obtain an integrated and balanced relationship between Downs and Weald in terms of recreational provision, conservation and economic development.
- The provision of a 'superior recreational experience'.
- The need to ensure that planning and land-management policies for the National Park can be of direct assistance to farming and the rural economy.
- The development of the service role of the towns in relation to National Park managerial purposes.
- The need for management policies in the National Park coastal area to take account, as far as legally possible, of voluntary measures agreed between local sea-users and other interested parties for conservation of the adjoining marine area.

It is likely that the designation of the whole area as a National Park would be widely welcomed. If it were not approved, however, it is probable that the present South Downs Joint Committee, which is a statutory Joint Committee, would continue as such. To establish a statutory Conservation Board for the whole area, as an alternative, is now thought to be so difficult procedurally and might also have financial disadvantages, that this does not seem to be a viable option. The Joint Committee could readily focus on aspects of the principles set out above, but only to the lesser extent applying to an Area of Outstanding Natural Beauty than would be possible if the South Downs were to become a National Park. From all points of view, the case for a National Park is an extremely strong one.

REFERENCES

Countryside Agency (2002) *A South Downs National Park, Local Authority Consultation.* CA 111. CA, Cheltenham.

Countryside Agency (2004a) *Position Paper 1 (Principle) for South Downs National Park Designation Order Public Inquiry.* Inquiry Document No.CD/069. CA,Cheltenham.

Countryside Agency (2004b) *Statements of Evidence.* Inquiry Documents 5770 series.

Countryside Commission (1991) *Fit for the Future. Report of the National Parks Review Panel.* CCP 334. Cheltenham. ('**The Edwards report**'.)

Countryside Commission (1998) *Protecting our Finest Countryside; Advice to Government.* CCP 532. Cheltenham.

Department of the Environment (1974) *Report of the National Park Policies Review Committee.* HMSO, London. ('**The Sandford report**'.)

Ministry of Town and Country Planning (1947) *Report of the National Parks Committee (England and Wales).* Cmd 7121. HMSO, London.

Planning Inspectorate (2003) *Terms of Reference for the South Downs National Park Inquiry.* Planning Inspectorate web-site, and interview with Inquiry Manager.

South Downs Campaign (2003) *Support for a South Downs National Park, 'In Principle' Support Paper for South Downs National Park Public Inquiry.* Inquiry Document No. 3275/3/1. Brighton.

South Downs Campaign (2004a) *Opening Statement to South Downs Designation Order Public Inquiry.* Inquiry Document No.3275/12/1. SDC, Brighton.

South Downs Campaign (2004b) *Qualities of the Marine Area.* Inquiry Document No. 5770/1/1/3275. SDC, Brighton.

West Sussex County Council, East Sussex County Council, Chichester District Council, Winchester City Council, Mid Sussex District Council, Wealden District Council (2003) *Statements of Evidence to the South Downs National Park Designation Order Public Inquiry.* Inquiry Documents 1181, 3293, 2698, 2437, 2708, 3068.

COCKING V.M.EVANS

Commentary on Part 3

The two chapters in this part of the book record the significant progress made in the last ten years towards conservation of the South Downs by the Conservation Board and the Joint Advisory Committee, now merged into the South Downs Joint Committee. The chapters also point to the underlying tensions that surfaced in the debate on future organization during the National Park Inquiry. Chapter 12 recounts the very thorough negotiations to set up the Board and the Advisory Committee. It is hoped that this, and the fact that current tensions about the future have been aired, may ease the task of any new National Park authority, once there has been a definitive statement about the form that combined management of the area should take.

The Board and the Advisory Committee have been two very different types of organization, with dissimilar resources and powers. A high initial level of funding from government gave Sussex an early advantage over Hampshire, especially in its ability to undertake a large programme of capital projects. The progress made underlines the benefit of such central funding. This is emphasized by the drastic reduction in the Board's programme in the last few years when central funding decreased, resulting in the diversion of effort into raising funds from other sources. It is absolutely essential for the Downs to have assured and generous levels of grant, such as applies to existing National Parks.

The variety of projects in both areas described in Chapter 12 is nevertheless impressive. This ranges from initiatives to improve countryside access, including bus and rail, to landscape enhancement, design guidance, interpretation, preservation of historic features, participation by communities and schools, and the day-to-day work of volunteer rangers. Mistakes have inevitably been made, but overall the programme has provided a firm base of achievement in land management and finance, and in effective consultation with planning authorities, especially in development control. All this will stand the new organization in good stead, whether it is a National Park Authority or a continuation of the South Downs Joint Committee. Furthermore, the preparation of the *South Downs Interim Management Plan*, with an intensive effort to collect area-wide data, shows a determination by the former Board and Advisory Committee to view the two areas as a single entity, and to give the new organization a good start.

Against this background it might have been thought that the National Park Public Inquiry would deal largely with boundary issues, but as Chapter 13 indicates, the tensions about future organization raised major questions of principle for the Inquiry Inspector and the Secretary of State to deal with. Fundamentally these questions were concerned with the distribution of powers, especially planning, between the proposed National Park Authority and the existing Local Authorities, and hence the very form of the new organization and the area to be covered, its democratic accountability and its relationship with communities, especially farming. To reduce these tensions must be an urgent priority for the new Authority, once established.

More generally, drawing conclusions from the interplay of themes from both chapters in this part of the book, and from the build-up of confidence that has been experienced, it could be argued that, in terms of planning and of countryside management functions:

- The Authority should aim for a constructive accord and the closest of working arrangements with Local Authorities, especially in planning and transport matters;
- Staff should be deployed on the ground in sufficient numbers to foster regular two-way contact with Parish Councils, community groups, landowners and farmers, and also with local staff of other official bodies;
- In rightly having overall responsibility for Park-wide forward-planning, the Authority should ensure that its policies are co-ordinated closely with those of adjoining areas;
- It should delegate to the local planning authorities all development-control decisions, other than ones with an important strategic content;

- While offering services, such as guidance on design and a Park-wide environmental data-bank, the Authority as far as possible should seek to make use of the skills of professional staff already working in the area;

- In its management-planning, the Authority must develop policies and programmes, including financial ones, that are of direct assistance to sustainable agriculture, the rural economy, the service-role of towns, and the interests of local-community groups;

- While additional recreational pressures are inevitable, the Authority's prime aim for recreation should be to create in depth 'a superior recreational experience'; it should not attempt deliberately to increase visitor numbers;

- Policies for coastal management should extend, informally, to off-shore areas, encouraging, in particular, voluntary co-operation between local sea-users;

- The Authority must champion the needs, including financial ones, of the area as a whole, but in doing so must be aware of the differing requirements of the Downs and the Weald, especially in agriculture, forestry and recreational opportunity.

As with those emerging from Parts 1 and 2 of the book, the ideas arising from the preceding two chapters are inter-related and will be developed further in Chapter 14.

OLD HENLEY HILL   J. EVANS

CHAPTER 14
Sustainability: A Vision for the South Downs

GERALD SMART & PETER BRANDON

AN UNCERTAIN FUTURE?

Previous chapters have looked at the character of the South Downs, some key environmental issues affecting the area, and the steps taken to promote its conservation as one of the best loved landscapes in southern England. Chalk downland and scarp, wealden fields and woods, river valleys, estuary and coastal cliffs create, together and individually, a distinctive beauty that is enjoyed daily by thousands of residents and attracts more visitors than any of our National Parks.

It is clear from these chapters, nevertheless, that a critical stage has been reached in the age-long history of human influence in the area. The traditionally grazed landscape and diverse wildlife of the chalk has, sadly, almost disappeared in the last fifty years as a result of insensitive agricultural policies. Important historic sites have gone. The fragile ecosystems that are streams and rivers, are under continuing threat from drainage and water abstraction. The coastline and marine environment is at risk from development, pollution, climate change and fishing. The familiar town and village scene is in danger of losing its local texture. Many of the communities that live there are suffering from a serious decline in services and no longer include all sections of society. The pressure of recreational visitors and traffic on countryside and communities grows daily. Nevertheless, valiant and innovative progress has been made in the last 15 years towards conservation and enhancement by local government, albeit constrained by limited powers

and finance, and by means of agricultural environmental policies. More recently, the possibility of a National Park has been on the cards and widely debated.

This final chapter now peers into an uncertain future. It offers a vision of long-term sustainability, and highlights what this might mean for the management of the South Downs' very special environment, preferably as a National Park for the whole area.

Forecasts underlying the Countryside Agency's publication *The State of the Countryside, 2020* (2003), and local trends revealed in this book, give some indication of the economic, social and environmental context within which such management needs to operate.

There will be growing economic pressures for development:

- While new housing estates, major roads, superstores, waste-disposal sites and such like should be resisted in protected landscape such as the Downs, the countryside, villages and small towns of the area will be affected in other ways. There will, for example, be pressure for changes in the nature and patterns of work and skills which will be one of the factors causing a considerable increase in traffic on rural roads, particularly at peak hours. Equally, the economic problems of maintaining services in scattered settlements are causing the loss of facilities such as village shops, post offices and public transport, also leading to increased car traffic.

At the same time, powerful social pressures are affecting rural communities:

- There is likely to be continued growth in the number of households, especially of single people and small families, all requiring more personal space. At the same time there will be further movement into villages by families who prefer country living to towns. These trends, together, will affect the housing market, especially the supply of homes at prices affordable by less well-off local people who need to live in the area.

Environmentally, four matters need specific mention:

1. **Agriculture**, so long the mainstay of local employment but now a minor factor in it, faces an uncertain future due to radical changes in the Common Agricultural Policy which will see the removal of production subsidies and increased competition from imported produce. This could lead to some further farm-diversification, and new agri-environmental grants will open an opportunity for more environment-friendly land management.

2. The continuing growth of **recreation and tourism** in the area, due to increases in wealth and leisure time, will intensify pressure on existing access facilities and create demands to accommodate new activities such as paragliding and quad-biking. This is likely to focus pressure on places that have hitherto experienced little use, such as woodlands and the remoter footpaths and bridleways. With such pressure will come an extended need for facilities, country-parks, informal-access land, car-parks, picnic-sites, hiking-trails, cafes, restaurants, and overnight-accommodation. All will add to the growth of traffic in villages and rural roads, especially at weekends, and cause further loss of ease of movement, safety, and tranquillity.

3. Much of **the characteristic wildlife** of the Downs is still severely stressed by the pressures of farming, in particular, and some important species survive only because of the presence of reserves managed by public and voluntary bodies. Unless wildlife management can be put on a more sustainable basis by the creation of larger ecologically-friendly areas of chalk grassland, forest, heathland and wetlands, the outlook is not good.

4. **Climate change**. This is now widely accepted as inevitable, but there is great uncertainty as to its intensity, short and long-term, and thus of its effects on landscape, including rivers and water supply, the coast, on wildlife, agriculture, and on countryside recreation.

All these and other trends, such as the cumulative impact of 'clutter' exempt from planning control (ill-designed road signs and street furniture, aerials, unsightly alterations or extensions to buildings, for example), is the context within which the many and often conflicting uses of the South Downs' countryside will need to be managed. The task may be helped by changes in public attitudes, now increasingly favourable to conservation, albeit perhaps less tolerant of restraints on job-creating development.

A LONG-TERM VISION FOR THE SOUTH DOWNS

Before looking at objectives and priorities for the task of management, it is worth standing back a little to consider what strategic vision or ambition for the South Downs many residents and visitors are likely to share for the long-term future. The following suggestions are made:

- The South Downs should have permanency as a beautiful, dramatic and varied landscape, chalk downland, farmland and forest, pasture and woods, river valleys, estuary and sea cliff, a diversity of wildlife, an age-old historic heritage, and a wealth of local character. This, and the standard of its conservation, should be of the highest order, when judged nationally and internationally.

- The Downs should provide an unsurpassed environment for living, working and enjoying an unspoilt and peaceful countryside. In this, villages and towns blend with their landscape and historic setting, agriculture and forestry are dedicated to sustainability, cultural and geological sites are conserved, and pollution of air, land and water, including pollution by noise and light, is minimized.

- In harmony with this, residents should be housed in a range of dwelling types suited to their needs and ability to afford. They should be able to find work and services, including public transport, within a reasonable distance. They should be able to partake in a full community life and to influence decisions taken on their behalf. Visitors, including those who are disabled or disadvantaged, should have a wide choice of access to the highest quality of quiet recreation, of year-round benefit to the local economy.

A SOUTH DOWNS AUTHORITY: THE AREA TO BE COVERED, AND THE NATURE OF ITS POWERS

Two matters affecting the agency through which this vision is achieved were debated very fully at the National Park Public Inquiry. The first was the extent of the land needing to be treated as a whole. Should it be, broadly, the area covered by the two AONBs? Some Local Authorities maintained that, if there were to be a National Park at all, it should be limited solely to the chalk landscape. In response, the Countryside Agency argued powerfully that the geological, visual and cultural relationship between downs and weald, reflected in the boundaries chosen for the AONBs, was of over-riding importance. The second challenged the very nature of the body to be responsible for management. Should it be a National Park Authority or an extended Conservation Board? National Park status was opposed by Local Authorities who feared that it would have a serious effect on their own services, would not be democratically accountable and would be unacceptably expensive. In response, the Agency argued, again persuasively, that the existence of 15 Local Authorities in the area would make local planning and management unduly complex. A National Park Authority would lead and co-ordinate this process satisfactorily. It would have a majority of elected local-authority members; it would consult widely in the course of its work; and, due to the financial arrangements for central governmental grant to National Parks, would not add direct costs for local taxpayers to bear. In its opinion, the alternative of an enlarged Conservation Board could not do the job effectively, as it would have no planning powers, and its funding, considerably lower than in the case of a National Park, would have no permanent basis.

The Countryside Agency's arguments and the support it had from organizations such as the South Downs Campaign are convincing. It is therefore reasonable to anticipate that the task of management should relate to the area proposed in the Designation Order (amended in detail if necessary), and that the most effective way of providing for this would be to establish a National Park Authority.

Aims and priorities

The statutory purposes of a National Park are clearly set out in legislation. They are to conserve and enhance natural beauty, wildlife and cultural heritage, to promote opportunities for the public to understand and enjoy the Park without harming its special qualities, and also to foster economic and social well-being of its communities. If there were conflicts between these purposes, conservation should be the primary aim. In the light of this, and the context and vision set out above, the National Park Authority should provide imaginative leadership and versatile resources to fulfil the statutory purposes, working in constructive partnership with Local Authorities, agencies, landowners and communities. It should attend specially to the need for sustainable development, and to

strengthening the links between economic, social and environmental considerations.

What would this mean for the essential priorities in running a National Park, that is, those concerned with land, the environment and with communities, in which there is no lack of experience?

Managing the land, caring for the environment and promoting understanding and quiet enjoyment of it, having regard to the detailed implications of the pressures outlined at the beginning of this chapter:

- Creating the best conditions for conserving and enhancing, in a cost-effective way, valuable landscapes and habitats, especially on the chalk downland, the woodlands, rivers and coast, and maintaining local distinctiveness;

- Understanding the needs of rural landowners, farmers and foresters and enabling them to manage land sustainably in a way that supports National Park purposes, to diversify sensitively, to build up new markets, including local speciality products and rural crafts, and to support new infrastructure of benefit to the local economy;

- Encouraging public bodies such as Local Authorities, English Nature, English Heritage and the Environment Agency to exercise their powers and manage their land in a manner that is of benefit to landscape quality, bio-diversity, cultural heritage, river systems, the local economy and recreational needs;

- Ensuring that there are superior recreational opportunities, especially for access to the countryside by an augmented rights-of-way system;

- In conjunction with public agencies, the tourism industry, interest groups and landowners, promoting the enjoyment and understanding of the National Park, but not to the extent of damaging it, and co-ordinating the provision of information on its natural and cultural assets;

- Making certain that the National Park's own planning, management and financial-support policies, its landholdings and ranger services, including volunteer rangers, give positive encouragement to these priorities. This should aim especially to distribute the locations for quiet recreation in a way that relates well to the centres of population in and around the area, and to the possibility of new sustainable opportunities and means of access.

Providing for communities, again in the light of detailed understanding of the implications of the pressures already outlined:

- Helping Local Authorities, interest groups and communities to create opportunities in towns and villages for affordable housing, suitable economic development, attainment of new skills, and for improvements to public transport;

- Offering participation openly in the preparation of planning and managerial policies;

- Collaborating closely with Local Authorities when the latter are preparing Community Strategies.

Administrative co-operation:

- Carrying out forward-planning responsibilities in full consultation with planning and transportation authorities in order to obtain consistency of policies within and adjoining the area;

- Similarly, working in full consultation with them when preparing the statutory National Park Management Plan;

- Delegating to the existing planning authorities the responsibility for determining all planning applications except those of strategic importance to the area, offering landscape, building design and other specialist guidance as necessary;

- Providing a comprehensive database and monitoring system for the Park's planning and management functions;

- Sharing, where possible, the use of experienced staff available in the area;

- Working closely with voluntary-sector bodies such as the National Trust, the Wildlife Trusts, the South Downs Society (formerly the Society of Sussex Downsmen), and with the landowners, especially of large estates, particularly in matters of provision of access and wildlife conservation;

- Acting as a champion, locally, regionally, nationally and internationally for the needs, especially for project-finance and sponsorship, of the National Park as a whole, and of its individual parts.

The setting of priorities amongst many of these items is a task that will be governed by the interplay of timescales and spatial factors, inter-agency relationships, the availability of finance, and value for money as seen by members of the National Park Authority. Such priorities, together with the working up of policies and action programmes for each item will be the raw material of the statutory Management Plan as it evolves from the Plan currently being prepared by the South Downs Joint Committee.

SOME FINAL THOUGHTS

Nothing will be as important for the Downs as care for the environment. Their corrosion must be stopped for ever. This means no insidious creeping tide of development from the coastal towns, no more damage to historic skylines, no trunk-roads across the area, no crowd-attracting leisure-facilities, no shopping-malls, no business and industrial parks, no identikit or unsightly buildings; in fact nothing which is in flat defiance of the very qualities that make the Downs a national treasure.

Equally, the restoration of the Downs to their natural splendour and beauty, begun under the auspices of the Conservation Board and the Joint Advisory Committee, and latterly of the South Downs Joint Committee, must be given the widest support and a special claim on national funding. There is a huge backlog of work to be caught up with, and it is vital that conservation and countryside enhancement in the area is properly financed and expertly staffed. There is, indeed, no better way to conserve the natural environment than by sensitive farming. Uncertain as the future is, enough farmers must continue to live on the land to do this, avoiding the consequences of recent intensive agriculture, by, for example, greater emphasis on lower-output farming made profitable through the creation of high-value products.

As implied earlier in this chapter, there is a new mood in the country as a whole that favours conservation, and a new commitment to restore what has been damaged in the past. The prospect of the care and protection that a well-established and accountable National Park Authority can give to the landscape of the South Downs presents a real opportunity. The mistakes that have plagued it for half a century must never be repeated. For an England steadily being built over, it is of momentous importance that there should remain prime countryside not desecrated by human hands. Present generations must leave to posterity a future South Downs in far better shape than when they received it. That would be an important contribution to the national quality of life.

REFERENCE

Countryside Agency (2003) *The State of the Countryside 2020*. CA138. CA, Wetherby.

Biographies of the authors

Phil Belden is Countryside Services Manager and Deputy Chief Officer for the South Downs Joint Committee. He is a Chartered Environmentalist and has a degree in Business Studies. After an early career in the City, he moved into conservation work beginning in 1977 as a warden on the Dorset Heritage Coast. Subsequently, he has been a countryside ranger in the Suffolk Coast and Heaths AONB (1979-83), Assistant Project Officer in the Sussex Heritage Coast and (East) Sussex Downs Area of Outstanding Natural Beauty (1983-88) and as Conservation Officer and Area Manager of the (West) Sussex Downs AONB (1988-93). From 1993 he has been with the Sussex Downs Conservation Board (now the South Downs Joint Committee). Phil has been responsible for, or involved in, a number of conservation initiatives, such as the Dorset long-distance National Trail, co-founder of the Suffolk Sandlings Group, founder of Brighton Urban Wildlife Group, and in the South Downs ESA Scheme, the Seven Sisters Voluntary Marine Conservation Area, development of the Volunteer Ranger Service and championing South Downs lamb.

Peter Brandon, co-editor of this volume, is well known for his many books on the landscape history of south-east England, particularly the most recent ones on the South Downs (1998), the Weald of Kent and Sussex (2003) and the North Downs (2005). He is a native of Sussex and a resident since 1958; since retiring he has been involved in promoting and protecting the countryside. He is a former Head of the Department of Geography at the University of North London, and is a Vice-President of the Sussex branch of the Campaign for the Protection of Rural England (CPRE) and of the Sussex Archaeological Society, and President of the South Downs Society (formerly the Society of Sussex Downsmen).

Trevor Cherrett has been involved in rural development for over 20 years in Sussex, till recently being Head of the Centre for Rural Development in Lewes, the rural community council for East and West Sussex. A planner by training, he has worked in the local government, academic and independent sectors. He is the author of several research projects and good-practice guides covering affordable housing and community-led planning. Trevor is Chairman of the South East Assembly's Rural Advisory Group, and is a Visiting Research Fellow at the University of Sussex. In 2004 he completed a Winston Churchill Fellowship study of local communities on the edge of national parks in Australia and New Zealand. In 2005 he was appointed Head of Planning, Housing and Transport at the newly-formed national Commission for Rural Communities, based in London.

Jason Lavender is originally from Zimbabwe, and has a degree in Environmental Archaeology and a master's degree in European Environmental Policy and Regulation. He has worked in the environmental sector in both southern Africa and the UK, the last ten years of which have been in Sussex and Kent.

After working for the Environment Agency for six years promoting the benefits of naturally-functioning floodplains and coasts, Jason was appointed Director of the High Weald Area of Outstanding Natural Beauty in September 2005. He is a trustee of the Bellhurst Nature Conservation Trust which owns approximately 800 hectares in Kent and Sussex, and he is a member of the Sussex Cattle Society, the Centre for Alternative Technology and Survival International.

Patrick Leonard OBE has an degree in agriculture from Wye College, University of London, and a postgraduate diploma in Agricultural Economics from the University of Oxford. He first became interested in the environmental effects of agricultural policy while working in Sarawak in the 1960s. Later he was Assistant Director at the Countryside Commission responsible for the pioneering agri-environmental experiments which led to the establishment of Environmentally Sensitive Areas (ESAs). He moved on to be responsible for rural development policy and agri-environmental matters at the Department of the Environment. He has been a council member of the Sussex Wildlife Trust and a member of the Executive of the South Downs Joint Committee. Since writing his chapter in this book, he has retired to live in the Antipodes, after spending most winters in New Zealand.

Donald Macdonald was born in Edinburgh in 1950 and brought up in Kikcudbright on the Solway Coast. An early interest in the natural world led him into forestry and, after graduating from the Cumbria College of Agriculture and Forestry in 1974, he took various posts in commercial forestry throughout Scotland. Since 1985 he has been Head Forester at the Cowdray Estate, West Sussex, the most wooded private estate in the south of England.

Paul Millmore came to the South Downs when he took up a post as a rural planner with East Sussex County Council. After the reorganization of local government in 1974, he grasped the opportunity to become the first Heritage Coast Officer in the UK, still based in East Sussex. This was the start of a long involvement with the South Downs in pioneering new initiatives in rights-of-way management, interpretation, marine conservation, guided walks, dewpond restoration, eyesore removal and countryside management in general. In his spare time he wrote the National Trail Guide to the South Downs Way, and has just completed the latest revised edition. In 1995 Paul left East Sussex County Council and, after a brief spell managing the Cuckoo Trail for Sustrans, established himself as a freelance conservation consultant. Believing in the need for aSouth Downs National Park for the last 20 years, he has been actively involved in the running of the South Downs Campaign, and was a Countryside Agency-appointed member of the Downs Conservation Board, now the South Downs Joint Committee, serving on the tourism without traffic steering group, the recreation and tourism working party and the South Downs Access Forum. Paul is now the Chairman of the SDJC's Planning Committee.

David McOmish is a Senior Archaeological Investigator within the Research and Standards Department of English Heritage, based at Cambridge. He read archaeology at the University of Glasgow, and then undertook work on a number of prehistoric sites in Scotland. In 1984 he joined the Royal Commission on the Historical Monuments of England based at Salisbury in Wiltshire, working on its final county inventory of South Wiltshire and carrying out fieldwork throughout much of southern England. He later moved to RCHME's Swindon headquarters in 1992 and worked on EH's volumes covering Salisbury Plain and the Marlborough Downs, as well as participating in major field projects looking at Neolithic causewayed enclosures and flint mines. After RCHME's merger with English Heritage, David moved to EH's Cambridge office, from which he carries out work on sites throughout much of the South East. He is currently a Vice President of the Prehistoric Society and a Fellow of the Society of Antiquaries. His research interests include European late prehistory, chalk landscapes and prehistoric settlement archaeology, and a personal involvement in a major landscape project in the Northumberland National Park.

Lord Selborne is Chairman of Blackmoor Estate Limited, a family farming business based at Selborne, Hampshire, with interests in fruit growing, milk production and nursery enterprises. He served as Chairman of the Agricultural and Food Research Council from 1983 to 1989, of the Joint Nature Conservation Committee from 1991 to 1997, and of the South East Rural Affairs Forum from 2001 to 2005. He was a member of the Government Panel on Sustainable Development from 1994 to 1997 and President of the Royal Geographical Society from 1997 to 2000. He is currently Chairman of the Trustees of the Royal Botanic Gardens, Kew, and Chancellor of the University of Southampton.

Martin Small is Planning and Policy Manager of the South Downs Joint Committee, having held the same post at the Sussex Downs Conservation Board since 1998, based at Ford, West Sussex. He has degrees in Town and Country Planning from the University of Manchester, and a Diploma inCountryside Management from Birkbeck College, University of London. Between 1988 and 1998

Martin worked for Winchester City Council both in forward planning and development control, and was seconded for a year to write the Management Plan for the East Hampshire Area of Outstanding Natural Beauty. He is married with a small son, and lives on the Hampshire-West Sussex border.

Gerald Smart CBE, co-editor of this volume, is Emeritus Professor of Planning at University College London and formerly County Planning Officer for Hampshire. In addition to contributing to books on planning and countryside management, he was co-author in 1990 of the Countryside Commission's *Review of Areas of Outstanding Natural Beauty,* and in 2001, was co-author of the book, *Landscapes at Risk? The Future for Areas of Outstanding Natural Beauty.* He has been a council member of the RSPB, and is currently on the council of the Solent Protection Society. Professor Smart was appointed CBE in 1991 for his contribution to strategic planning, and in 2001 was the first recipient of the Bowland Award of the National Association of AONBs. He lives on the New Forest coast near Lymington.

Alison Tingley has an Environmental Science degree from the University of the South West and a Masters degree from Imperial College, London University. She has been involved in conservation since 1984 when she joined Essex Wildlife Trust as Project Officer for its Manpower Services Commission Team. In 1986 she became the Hampshire Farming and Wildlife Advisor. After two years she moved to Hampshire County Council, working in its landscape and then ecology sections. In 1994 she took up the post of East Hampshire AONB Officer, where she was responsible for the team involved in discussions about a South Downs National Park. With the formation of the South Downs Joint Committee, she has taken on the role of Countryside Manager (Strategic) with responsibility for the South Downs Advisory Forum amongst other matters.

Peter Topping is Head of English Heritage's Archaeological Survey and Investigation Team which specializes in landscape analysis, based at Cambridge. He studied archaeology at the University of Durham, and then joined the Royal Commission on the Historical Monuments of England's Newcastle upon Tyne office in 1983. He has been involved in excavation and fieldwork throughout the UK and also the American Midwest. He moved to the RCHME office in Cambridge in 1993, where he devised and led the national fieldwork project which focused on causewayed enclosures and flint mines, many of which are in the South Downs. The RCHME was later merged with English Heritage. Peter's personal research interests include the Neolithic period and prehistoric farming.

Tony Whitbread is Chief Executive at the Sussex Wildlife Trust (SWT). After gaining a BSc in applied biology and a PhD in grassland ecology from Hatfield Polytechnic, he worked for the then Nature Conservancy Council from 1981 to 1988, initially as a biological surveyor but later specializing in woodland surveys. In 1987 he assisted with survey and inventory work for the NCC following the great storm of that year. This work later led him to join the Royal Society for Nature Conservation (RSNC) in 1989 to co-ordinate the responses of the Wildlife Trusts to the positive effects of the storm. In 1991 Tony joined the SWT where, before his most recent appointment, he was Head of Conservation. He continues his participation in woodland issues, for example in advising the Wildlife Trusts' National Office, sitting on woodland forums and on the Forestry Commission's South East Regional Advisory Committee. He also sits on Environment Agency committees and several local nature reserve advisory committees. He is a member of the British Ecological Society and the Institute of Ecologists and Environmental Managers. Tony has co-authored in particular two important SWT publications – quoted in this book – concerned with the development of local biodiversity action plans, and in proposing a positive agenda for landscape-scale approaches to maintaining near-natural areas in the South Downs: *A Vision for the South Downs* (1993) and *A Vision for the Wildlife of Sussex* (1996).

Rendel Williams was a Reader in Physical Geography at the University of Sussex, where he taught from the late 1960s. He has researched extensively on rock weathering and landform evolution, and in recent years on coastal erosion, particularly beaches. He is author of two books on statistics and joint editor of a book on rock weathering, and is currently working on a book covering the coastline of the eastern channel. He is a keen supporter of nature conservation, and has been a Council member of the Sussex Wildlife Trust for many years.

THE SMALL BRIDGE AT PULBOROUGH. D.V.GORDON.

Colour Plates and Maps

Several acronyms appear below in the interests of brevity. These are: SDJC for the South Downs Joint Committee; SWT for the Sussex Wildlife Trust; and NMR for National Monument Record.

Cover painting Black Cap, Ditchling Beacon, East Sussex by Roy Adams, 1992.

Endpapers (front) Map of the South Downs Area of Outstanding Natural Beauty (AONB) and designated National Park boundary. Data from Natural England and SDJC; map produced by the University of Southampton Cartographic Unit.

Endpapers (back) Map of the proposed South Downs National Park showing the designated area compared with the Inquiry Inspector's recommended revised boundary, June 2007. Courtesy of DEFRA and Natural England.

Half-title page Butser Hill, Hampshire, in snow, looking north. Photo: Garrick Palmer, courtesy of SDJC.

Frontispiece Alfriston, East Sussex, taken from the south-east with the escarpment of the South Downs in the background, dip-slope on the left and the steep, north-facing scarp-slope to the right. Photo: English Heritage, NMR 23375-21.

Title page The Cuckmere valley at sunrise. Photo: SDJC.

Verso of title (copyright) page What Future for the South Downs? – cover of a CPRE leaflet of the 1990s. Courtesy of the Campaign to Protect Rural England/SDJC.

Plate (map) 1 The South Downs in their regional setting. Map by the University of Southampton Cartographic Unit.

Plate (map) 2 The extent of protected landscapes and heritage coasts in the United Kingdom. Map by the University of Southampton Cartographic Unit.

Plate 3 Environmental vandalism at its worst: the cutting through Twyford Down for the M3 Motorway, near Winchester, Hampshire. Photo: Alison Tingley, courtesy of SDJC.

Plate 4 The Fulking escarpment, looking west from the Devil's Dyke area. The steep scarp-slope can be clearly seen. Photo: John Tyler, courtesy of SDJC.

Plate 5 A poster painted by Frank Newbould as encouragement during the Second World War. The scene nowadays is well preserved by Eastbourne Borough Council. Image courtesy of the Imperial War Museum, London.

Plate 6 The village of Selborne, Hampshire, where the naturalist Gilbert White lived, viewed from Selborne Hanger. Photo: Mike Read (www.mikeread.co.uk).

Plate 7 Visitors to Beachy Head. A *Punch* cartoon of 1935.

Plate 8 The Woodingdean teashop in the 1930s, East Sussex, sited to cater to the increasing numbers of visitors to the area. From Mercer, P. & Holland, D. (1930) *The Huns MerePit: the Story of Woodingdean and Balsdean*, Lewes, courtesy of Peter Brandon.

Plate 9 Birling Gap, East Sussex, looking east, in 1931; increasing use of the motor car enabled such formerly remote sites to become popular. Severe cliff erosion has taken place since then: the cottage centre left has now fallen into the sea. Photo from an old postcard, photographer unknown, courtesy of Paul Millmore.

Plate 10 In the Eastern Downs near Lewes, flocks of Southdown sheep grazed the hills by day. Photo from an old postcard, photographer unknown, courtesy of Rendel Williams.

Plate 11 Hampshire Down sheep, specially bred for the conditions of the Western Downs. Photo: Nick Heasman, courtesy of SDJC.

Plate 12 Getting ready to plough, Falmer, East Sussex , 1940. Photo from a national newspaper in World War II, photographer unknown, courtesy of Peter Brandon.

Plate 13 Dust from ploughing, near Shoreham, West Sussex, September 1989; the fragile downland soil has been constantly reworked, and is now in danger of being severely eroded. Photo: Phil Belden.

Plate 14 The Seven Sisters, Sussex Heritage Coast, viewed from Hope Gap, Seaford Head, East Sussex, August 1984. Photo: Phil Belden.

Plate 15 Urban encroachment; post-war housing on the Downs at North Lancing, West Sussex, following the contour, June 1992. Photo: Phil Belden.

Plate 16 The view from Harting Down looking towards Tower Hill, West Sussex., showing the more wooded nature of the Western Downs. Photo: Mike Read (www.mikeread.co.uk).

Plate 17 Old Winchester Hill, Hampshire; a most important archaeological site and National Nature Reserve. The photo shows the Iron Age ramparts (for an aerial photo see Plate 41); the NNR includes the largest colony of juniper in south-east England, and attracts a variety of invertebrates including the Duke of Burgundy fritillary. Photo: Nick Heasman, courtesy of SDJC.

Plate 18 The River Meon in east Hampshire, less affected by water extraction than other chalk streams. Photo: Mike McGoran, courtesy of Natural England/SDJC.

Plate 19 Amberley Wildbrooks, West Sussex, taken from the South Downs Way looking north, January 1991. Photo: Phil Belden.

Plate 20 Amberley Wildbrooks showing the drainage ditches that are important for wildlife. Photo: Cris Brunnen, courtesy of SDJC.

Plate 21 The Adur Valley looking south to the sea from the edge of Upper Beeding, West Sussex. Photo: Cris Brunnen, courtesy of SDJC.

Plate 22 The Arundel skyline (left and centre) looking westwards over the River Arun with the Downs to the right. Photo: SDJC.

Plate 23 The view from Lewes Castle keep – a thousand years of history in the town's roofscape below. Photo: Harry Montgomery.

Plate 24 Houses at Amberley, West Sussex; formerly a street village inhabited by small farmers, which from the 1920s was invaded by writers, artists and retired folk so that it has now become a 'chocolate box' type of settlement. Photo: Peter Brandon.

Plate 25 The Wealden countryside below Linchmere, West Sussex, in late afternoon, autumn 2006, looking south towards the chalk Downs in the distance. The first line of (blue) hills is part of the sandy ridge between Fernhurst and Midhurst; the highest hill on the horizon is Harting Down. Photo: Michael Packard.

Plate 26 Scrub clearance of a heathland environment, Forest Mere. Photo: Keith Fryer, courtesy of SDJC.

Plate (map) 27 Geological map of the South Downs area. Data from Rendel Williams; map by the University of Southampton Cartographic Unit.

Plate 28 Chalk blocks, known as 'clunch', used as building material in the outside walls of this recently restored tied cottage at Cocking, West Sussex, 2006. Photo: Jane Bowden, courtesy of SDJC.

Plate 29 A sea urchin (*Echinocorys*) chalk fossil, dia. 8.5 cm; fossils such as this were often found on the Downs and known as 'shepherds' crowns'. Photo: Gerald Legg, © The Booth Museum of Natural History, Brighton.

Plate 30 A fossilized prehistoric cockle shell (*Spondylus spinosus*) on flint (19 cm including the flint), found at Telscombe Cliffs, East Sussex. Photo: Gerald Legg, © The Booth Museum of Natural History, Brighton.

Plate 31 A fossilized fish (*Holopterix lewesiensis*) in chalk, 15 cm in length, found at Southeram, Lewes. Photo: Gerald Legg, © The Booth Museum of Natural History, Brighton.

Plate 32 (a,b,c,d) Flint used respectively as a) randomly-placed, knapped building material set in lime mortar in a 19th century wall (photo – Peter Greenhalf, courtesy of Natural England/SDJC); b) elegant 18th century squared knapped flint in the porch of St. Andrew's church, Steyning (photo – Brian Dawson, courtesy of West Sussex County Council); c) partially knapped and galleted (use of the small chippings for additional decoration) at West Dean farm buildings (photo – Michael Packard); and d) less imaginatively, though pleasantly, set in cement with brick courses today (photo – Tina Stallard, courtesy of Natural England/SDJC).

Plate 33 A Neolithic flaked flint axe-head 14.5 cm long, with evidence of cortex close to one end, where it could have been attached to a wooden shaft; found at Portslade, East Sussex, in 1885. Photo: Gerald Legg, © The Booth Museum of Natural History, Brighton.

Plate 34 Erosion at Beachy Head, East Sussex; a headland such as this impedes the longshore movement of flint shingle, creating deficits further along the coast. Photo: Rendel Williams.

Plate (map) 35 Archaeological sites in the South Downs area. Source: English Heritage; map produced by the University of Southampton Cartographic Unit.

Plate 36 The flint mines at Harrow Hill, West Sussex, are located on a prominent downland spur opposite those at Black Patch. A later prehistoric enclosure overlies the mines, as at Cissbury. Photo: English Heritage, NMR 23311-33.

Plate 37 The flint mines at Cissbury, West Sussex, now partly enclosed by later Iron Age hill-fort defences. Photo: English Heritage, NMR 23312-19.

Plate 38 The Early Neolithic enclosure at Barkhale, West Sussex, which subsequently became a focus for later Bronze Age round barrows. Photo: English Heritage, NMR 23310-30.

Plate 39 St Roche's Hill (The Trundle) at Goodwood, West Sussex. The circuit of the Middle Iron Age enclosure is clearly visible, and within it a number of Neolithic enclosures can be seen. Photo: English Heritage, NMR 23310-15.

Plate 40 A bell barrow on Kingley Vale, near Chichester, West Sussex. Photo: Mark Bowden, courtesy of English Heritage.

Plate 41 Old Winchester Hill, near East Meon, Hampshire, August 1995. This aerial photo taken from the east shows the outline of the hill fort very clearly, its circuit punctured by two entrances; that at the foot of the picture is the main one. What is not so clear is the dramatic ridge-top location (but see Plate 17), evidently significant long before the construction of the Iron Age boundary; within the site there are several Bronze Age burial mounds, now scarred by footpaths, and other round barrows underlie the bank to the east and south. The slight remains of prehistoric constructions can be seen inside the hill fort, as well as other later features, including a pond, close to the east entrance, and smaller hollows probably dating from World War II. Photo: English Heritage, NMR SU6420/53.

Plate 42 St. Catherine's Hill, near Winchester, Hampshire, July 1987. The oval outline of this large hill fort is picked out by the erosion caused by walkers, though the defences remain in good condition. The large internal rampart is flanked by a ditch and a further bank outside this, so originally it must have presented a formidable barrier. The remains of a medieval chapel, built before the middle of the 12th century, lie in the circular copse at the highest point of the site; beside this are the remains of a small mizmaze originally cut between 1647 and 1710. To the north, remains of medieval strip cultivation encroach on the Iron Age boundary. Photo: English Heritage, NMR SU4827/51.

Plate 43 Chanctonbury Ring, West Sussex; the hill fort can be seen top centre, and a medieval or later pond at bottom right. Between the two are the remains of a cross-ridge boundary. Photo: English Heritage, NMR 23312-31.

Plate 44 An aerial view of Arundel Castle. Originating in the late Norman Period (AD 1066–1154), the castle has survived over the centuries, and has been preserved by the Fitzalan-Howard family, latterly headed by the Dukes of Norfolk. Photo: English Heritage, NMR 18125-07.

Plate 45 Reconstruction of an Iron Age house, formerly at Butser but now sited at Chalton, Hampshire, based on studies by Peter Reynolds. Photo: Peter Brandon.

Plate 46 The Great Barn at Alciston, East Sussex, with 13th century foundations; built by the monks of Battle Abbey forthe storage of the produce of their farms. Photo: Peter Brandon.

Plate 47 A medieval cottage, originating from Hangleton, East Sussex and rebuilt at the Weald and Downland Museum, Singleton, West Sussex. Photo: Peter Brandon.

Plate 48 The Clergy House at Alfriston, East Sussex, before restoration. Built in c.1350, this timber-framed 'Wealden' house was partially rebuilt in the 17th century. It was bought by The National Trust in 1896 for £10.00. Photo: © The National Trust Photographic Library; www.ntpl.org.uk

Plate 49 A view of the west front of the restored Clergy House at Alfriston taken from the graveyard. Photo: Andrew Butler, © The National Trust Photographic Library; www.ntpl.org.uk

Plate 50 Southdown sheep in their fold. The animals were kept in such portable enclosures at night; their dung fertilized the valley fields for later planting of corn and oats, and their hooves consolidated the downland soil. From an old postcard, photographer unknown, courtesy of Peter Brandon.

Plate 51 A Southdown ram. Photo taken in 1939 by an unknown photographer, which appeared in a national newspaper. Courtesy of Peter Brandon.

Plate 52 Sussex red cattle; originally bred from the oxen used for ploughing in the Downs, but now being revived for production of beef. Photo: Janina Holubecki, courtesy of High Weald AONB.

Plate 53 Harvest at Falmer, East Sussex, 1941. Here the emphasis is on growing corn to help fed the nation in wartime. Note the 'land girls' who worked on the farms while most of the men were away at war. Photo by an unknown photographer from a national newspaper. Courtesy of Peter Brandon.

Plate 54 A chalk-pit near Glynde, East Sussex; one of the many quarries associated with Gideon Mantell, whose greatest work was *The Fossils of the South Downs* of 1822, based on studies made of the chalk workings in the Ouse Valley near Lewes. Photo: Peter Brandon.

Plate 55 Traditional flint barns near Birling, East Sussex. Photo: Peter Brandon.

Plate 56 The deserted village of Idsworth, Hampshire, winter 2000. All that remains is the medieval church, St. Hubert's, with a few scattered houses many metres away built in much later periods or moved in Victorian times to make way for the London to Portsmouth railway. Photo: SDJC.

Plate 57 The church of St. Andrew, Jevington, East Sussex, with its Saxon tower. It has an effigy of a 'Saxon' Christ in the nave. Photo: Peter Brandon.

Plate 58 The church of St. Andrew, Didling , West Sussex, one of the numerous little, 'lost' churches of humble origin. Photo: Peter Brandon.

Plate 59 A near-perfect example of a 13th century church, St. Mary, Tarring Neville, East Sussex; such buildings never evolved into the Decorated or Perpendicular styles due to lack of money, the result of population-loss in the 14th century. Photo: Peter Brandon.

Plate 60 A double-chambered dovecot of medieval origin at Alciston, East Sussex; built by the monks of Battle Abbey to house the birds that provided succulent meat for the table. Photo: Peter Brandon.

Plate 61 Halnaker Windmill, West Sussex; recently restored, but famed through Hilaire Belloc's verse of 1913, when he regarded it as a symbol of rural decline. Photo: Peter Brandon.

Plate 62 One of the surviving 18th century water-mills, here at Steyning, West Sussex, and now a private residence. Photo: Peter Brandon.

Plate (map) 63 The different habitats in the South Downs area. Map produced by the University of Southampton Cartographic Unit from data supplied by SWT, courtesy of East Sussex, West Sussex and Hampshire County Councils (heathlands), the Environment Agency (grazing marshes and rivers), Natural England (ancient woodland), SDJC (chalk grassland and the proposed National Park boundary).

Plate 64 Common spotted orchid (*Dactylorhiza fuchsii*) seen here at Malling Down, West Sussex. Photo: Sussex Wildlife Trust (SWT).

Plate 65 Bee orchid (*Ophrys apifera*), characteristic of dry chalk grassland. Photo: Tony Whitbread.

Plate 66 Musk orchid (*Herminium monorchis*); an uncommon species found in only a few locations on the Downs. Photo: David King, courtesy of SWT.

Plate 67 Burnt-tip orchid (*Orchis ustulata*); a rare species confined to a few locations in the Downs. Photo: SWT.

Plate 68 Early spider orchid (*Ophrys sphegoides*); found on a few high-quality chalk grasslands, such as Castle Hill near Brighton. Photo: Tony Whitbread.

Plate 69 Horseshoe vetch (*Hippocrepis comosa*); a characteristic downland plant and food-plant of the Adonis blue butterfly. Photo: Mike Read (www.mikeread.co.uk).

Plate 70 Round-headed rampion (*Phyteuma orbiculare*); frequently found in the South Downs but rare elsewhere, hence its nickname 'Pride of Sussex'. Photo: Tony Whitbread.

Plate 71 Yellow-rattle (*Rhinanthus minor*), so called because of the sound made when the ripe seed-heads are shaken; a semi-parasitic plant characteristic of neutral, traditionally grazed grassland. Photo: SWT.

Plate 72 Ling (*Calluna vulgaris*) with birch scrub and Scots pine, characteristic of heathland. Photo: Mark Monk-Terry, courtesy of SWT.

Plate 73 A beech wood (*Fagus sylvatica*) in winter, Selborne Hanger, Hampshire; its dense canopy in summer shades out most ground floras. Photo: Mike Read (www.mikeread.co.uk).

Plate 74 Kingley Vale National Nature Reserve (NNR) and its internationally important yew forest, near Chichester, West Sussex, viewed from the air in 1964. Photo: Richard Williamson.

Plate 75 Ancient yew trees (*Taxus baccata*) at Kingley Vale NNR, West Sussex. Photo: Richard Williamson.

Plate 76 The Duke of Burgundy fritillary (*Hamearis lucina*), characteristic of scrubby grassland and sunny woodland clearings. Photo: Andy Vidler, courtesy of SWT.

Plate 77 The white admiral butterfly (*Ladoga camilla*), a locally common woodland species. Photo: Mark Monk-Terry, courtesy of SWT.

Plate 78 The Adonis blue butterfly (*Lysandra bellargus*) characteristic of the South Downs, pictured on its feed-plant, horseshoe vetch (*Hippocrepis comosa*). Photo: Simon Culpin, courtesy of SDJC.

Plate 79 A female brown hairstreak butterfly (*Thecla betulae*), a species characteristic of woodland and hedges; it spends much of its life high in the tree canopy or deep in hedgerows. Photo: SWT.

Plate 80 A young roe deer (*Capriolus capriolus*); a welcome sight, but its browsing of regenerating woodland causes problems for foresters. Photo: Jamie Cordery.

Plate 81 A dormouse (*Muscardinus avellanarius*); isolated colonies are found in the South Downs area. Photo: Hugh Clark, courtesy of SWT.

Plate 82 A female sand lizard (*Lacerta agilis*); a very rare species that favours dry-heath where it inhabits stands of ling in sandy areas. Photo: SWT.

Plate 83 A barbastelle bat (*Barbastella barbastellus*), one of the rare species roosting in places such as Ebernoe Common, but flying a great distance at night for food. Photo: Frank Greenaway, courtesy of SWT.

Plate 84 Marsh tits (*Parus palustris*), favours the dense woodland habitat of the Western Weald. Photo: David Plummer, courtesy of SWT.

Plate 85 Buzzards (*Buteo buteo*) are now spreading through the South Downs area. Photo: Darin Smith, courtesy of SWT.

Plate 86 Dartford warbler (*Sylvia undata*); a resident bird, populations of which are expanding in suitable heathland habitats in the South Downs area. Photo: Andy Vidler, courtesy of SWT.

Plate 87 A male stonechat (*Saxicola torquata*); another heathland bird often seen displaying on top of bushes and tall vegetation. Photo: Darin Smith, courtesy of SWT.

Plate 88 Nightjar (*Caprimulgus europaeus*), a mainly heathland or woodland bird, characteristically active at night; it can stay motionless on the ground if approached. Photo: Mike Read (www.mikeread.co.uk).

Plate 89 Woodlark (*Lullula arborea*), a scarce bird which tends to nest on the ground, sometimes close to woodland rides. Photo: Mike Read (www.mikeread.co.uk).

Plate 90 Lapwings (*Vanellus vanellus*) congregate on the flooded marshes of the Adur and Arun river valleys in winter. Photo: Darin Smith, courtesy of SWT.

Plate 91 Bewick's swans (*Cygnus columbarius*) migrate to Britain in winter and can be seen particularly in the flooded river valleys of the South Downs area. Photo: Mike Read (www.mikeread.co.uk).

Plate 92 Ebernoe Common, West Sussex; woodland pasture, which is an internationally important habitat for bats. Photo: SWT.

Plate 93 Cross-leaved heath (*Erica tetralix*), characteristic of humid and wet-heaths. Photo: Mike Read. (www.mikeread.co.uk)

Plate 94 Adderstongue fern (*Ophioglossum vulgatum*), typical of damp, neutral grassland. Photo: Mike Read (www.mikeread.co.uk).

Plate 95 The River Arun flooding;. the annual cycle of flooding in winter and marshy conditions in summer create wetlands of national importance to wildlife. Photo: Julian Gray, courtesy of SDJC.

Plate 96 Restored sheepwalk at Harting Down, West Sussex, looking north, with buttercup, crosswort, bird's foot trefoil and plantain flourishing. Photo: Patrick Leonard.

Plate 97 East Meon village, Hampshire; visibly linked to the landscape and purposefully sited. Photo: SDJC.

Plate 98 Newly-built affordable housing at Rodmell, East Sussex. Photo: Martin Small, courtesy of SDJC.

Plate 99 The new Westmeston village hall, East Sussex. Well-equipped centres such as this provide important facilities for the inhabitants of country villages, and a focal point for the local community. Photo: Martin Small, courtesy of SDJC.

Plate 100 Downland pubs are very popular, thereby encouraging local employment; with increasing mobility people now enjoy the traditional Sunday lunch away from home or by picnicking outside, as here, at East Dean, East Sussex, August 1983. Photo Phil Belden.

Plate 101 With the continuing interest in riding horses on the Downs, the demand for a farrier's services is strong. Photo: Peter Greenhalf, courtesy of Natural England/SDJC.

Plate 102 Thatching for cottages in the South Downs is still in demand, although the thatching reeds often originate from outside the area. Photo: Peter Greenhalf, courtesy of Natural England/SDJC.

Plate 103 Firle village stores, East Sussex; vital to the local community, but such shops are continually under threat of closure due to lack of custom or competition from larger towns. Photo: Peter Greenhalf, courtesy of Natural England/SDJC.

Plate 104 The launch of 'bus walks', to encourage urban dwellers to explore the Downs in a controlled way, Stanmer Park, Brighton, July 1997. Photo: Phil Belden, courtesy of SDJC.

Plate 105 A millennium project to encourage local awareness in East Hampshire; a montage of typical pictures of parishes, cut to shape, and the whole made into a jigsaw puzzle. Building on the Countryside Agency's encouragement of parish maps, it was hoped to create a picture of the South Downs area. Photo: Nick Heasman, courtesy of SDJC.

Plate 106 Hurdle-making at Harting Coombe, West Sussex; a posed picture from an old postcard showing the tools of the trade, and the resulting product used for folding sheep. Photographer unknown, courtesy of Rendel Williams.

Plate 107 Threshing corn *c.* 1904/5 at East Dean, East Sussex; a posed photograph showing the transition from animal-based to mechanized farming. The steam-powered traction engine drives the belts of the threshing machine (centre), where the grain flows into sacks, and the elevator lifts the straw to be stacked. Piles of chaff can be seen to the right of the picture. The sacks of corn are then taken away by horse and cart, to be stored before being sold, or milled for animal feed. Photographer unknown, courtesy of Rendel Williams.

Plate 108 The way it used to be between the two world wars; Newmarket Hill taken from the Rottingdean road, 1932. Photo: Edward Reeves, Lewes.

Plate 109 Prairie-like arable fields; Loose Bottom, near Falmer, East Sussex, looking north-east, October 1983. Photo: Phil Belden.

Plate 110 An Environmentally Sensitive Area (ESA) landscape; looking south from Chanctonbury Ring, West Sussex, 1990. Photo: Phil Belden.

Plate 111 Part of Offham Down, East Sussex, 1997; ploughed by the farmer, who could earn more from government subsidy for crops than from payments to protect the site. Photo: Julian Gray, courtesy of SDJC

Plate 112 'Unploughing'; local people, enraged by the ploughing up at Offham Down try to put back the sward, 1997. Photo: Julian Gray, courtesy of SDJC.

Plate 113 A close-up of restored sheepwalk at Harting Down, West Sussex, with crossword, bird's-foot trefoil and common spotted orchid in the sward, and bramble already starting to invade. Photo: Patrick Leonard.

Plate 114 Sheepwalk beside ploughed downland, which is now severely eroded, near Eastbourne. Photo: Patrick Leonard

Plate 115 The changing arable landscape today: potatoes and power lines. Photo: Patrick Leonard.

Plate 116 'Lettuscapes'; intensively planted salad crops brought on early by the use of horticultural fleece. Photo: Patrick Leonard.

Plate 117 'Plasticization' of the landscape; vegetable crops protected from the elements in order to gain quicker maturity. Photo: Patrick Leonard.

Plate 118 Ancient semi-natural woodland at Paddock Wood, Cowdray Estate, West Sussex, 2005. Photo: Donald Macdonald.

Plate 119 Seventeen year-old sweet chestnut (*Castanea sativa*) poles being coppiced at Pathfield, near Lodsworth, on the Cowdray Estate, October 2006. Photo: Donald Macdonald.

Plate 120 More modest woodland products from hazel (*Corylus avellana*) coppicing at Blagdon Farm, near Clanfield, Hampshire: in the foreground, bean poles (left) and a wattle hurdle (right). In the background the coppiced stools can be seen, which will re-grow; in the meantime a rich ground flora will burst forth on the cleared site. Photo: Nick Heasman, courtesy of SDJC.

Plate 121 Fifty-three year-old Douglas fir (*Pseudotsuga menziesii*) on the Cowdray Estate at Minepits, near Fernhurst, West Sussex. Photo: Val Carver LRPS.

Plate 122 Fifty-eight year-old Corsican pine (*Pinus nigra* var. *calabria*), near Easebourne, West Sussex, 1987, for which the Cowdray Estate was awarded a Gold Medal in the Royal Agricultural Society of England competition. Photo: Val Carver LRPS.

Plate 123 Large Corsican pine sawlogs for ultimate use as building timber awaiting transport. Photo: Val Carver LRPS.

Plate 124 Small round fencing material; products of an early thinning of larch (*Larix x eurolepis*) at Poors Common road on the Cowdray Estate, 2003. Photo: Val Carver LRPS.

Plate 125 Oak timber (*Quercus robur*) of a quality for potential use in joinery or furniture, ready to be extracted for roadside collection. Photo: Val Carver LRPS.

Plate 126 A typical downland scene at West Dean; a beech (*Fagus sylvatica*) hedge fronting a beech shelter belt. Photo: Val Carver LRPS.

Plate 127 A mini-swipe weeding a five year-old plantation of Corsican pine in Goldballs Plantation, Cowdray Estate, West Sussex, 2005. Photo: Donald Macdonald.

Plate 128 A timber harvester carrying out thinning work in a 40 year-old Norway spruce (*Picea abies*) plantation, Cocking Forest, Cowdray Estate, West Sussex, 2005. Photo: Donald Macdonald.

Plate 129 Lonesome pine: the woodland devastation near Midhurst, West Sussex, after the 1987 storm. Photo: Val Carver LRPS.

Plate 130 A mobile sawmill preparing Douglas fir sawlogs to be converted into 'rustic' sleepers for the garden trade in Cocking Forest, Cowdray Estate, West Sussex, 2005. Photo: Donald Macdonald.

Plate 131 Part of the lower Cuckmere Valley; the artificial embankments can be seen which, if removed, could allow water to disperse across the floodplain, thereby providing a natural and temporary storage of flood water. Photo: John Tyler, courtesy of SDJC.

Plate 132 Floods at Bramber, West Sussex, *c.*1931; from an old postcard, photographer unknown, courtesy of Rendel Williams.

Plate 133 Bell Lane, Uckfield, East Sussex, at 10.30 a.m., 12 October 2000. Land-drainage policy has encouraged building on floodplains, the catastrophic results of which can be seen. Uckfield is in the catchment area of the River Ouse just outside the proposed South Downs National Park. At times of heavy rainfall, flood water cannot remain within artificially deepened river channels, altering dramatically the amount of overflow, the results of which can lead to misery for local residents and millions of pounds worth of damage to built property. Photo: Alan Thompson, the Symonds Group.

Plate 134 The centre of Lewes, East Sussex, at 2.00 p.m., 12 October 2000. Typical of many lowland rivers, the Sussex Ouse has been heavily engineered and artificially modified, resulting in the loss of wetland habitats in naturally functioning floodplains. This has robbed the river catchment of the ability to cope with flooding; downstream towns suffer as a consequence. Photo: John Gower, courtesy of the Environment Agency.

Plate 135 Mountain bikers on an 'open access' section of the South Downs Way west of Ditchling Beacon, March 1996. Photo: Phil Belden.

Plate 136 Guided walks are also popular, often organized through groups such as the Ramblers' Association. Photo: Mark Brookes, courtesy of SDJC.

Plate 137 Walkers on the Hampshire Hangers. Access and recreation are key uses of the Downs. Photo: Nick Heasman, courtesy of SDJC.

Plate 138 Visitors to the South Downs peacefully enjoying the scenery; the Long Man at Wilmington, East Sussex, is in the background. Photo: Peter Greenhalf, courtesy of Natural England/SDJC.

Plate 139 The extensive bridleway network and underlying dry chalk geology make the South Downs particularly popular with horse-riders, though not necessarily with hikers, who suffer from interrupted walks and churned up and often muddy pathways; here riders are pictured just south of Wilmington, East Sussex, *c.* 1985. Photo: Paul Millmore.

Plate 140 The bridleways up the steep scarp-slopes of the Downs can suffer from severe erosion if not properly maintained. Here rangers repair a deep gulley in Bridleway Westmeston 33 – an expensive procedure. Photo: Paul Millmore.

Plate 141 Paragliding, a more recent development from hang gliding using a cheaper, specially-designed parachute wing, has become increasingly popular. The scarp-slopes of the Downs provide ideal launch-sites for this sport. Photo: SDJC.

Plate 142 A mountain biker on the South Downs Way west of Lewes, *c.* 1996, negotiating and, importantly, closing the gates. Design improvements to the humble bicycle have made the Downs accessible to this form of sustainable recreation. Photo: Paul Millmore.

Plate 143 This extreme example of pressure on the South Downs trackways speaks for itself; the four-wheel drive 'Southern Hill Rally' on the escarpment at Kingston, near Lewes, East Sussex, August 1995. Photo: Phil Belden.

Plate 144 Clough Williams-Ellis's mythical 'Seaville': an aerial view of Peacehaven in 1936, showing the gridiron layout and clifftop position. Photo: East Sussex County Council, courtesy of Paul Millmore.

Plate 145 Bungalow city; post-war bungalow development at Saltdean on the Downs inland from the cliff edge. Photo: Martin Small, courtesy of SDJC

Plate 146 (a & b) A fair exchange? 'Executive' housing a) at the former Royal Navy establishment, HMS *Mercury*, East Meon, Hampshire, permitted in order to secure the removal of unsightly MoD buildings b). Photos: Alison Tingley, courtesy of SDJC.

Plate 147 Destruction of the downland countryside; construction of the Brighton bypass, May 1991, which emphasizes the damage done to the Downs, even after landscaping, by pushing polluting traffic into the hills due to the density of the ribbon housing of the coastal plain. Photo: Phil Belden.

Plate 148 Construction of the Southwick tunnel on the A27 Brighton bypass. Photo: Julian Gray, courtesy of SDJC.

Plate 149 The greatest eyesore in the South Downs: the derelict former Shoreham Cement Works, opened in 1950, closed 40 years later. Photo: Julian Gray, courtesy of SDJC.

Plate 150 How to wreck natural beauty: electricity pylons and the former Shoreham Cement Works frame a right of way, near Coombes, West Sussex, 1996. Photo: Phil Belden.

Plate 151 Wartime legacy; the twin masts on The Trundle (St Roche's Hill) at Goodwood, West Sussex. Photo: Martin Small

Plate 152 'Glorious Goodwood', a site for horse racing on the private Goodwood Estate. This hilltop scene shows the extent of the car parking and crowds attracted to such popular meets, which are serviced by three minor roads through the Downs, often causing extensive disruption to local traffic. The central stands can be seen from miles away. Photo: Phil Belden.

Plate 153 The site of the proposed Brighton & Hove Albion stadium at Court Farm, Falmer, East Sussex, and the University of Brighton, June 1999. Photo: Phil Belden.

Plate 154 Architects' CAD-generated image of Brighton & Hove Albion's proposed new stadium at Falmer. Image by KSS Design Group Ltd, courtesy of Brighton & Hove Albion Football Club.

Plate 155 Looking towards the Meon Valley, Hampshire, from Beacon Hill NNR. Photo: SDJC.

Plate 156   Scrub clearance at Malling Down, October 1986. Photo Phil Belden.

Plate 157   Volunteers mending fences at the Seven Sisters Country Park. Photo: Keith Fryer, courtesy of SDJC.

Plate 158   Enthusiastic volunteer rangers litter-picking on the beach at Seaford Head, December 1985. Photo: Phil Belden.

Plate 159   Intrusive superstores at Lyons Farm north of the A27 Sompting bypass near Broadwater and Worthing. Photo: Phil Belden.

Plate 160   The opening of the footbridge over the River Arun; built to provide walkers of the South Downs Way with a safe route away from the dangerous Amberley Houghton road, 1993. Left to right: Tim Yeo MP, then Conservative Environment Minister; Lord Nathan, then Chairman of the Sussex Downs Conservation Board; and Sir John Johnson, then Chairman of the Countryside Commission. Photo: Phil Belden.

Plate 161   Catching them young: education of school children about the environment, and the South Downs in particular, is vital for the area's future sustainability – here at the Seven Sisters Country Park. Photo: Julian Gray, courtesy of SDJC.

Plate (map) 162   (Left) National Parks and Conservation Areas in England and Wales proposed by the Hobhouse Committee in 1947. Note that the proposed National Parks, though largely in relatively wild upland areas, did include the South Downs. Map produced by the University of Southampton Cartographic Unit. (Right) National Parks and Areas of Outstanding Natural Beauty at December 2006. Note that the proposed South Downs National Park extends into the Western Weald beyond that proposed by Hobhouse. Map courtesy of Natural England.

Plate 163   Sustainable tourism at sea; looking south-west from the Allchorn Brothers' tour boat off Beachy Head lighthouse, *c.* 1993. Photo: Heritage Coast Forum

Plate 164   If the marine environment off the Seven Sisters becomes part of a South Downs National Park, there will perhaps be a need for shipwreck management for the diving community. The picture shows a member of the American park service undertaking archaeological research on a wreck off the Florida coast, *c.* 1990. Photo: US National Park Service, courtesy of Larry Murphy.

Figures and Maps (in black & white)

Tables

Appendices (Chapter 10)

Index

THE END.

Duck Lane, Midhurst.   M. Seeck.

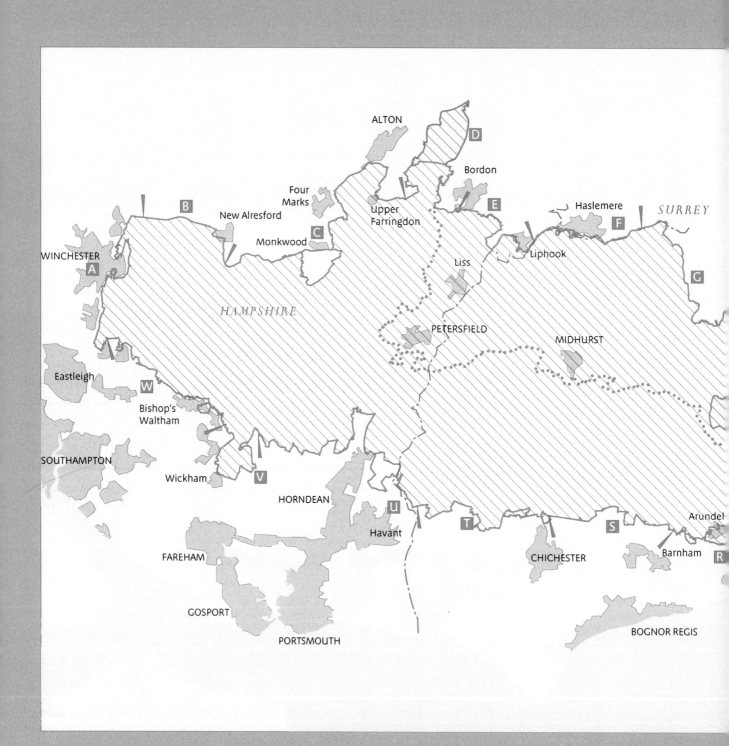

Proposed South Downs National Park
recommended boundary modifications - June 2007

COMPARISON WITH DESIGNATED NATIONAL PARK AREA

Proposed National Park boundary with section marker

Area designated as South Downs National Park

Revised boundary based on Inspector's recommendation

County/Unitary boundary

Settlement

0   10km

Burgess Hill

Hurstpierpoint

K

J

Hassocks

L

Steyning

LEWES

P

Brighton & Hove UA

M

Hove

Saltdean

Denton

BRIGHTON

EAST SUSSEX

WORTHING

Rottingdean

N

Peacehaven

Newhaven

EASTBOURNE

Seaford

O

FOR ILLUSTRATIVE PURPOSES ONLY